Motors and Drives
A Practical Technology Guide

D1496589

NEW ENGLAND INSTITUTE
OF TECHNOLOGY
LIBRARY

Motors and Drives

A Practical Technology Guide

Dave Polka

NEW ENGLAND INSTITUTE
OF TECHNOLOGY
LIBRARY

ISA–The Instrumentation, Systems,
and Automation Society

5/04

#50424530

Notice

The information presented in this publication is for the general education of the reader. Because neither the author nor the publisher have any control over the use of the information by the reader, both the author and the publisher disclaim any and all liability of any kind arising out of such use. The reader is expected to exercise sound professional judgment in using any of the information presented in a particular application.

Additionally, neither the author nor the publisher have investigated or considered the affect of any patents on the ability of the reader to use any of the information in a particular application. The reader is responsible for reviewing any possible patents that may affect any particular use of the information presented.

Any references to commercial products in the work are cited as examples only. Neither the author nor the publisher endorse any referenced commercial product. Any trademarks or tradenames referenced belong to the respective owner of the mark or name. Neither the author nor the publisher make any representation regarding the availability of any referenced commercial product at any time. The manufacturer's instructions on use of any commercial product must be followed at all times, even if in conflict with the information in this publication.

Copyright © 2003 ISA – The Instrumentation, Systems, and Automation Society

All rights reserved.

Printed in the United States of America.
10 9 8 7 6 5 4 3 2

ISBN 1-55617-800-X

No part of this work may be reproduced, stored in a retrieval system, or transmitted in any form or by any means, electronic, mechanical, photocopying, recording or otherwise, without the prior written permission of the publisher.

ISA
67 Alexander Drive
P.O. Box 12277
Research Triangle Park, NC 27709

Library of Congress Cataloging-in-Publication Data

Polka, David.
Motors & drives / by David Polka.
p. cm.
Includes bibliographical references and index.
ISBN 1-55617-800-X
1. Electric motors. 2. Electric driving. I. Title:Motors and drives. II. Title.
TK2514 .P65 2002
621.46--dc21
2002012843

Dedication

This book is dedicated to my wife, Candy, and my daughter, Korey. Their support, understanding and encouragement has been monumental in the creation of this literary work. (Maybe I'll get more projects done around the house, now that my work is complete.)

I also dedicate this book to my parents, Chet and Carol, who taught me to stick to my goals, and that you can't put a price-tag on the value of education. Teachers are essential to the creation of a well-trained and efficient functioning society.

Contents

About the Author

Dave Polka has devoted his professional career to training and education, in the areas of Electronics and Motor Speed Control. He graduated from the University of Wisconsin – Stout, Menomonie, WI, with a Bachelor of Science Degree in Industrial Education, and an emphasis in Electronics and Controls.

His first position was with Homestead High School, Mequon, WI, where he spent eight years as an Industrial Education teacher. His programs included: Basic Electricity and Electronics, Advanced Electronics and Instrumentation, and Broadcast Radio.

He held several positions at Allen-Bradley's Drives Division, Mequon, WI. He spent three years as a Technical Writer of operation and maintenance manuals, and seven years as Instructor and Supervisor of Drives Training, encompassing sales, service and customer training.

Mr. Polka has published several trade journal and website articles, dealing with topics such as: "What is a Drive?" "How to Maintain a VFD" and "Energy Savings with VFDs in Paint Spray Booths."

He currently holds the Training Center Manager position for ABB Inc, Drives & Power Electronics, in New Berlin, WI. For the past eight years, he has conducted distributor and customer classes on drive - applications, programming and operation, for ABB University.

Acknowledgments

There are many people that had a hand in the success of this project. It could not have been created by one person – working in a vacuum. I would like to thank the following people for their assistance in making this book, what it is.

I would be remiss in mentioning the people that inspired me throughout the years – to do my best, research until I find answers, and persist in the pursuit of excellence. I began my knowledge base, through the direction and guidance given by those at Allen-Bradley, now Rockwell Automation. I especially appreciated the assistance by the late Jim Bonham. His insight into the world of AC and DC drives gave me a foundation from which to grow. I also thank Howard Murphy, Dave Caruana, Scott Patterson, Clarence Phipps, Jerry Muehlbauer and Glenn Reinders, for their assistance throughout my formative years.

I also want to thank Ken Graber of Zigman Joseph Stephenson, for his guidance and encouraging me to accept the challenge of writing technical articles, and ultimately, the writing of this book. Ken has injected a shot of "reality" into a rather hectic writing schedule, both professionally and personally.

I want to thank my professional colleagues at ABB Inc. First and foremost, Chuck Clark, for his approval of the use of various written works, as well as photos and graphics. I also thank Roy Coleman and Joe Maloni for allowing me time to pursue my publishing goals. I also acknowledge the following individuals for their proofreading and technical suggestions: Becky Nethery, Mark Kenyon, John Sutschek, Randy Stevens, Dennis Miller, Michael Tews, Jim Nash, Tim Gladd, and Stuart Koym. I thank Jamieson Greig, for his insight into legal aspects of literature.

Mike Olson, has been my mentor, and very instrumental in the completion of this literary work. I appreciated his encouragement, proofreading and technical expertise. An accomplished author himself, Mike has always made time for my last minute questions and offered constructive criticism – that ultimately made my written documents more understandable and technically accurate.

I also thank Bill Wagner for his scanning, creation and digital photography techniques, as well as Randy Stevens, for his photo art rework and graphics assistance. I thank those affiliated with ABB, directly or indirectly, including: Chuck Cowie, Todd Vigorito and Walt Dembiczak for their insight, suggestions and comments on previously written material.

The people at ISA have been most helpful in guiding me through the maze of writing requirements. I especially thank Matt Lamoreaux for his encouragement, and Shandra Botts for her schedule keeping. I also thank Joice Blackson, for her assistance in the early stages of this project.

Introduction

To some, motor speed control is somewhat of a mystical science, a science that causes motors and machines to sometimes operate in unexpected ways. Over 30 years ago, AC drives were considered "new technology." If a company wanted to have reliable production, it should stick with known, proven technology – that of DC drives and motors. In many cases, the cost of transferring manufacturing machinery to AC technology, would not warrant the lengthy paybacks. It seemed that AC technology had a long way to go, to improve in reliability and reduced cost. In some technician's minds, you would need to have a new, back-up AC drive, because the first one would probably fail upon start-up.

As time marched on, low horsepower AC technology improved to the point where total installed costs, including the motor, were equal to – or even less expensive than the DC alternative. The size of the AC drive was equal to or smaller that its DC counterpart. Improvements in power electronics increased the reliability of AC drives, to the point where one would almost never hear of a drive failure upon start-up.

This book is intended to de-mystify drive and motor technology, used in today's modern manufacturing processes. The text has roots in the practical side of drive and motor use, with the "design engineering" side of technology, presented in commonly used terms. An attempt is made to help the reader "start from scratch," gathering and reviewing a collection of basic information – from basic electrical principles to DC and AC motor principles of operation. The initial cost of a motor only represents about 3% of its total lifetime expense, with operating costs representing the other 97%. Therefore, energy savings with VFDs (variable frequency drives) is a topic that faces many consumers in this day of rising energy costs.

From the basics, the reader is lead on a historical path – reviewing DC and AC drives that are 10 years old or more. The focus of this section however, points to the new and improved technology, in both types of drives.

From that point, the reader is lead into feedback methods and devices, and into closed loop control of drive systems. The concepts reviewed, are the basics of modern industrial and commercial HVAC systems.

An overall attempt is made to start with the basics, and move into the more complex concepts of drive operation and design. The book also compares the two technologies, AC and DC, and provides questions and issues to review when making any drive technology decision. The book ends with general principles of drive troubleshooting, and ideas on how to conduct routine drive maintenance.

Summary sections and "Test your Knowledge" questions are provided at the end of each chapter, to assist in confirming important points. In addition, the Appendices are offered as a reference section, providing terms and definitions, as well as formulas, conversions and enclosure information.

Many types of drives are on the market today – ranging from the size of a person's fist – to 14 bay cabinets, with the electronics to power thousands of motor horsepower. Open loop (V/Hz) AC drives are the most common drive in use today, with up to 70% use, according to some surveys. Behind the standard open loop drive, stands several other types of drive products: brush DC servo drives, DC drives, SCR DC drives, stepper drives / motors, AC servo drives, and brushless DC servo drives. Though in smaller percentage of use, encoderless flux vector, closed loop vector, and direct torque control type drives are gaining in popularity.

It is hoped that this book can be used as a resource for those that design, apply or maintain AC or DC motor speed controls. It is meant to be an overall "book of knowledge" on a student's, technician's or engineer's bookshelf.

What is a Drive?

In the most generic sense, a drive is a device that controls speed, torque, direction, and the resulting horsepower of a system. There are many different types of drives, and they will be discussed later in this chapter. For now, we will focus on the reasons for drive use in our industrial and commercial environments. To appreciate the use and benefits of any type of drive, we need to look at a generic application and determine how the system could be improved.

Figure 1-1 shows a prime candidate for a variable-speed drive—a conveyor in a manufacturing plant.

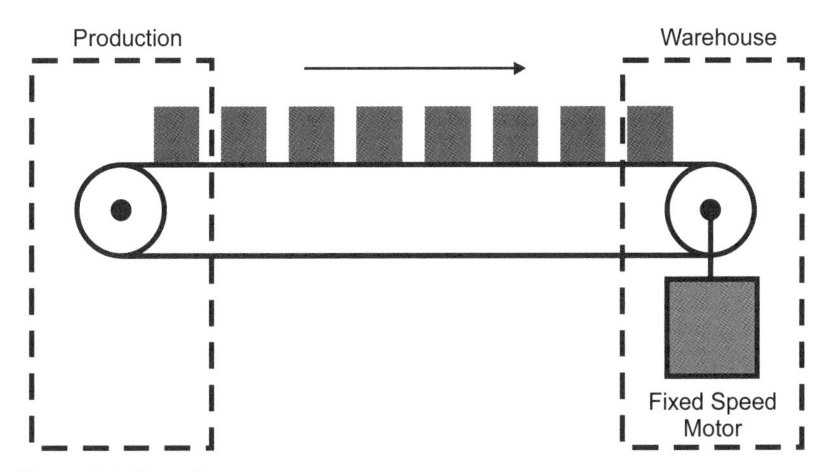

Figure 1-1. Generic conveyor system

In Figure 1-1, we can see that the conveyor's main intent is to move products from production to the warehouse. A typical way to move products is by means of a motor. The generic motor on this conveyor operates at only one speed. With only one speed of motion, this type of manufacturing system has its drawbacks.

The products can reach the warehouse only in a given timeframe. There is no way to gradually increase the conveyor speed. If it takes the motor a very short time to accelerate, the boxes may fall off the conveyor because of the accelerating forces. We will look at several factors that lead to the use of a variable-speed drive: efficiency gains, process changes and improvements, and system coordination.

Efficiency Gains

We may view the system in Figure 1-1 as very *inefficient*. We are locked into whatever efficiencies the motor can provide, given a somewhat variable amount of loading. If the motor in Figure 1-1 happened to be an alternating current (AC) motor, typically, the following would be true:

1. The more load on a motor, the more efficient that motor is.
2. The higher the motor's horsepower (HP) rating, the higher the efficiency.
3. The higher the operating speed, the more efficient the motor.

We will cover the physical makeup of AC and direct current (DC) motors in more detail in Chapter 3. For now, we will use an AC motor to explain the effects of efficiency on the total system.

As seen in Figure 1-2, efficiencies vary as indicated above.

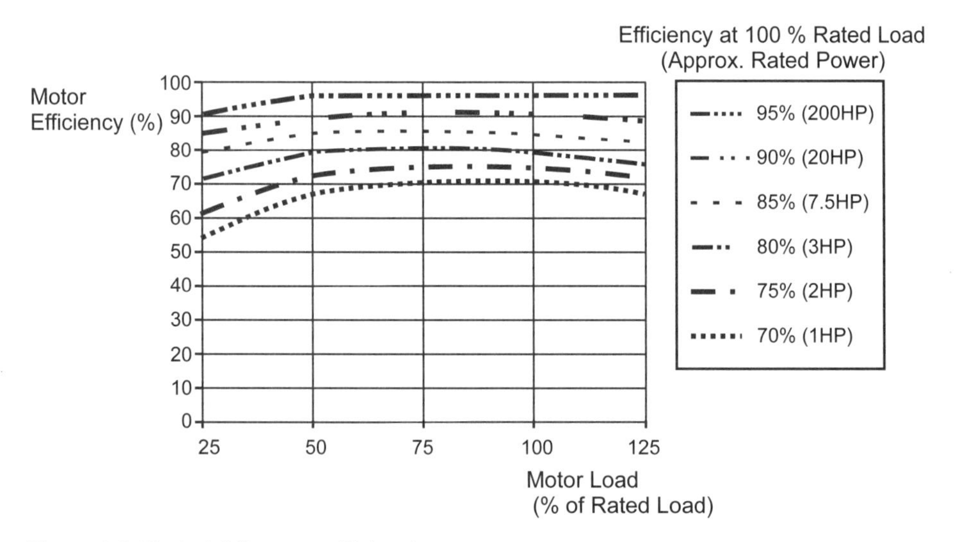

Figure 1-2. Typical AC motor efficiencies

If the conveyor motor happened to be 1 HP, we may expect to see only 70% efficiency, at 75–100% motor load. (% Efficiency = output power ÷ input power × 100). By strict definition, the 1-HP AC conveyor motor would be operating at a 30% loss at 75–100% motor load.

Figure 1-3 indicates AC drive and motor efficiencies at various speeds.

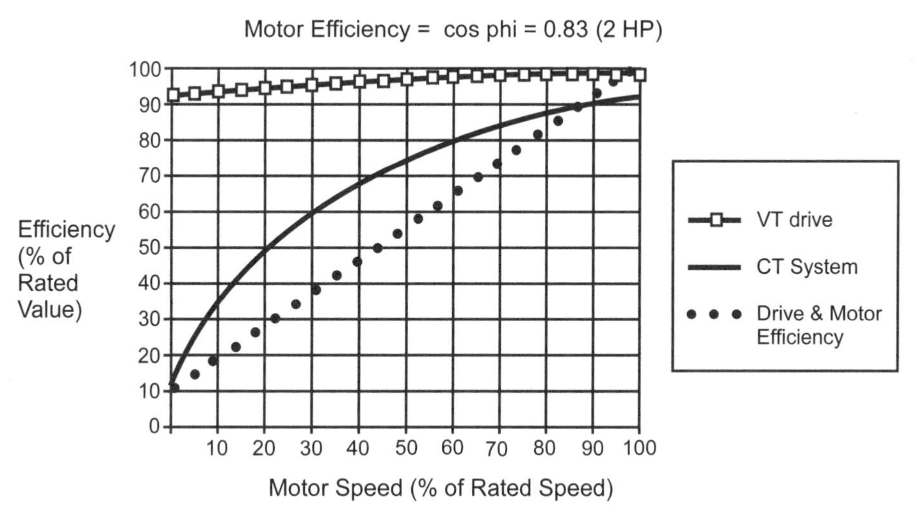

Figure 1-3. AC drive and motor efficiencies

Figure 1-3 shows an example of a 2-HP system. In this example, if we added a variable-speed AC drive, our efficiency of this constant torque (CT) system would be in the range of 80–90% when the conveyor is operated at 60% speed or higher. A conveyor is labeled a *constant torque load* and is indicated by a CT on the graphs.

It should be noted that the AC drive is an efficient means of varying the speed of an AC motor. Its 5–10% losses are attributed to thermal losses because of the alternating current's switching of power devices several thousand times per second. Variable-speed output from a drive has a direct impact on the total system efficiency. A manufacturer can operate the production equipment at the most efficient speed and load point—if drive and motor efficiencies are known.

Process Changes and Improvements

As previously indicated, in a fixed system there is no way to vary the speed of the conveyor. A fixed system will not allow for changes in the process or production cycle. Some manufacturing circumstances may require a slow speed, others, a faster pace.

The same conveyor system is used in processes such as baking. Figure 1-4 illustrates the same type of conveyor, with the addition of an industrial oven.

Certain materials may require a longer baking cycle because of thickness. If a fixed-speed motor is used, only one type of material could be processed in this system. To stay competitive, many companies require flexibility in manufacturing. A variable-speed system is often necessary to change production cycle times and increase capacity.

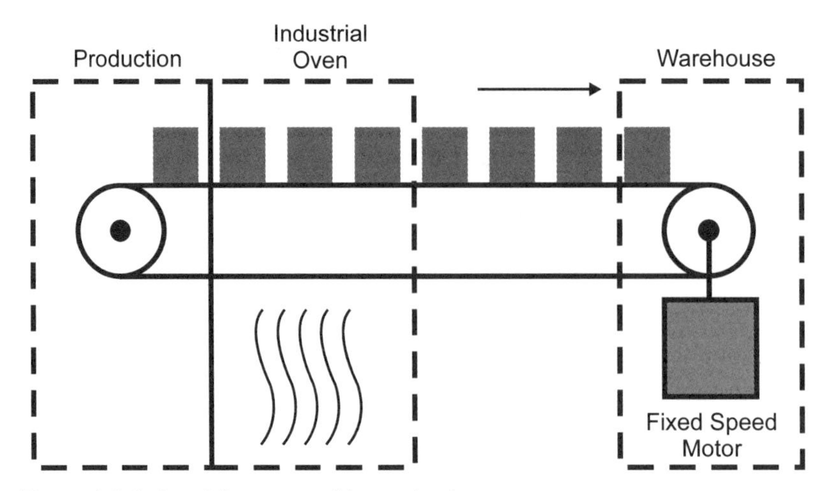

Figure 1-4. Industrial oven used in production

System Coordination

The system shown in Figure 1-4 is typical of many manually operated processes. An operator turns on the system and turns it off for maintenance or at the completion of the production cycle. However, in an age of increased flexibility requirements, few processes are manually operated. Production cycles are constantly monitored by some type of computer system.

Computer systems will automatically oversee the process and correct for load fluctuations, material density, and size requirements. In industrial processes, the use of PLCs (programmable logic controllers) is typical. Programmable logic controllers are beyond the scope of this book, but will be addressed at various points. Figure 1-5 illustrates a conveyor system that is manually operated by a control station.

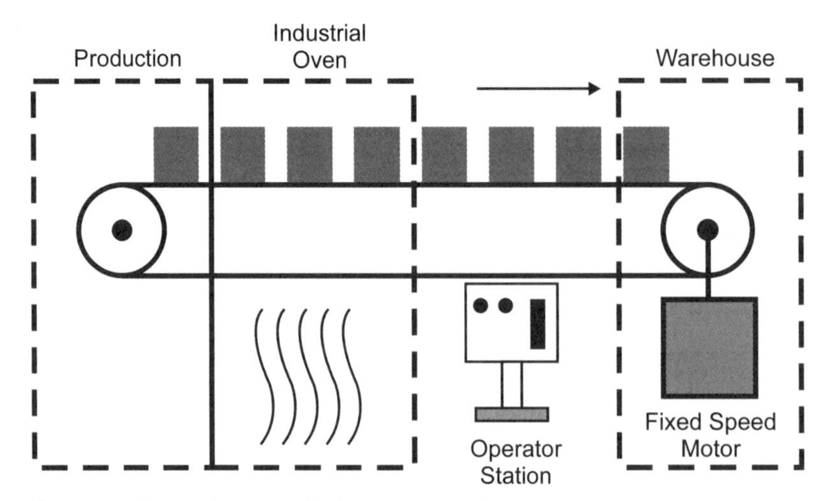

Figure 1-5. Manually controlled conveyor system

Programmable logic controllers work effectively in place of the manually controlled operator station. Automatic control of the motor could therefore be accomplished, but only STOP and START control, in this case. Variable-speed drives would be effective in providing the flexibility and control needed by motors to meet almost any application requirements.

Drive Principles of Operation

At this point, we will look at a variable-speed drive system—from a generic standpoint. All drive systems, whether, electronic, mechanical, or fluid in nature, have the basic parts indicated in Figure 1-6.

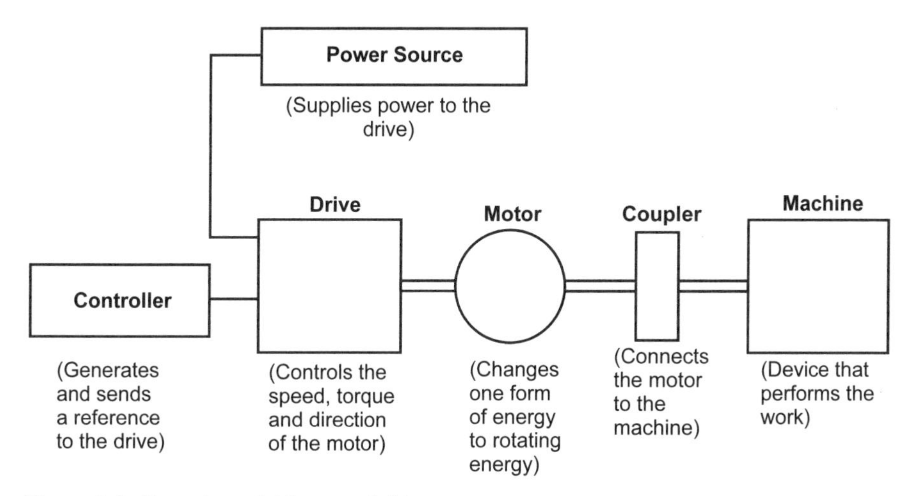

Figure 1-6. Generic variable-speed drive system

To understand a simple drive system, we will start at the end of the system and move backward. We will devote individual sections of this book to each of the basic components listed in Figure 1-6. For now, the intent is to develop a basic understanding of a drive system. A foundation will be built, which will allow more complex concepts to be discussed in later chapters.

Machine

The essence of any drive system is the application, or machine. This is the heart of the system, since it ultimately needs to perform the work. Consider the machine—the application. It could be a conveyor, a press, a packaging machine, or literally hundreds of applications that operate at variable speed.

Coupler

The coupler is the device that connects the machine to the motor. Couplers come in all shapes and sizes. Its basic task is to make a solid connection between the motor and the machine. Couplers may accept one diameter of motor shaft and convert the output to another size shaft. In some cases, the coupler may actually be a device called a *gearbox*, which may include some type of speed-reducing or speed-increasing gears. Couplers could also be considered *matching* devices because of their ability to deliver power smoothly to the machine. To a certain extent, this device can also cushion shocks delivered by the motor to the machine.

Motor

This device changes one form of energy to rotating mechanical energy. It can be considered the *prime mover* because it takes power from the drive unit and translates it into motion. As we will see shortly, there are several types of motors using various forms of energy. In this book, we will discuss mechanical, hydraulic, AC, and DC motors. The size of the motor usually dictates the amount of rotating motion it can generate from incoming power. We will see later that there are a few exceptions to this principle.

Drive

The drive can be considered the heart of the whole system. This section controls the speed, torque, direction, and resulting horsepower of the motor. The drive is very similar in nature to an automobile drive system. The transmission and drive shaft controls the speed, direction, and power delivered to the wheels. Much of this book will be devoted to AC and DC drives. However, we will take a brief look at other types of drive systems that exist in industry.

Power Source

The drive must have a source of power to operate effectively. If the drive is electrical, it must have either single- or three-phase power available. The drive then accepts this power and modifies it to an output that is usable by the motor. If the drive is hydraulic, the power source could be considered the hydraulic-fluid reservoir, since it supplies the drive with the form of power it needs to accomplish the job.

Controller

The controller supplies a reference signal to the drive unit. Typically controllers are electronic and supply a small voltage or current signal to the drive. The larger the signal, the more power the drive generates, and the faster the motor rotates. In many cases, the controller is an automatic device such as a computer. The computer has the ability to take in signals from external devices such as switches or sensors. The controller then processes the signals, does calculations based on the sensor inputs, and generates a reference signal. This *output* reference signal is usually a speed signal to tell the drive how much power to generate. As we will see in later chapters, this is not always the case. The controller could generate an output signal to tell the drive how much power to generate in order to control motor torque or motor shaft position. The operator station in Figure 1-5 can also be considered a controller. Instead of being an automatic device, the operator station provides a signal based on a manually operated switch or speed control set by a human operator.

Types of Drives, Features and Principles

In this section, we will briefly review the different types of variable-speed drives used in industry. For the most part, electronic AC and DC drives find their dominance in manufacturing and commercial HVAC applications of today. This brief look at drive technologies will assist you, should you encounter any of these types in the future. In addition, we will also review the benefits and limitations of each type. The types of drives we will consider are mechanical, hydraulic, and electrical/electronic (eddy-current coupling, rotating DC, DC converters, and variable-frequency AC).

Mechanical

Mechanical variable-speed drives were probably the first type of drive to make their way into the industrial environment. Figure 1-7 shows a basic mechanical variable-speed drive.

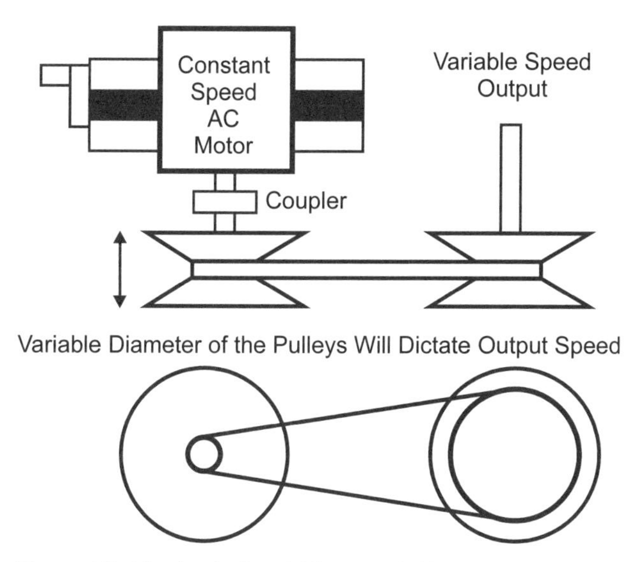

Figure 1-7. Mechanical variable-speed drive

As seen in Figure 1-7, the mechanical drive operates on the principle of variable-pitch pulleys. The pulleys are usually spring-loaded and can expand or contract in diameter by means of a hand crank (shown on the left side of the constant speed AC motor). The mechanical drive still gets its power source from an AC power supply—usually three-phase AC. Three-phase AC is then fed to the fixed-speed AC motor. The ability to vary the diameter of one or both pulleys gives this drive unit the ability to change its output speed (seen in the lower portion of Figure 1-7). The principle of variable speed is exactly the same as the gears of a 15-speed bicycle. Shifting gears causes the chain to slip into a wider- or narrower-diameter sprocket. When that happens, a faster or slower speed is achieved with basically the same input power.

Years ago, the benefits of this type of drive were low cost and the ability to easily service the unit. Many technicians liked to work on mechanical problems. The malfunction was rather obvious. However, the benefits of yesterday have turned into the limitations of today. Mechanical devices have a tendency to break down—requiring maintenance and downtime. The efficiency of the unit can range from 90% down to 50% or lower. This is due to the eventual slipping of the belt on the pulleys (sometimes called sheaves). Sometimes the speed range can be a limitation because of fixed diameter settings, a characteristic of the mechanics of the device. Size can also be a limitation. Typically floor-mounted, this device sometimes stood 3–5 feet tall for general applications. Size and weight could prohibit the use of this device in areas that would be required for mounting a drive.

Hydraulic Drives

Hydraulic drives have been, and continue to be, the workhorse of many metals processing and manufacturing applications. The hydraulic motor's small size makes it ideal for situations where high power is needed in very tight locations. In fact, the hydraulic motor's size is 1/4–1/3 the size of an equivalent power electric motor. Figure 1-8 indicates a hydraulic drive.

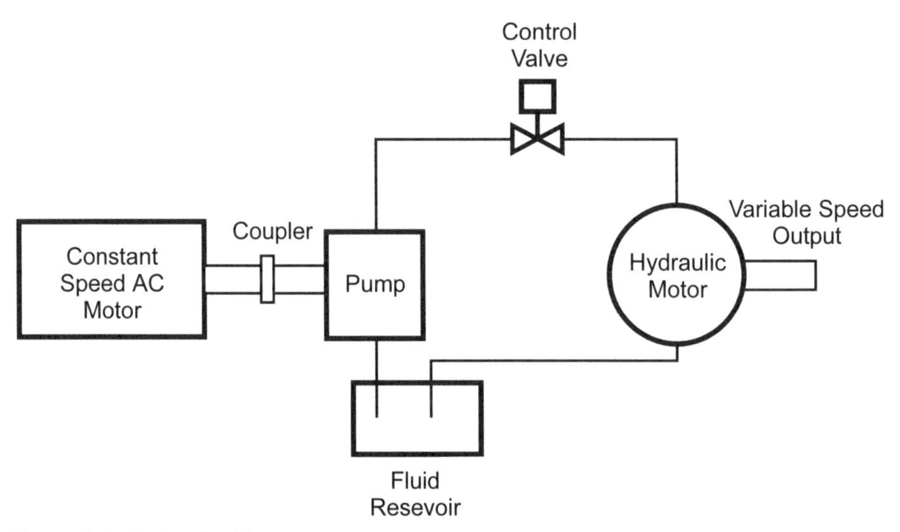

Figure 1-8. Hydraulic drive

In Figure 1-8, a constant-speed AC motor operates a hydraulic pump. The pump builds up the necessary operating pressure in the system to allow the hydraulic motor to develop its rated power. The speed control comes from the control valve. This valve operates like a water faucet—the more the valve is open, the more fluid passes through the system, and the faster the speed of the hydraulic motor. Note that this system uses a coupler to connect the AC motor to the pump.

The benefits of this type of drive system is the ability of the hydraulic motor to develop high torque (twisting motion of the shaft). In addition, it has a fairly simple control scheme (a valve), which operates at a wide speed range and has an extremely small size compare to most AC motors of the same power.

However, this type of system has several major limitations. The most limiting factor of this system is the need for hydraulic hoses, fittings, and fluid. This system is inherently prone to leaks, leading to high maintenance costs. In addition, there is virtually no way to connect this system to an electronic controller. Automatic valve-type controls have been developed, but their use is limited in today's high-speed manufacturing environment.

Eddy-Current Drives

Eddy-current drives have their roots in the heavy machinery part of industry. Grinding wheels are prime candidates for eddy-current drives. This system uses an AC-to-DC power-conversion process, which allows variable shaft speeds, depending on the amount of power converted. Figure 1-9 indicates a simple eddy-current drive system.

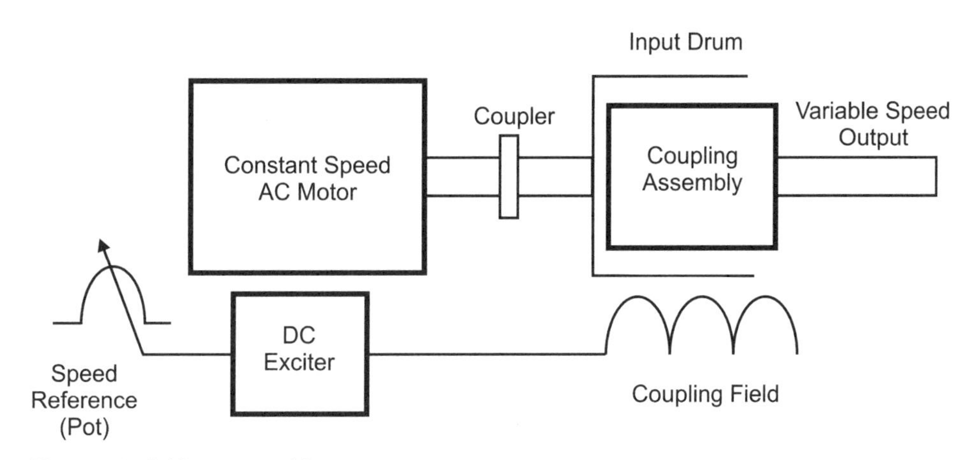

Figure 1-9. Eddy-current drive system

As seen in Figure 1-9, an AC motor operates at a fixed speed. This causes the input drum to operate at the same speed. The function of the DC *exciter* is to convert AC power to DC power. This power is then fed to the *coupling field*. The coupling field generates a magnetic field based on how much DC power is being produced by the DC exciter. The more power produced, the more magnetic field is produced and the stronger the attraction of the *coupling assembly* to the *input drum*. How much power produced by the DC exciter is determined by the *speed reference potentiometer* (speed pot).

The benefits of an eddy-current system include initial cost and the simple control method (usually 1 speed pot). In addition, this type of system can produce regulated torque because of its ability to fairly accurately control the DC exciter.

However, several limitations dictate where and how this type of system is applied. Heat generation and power consumption are the major issues. For the coupling assembly to magnetically couple to the input drum, a large amount of power must be produced. When power is produced, heat is the by-product, and energy savings are not realized. Compared with other types of variable-speed drives, this type can be several times larger, thereby limiting the locations where it can be mounted. Size is also an issue when maintenance is required on the rotating machinery. Typically on-site repairs are required, which is more costly than shipping the unit back to the repair location.

Rotating DC Drives

This system dates back to the mid 1940s. The system also gained the name M–G set, which stands for motor–generator set. As seen in Figure 1-10, that description is quite accurate.

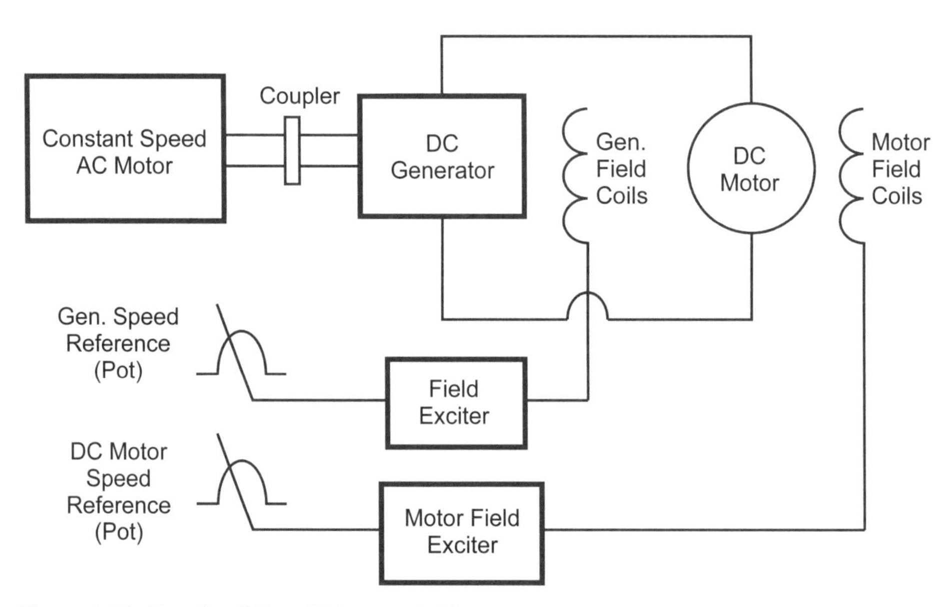

Figure 1-10. Rotating DC variable-speed drive

As seen in Figure 1-10, the variable-speed system is more complicated than an eddy-current system. The constant-speed AC motor causes the DC generator to produce DC power. The amount of power produced by the generator is dependent on the magnetic strength of the field exciter of the generator. The field exciter strength is determined by the position of the speed pot. As will be shown later, the DC motor requires two circuits in order to operate properly. In this case, the DC generator feeds power to the main circuit of the DC motor (called the *armature*). The DC motor also needs another circuit called the *field.* The field magnetism interacts with the magnetism in the main circuit (armature) to produce rotation of the motor shaft. The strength of the field magnetism depends on how much power is produced by the motor field exciter. The field exciter strength is determined by the position of the DC-motor speed pot.

This system has several benefits. Years ago in the rotating machinery industry, this equipment was very traditional equipment. This system also had the ability to control speed accurately and had a wide speed range. It typically used motors and generator equipment that had a very large overload capacity, compared with modern-day motors.

Today, a system of this type, however, would carry several limitations. Because of the need for three rotating units (AC motor, DC generator, and DC motor), this system is prone to maintenance issues. DC equipment uses devices called *brushes,* which transfer power from one circuit to the other. These devices need periodic replacement, meaning the machine needs to be shut down. This system is also larger than many of the other variable-speed units. In today's industrial environment, replacement parts are harder to find. The early units used a power conversion device called a *vacuum tube* (high-temperature electrical conduction), which is very difficult to acquire as a spare part. As to be expected, three rotating units increases the maintenance required on mechanical parts.

Electronic Drives (DC)

DC drives have been the backbone of industry, dating back to the 1940s. At that time, vacuum tubes provided the power conversion technology. Vacuum tubes led to solid-state devices in the 1960s. The power conversion device, called the *silicon controlled rectifier* (SCR), or *thyristor,* is now used in modern electronic DC drives. Figure 1-11 indicates the main components of a simple DC drive system.

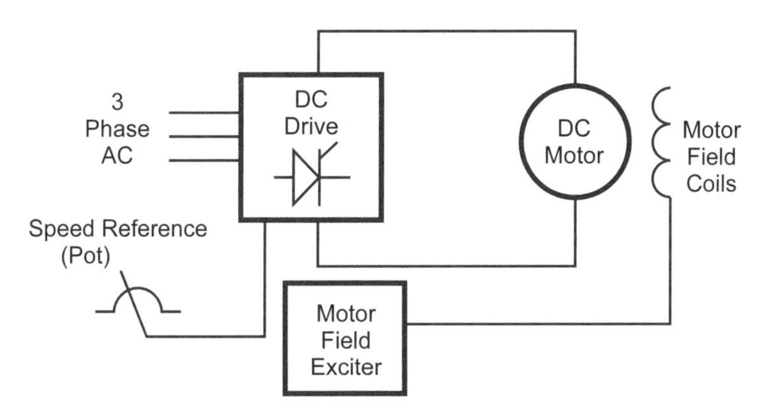

Figure 1-11. Electronic DC drive

As seen in Figure 1-11, the DC drive is basically a simple power converter. It contains two separate power circuits, much like that of the rotating DC unit. Typically, three-phase AC power is fed to the drive unit. (**Note:** Some small horsepower DC drives will accept one-phase power.) The drive unit uses SCRs to convert AC power to DC power. The speed pot determines how much the SCRs will conduct power. The more the SCRs conduct power, the more magnetic field is generated in the main DC motor circuit, the armature.

In a DC-drive system, there is always a separate magnetic circuit, called a field. The strength of the magnetic field is determined by the separate motor field exciter, or a permanent magnet. The motor field is usually kept at full strength, although in some cases, the field will be weakened to produce a higher-than-normal speed. The interaction between the motor armature and field produces the turning of the motor shaft. We will go into further detail on DC-drive technology later in this book.

There are some definite benefits to a variable-speed drive system of this type. This mature technology has been available for more than 60 years. Because electronic technology is used, a wide variety of control options are available.

Monitors such as speed and load meters and operating data circuits can be connected to illustrate drive operation. A remote operator station, including an isolated speed reference and start/stop circuits, can also be connected to the drive. This type of remote control allows commands from distant locations in the building. The DC drive offers acceptable efficiency, when compared with other variable-speed technologies. In addition, DC drives offer a small size power unit and comparable low cost in relation to other electronic drive technologies. However, when comparing electronic DC-drive technology with AC technology, several limitations should be considered.

Probably the largest issue with DC-drive systems is the need for maintenance on the DC motor. As indicated in the rotating DC-drive section, DC motors need routine maintenance on brushes and the commutator bars. Another issue that is critical to many manufacturing applications is the need for back-up capability. If the DC drive malfunctions, there is no way to provide motor operation, except through connection of another DC drive. In this day of efficient power usage, the DC drive's varying power factor must be considered when planning any installation. Total operational costs (maintenance, installation, and monthly operating costs) may be a limitation when comparing the DC system with the AC-drive system.

Electronic Drives (AC)

Basically, three types of AC drive technologies are currently available. Though each type differs in the way power is converted, the end result is the use of a variable-speed AC induction motor. All AC drives take AC input, convert it to DC, and change DC to a variable AC output, using a device called an *inverter* (i.e., inverts DC back to AC voltage). For purposes of this section, we will confine our discussion to a generic AC drive.

Figure 1-12 indicates a generic AC drive and its basic components.

The basic objective involved in an AC drive is to change a fixed incoming line voltage (V) and frequency (Hz) to a variable voltage and frequency output. The output frequency will determine how fast the motor rotates. The combination of volts and Hertz will dictate the amount of torque the motor will generate.

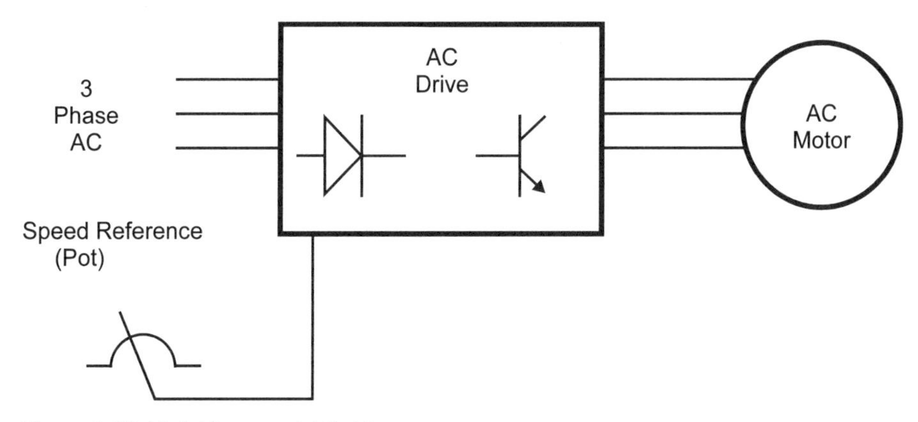

Figure 1-12. Variable-speed AC drive

When we look closer at the principles involved, we find that the AC drive essentially changes AC power to DC power. The DC power is then filtered and changed back to AC power but in a variable voltage and frequency format. The front end section consists of diodes. Diodes change AC power to DC power. A filter circuit then cleans up the DC waveform and sends it to the output section. The output section then inverts the DC power back to AC. This is accomplished through a series of transistors. These are special transistors that only *turn on* or *turn off*. The sequence and length in which these transistors turn on will determine the drive output and ultimately the speed of the motor.

With this type of variable-speed system, there are more benefits than limitations. When compared with DC drives, small-sized AC drives are equal to or lower in cost (5 HP or less). The efficiency of power conversion is comparable to that of DC drives. Also comparable is the ability to be controlled remotely and to have various monitor devices connected. Because of modern transistor technology, the size of the AC drive is equal to or even smaller than that of an equal horsepower DC drive (125–150 HP or less). One major advantage of AC drives is the ability to operate an AC motor in *bypass* mode. This means that while the drive is not functioning, the motor can still be operating, essentially across line power. The motor will be operating at full speed because of the line power input. But the benefit would be that the system continues to operate with little or no downtime.

There may be a few limitations when considering AC drive technology. With low horsepower units (above the 25- to 30-HP range), AC drives may carry a higher purchase price. However, the installation costs may be less because of less wiring (there is no separate field exciter). Some applications, such as printing and extrusion, lend themselves to DC technology. Comparable AC drives may need to be sized 1 or 2 HP frame sizes higher to accommodate the possible overload requirements. Chapter 4, section "Torque Control AC Drives" is devoted to flux vector and torque-controlled AC drives. More detail is presented on the issue of overload, torque control, and AC/DC drive comparisons. Today's AC-drive technology can provide impressive response, filling the application needs that traditionally used DC drives.

Chapter Review

There are various types of variable-speed drive systems. There are many reasons to use variable-speed drives, but basically they fall into three categories: efficiency gains, process changes and improvements, and system coordination. For example, efficiency of AC motors can be quite high, which reduces the overall monthly cost of operating the system. Variable-speed drives also allow for changes in the process, as well as process improvements. Some processes operate at less than full speed, so optimum product quality can be achieved. System coordination is a major factor in today's industrial environment. AC- and DC-drive systems are typically applied in a manufacturing process. Computers control the entire process, from infeed rate to output of the machine. Today's electronic drives offer easy connection to many types of automated equipment.

A generic drive system includes the following components: machine, coupler, motor, drive, controller, and power source. No matter what type of system is discussed, these main components are involved.

Various types of variable-speed drives are available in industry. The basic categories are mechanical, hydraulic, and electrical/electronic. Electronic drives can be further divided into the following categories: eddy current, rotating DC, DC converters, and variable-frequency AC.

Each type of variable-speed drive system has its set of benefits and limitations. The trend today is moving away from mechanical and hydraulic types of variable-speed systems, and toward electronic systems. The reasons are again identified in the ability to control the process by computerized systems. This also allows for quick changes in the process to meet the rigorous demands of production schedules.

Check Your Knowledge

1. What is a drive?
2. What are three reasons why variable-speed drives are used?
3. Name three factors that cause the efficiency of an AC motor to improve.
4. Coordination of variable-speed drive systems in industry are typically controlled by what type of device?
5. Name the basic parts and functions of a variable-speed drive system.
6. Name the categories of variable-speed drives and their principles of operation.
7. What are the two separate electrical circuits in a DC-drive system?
8. What three principles are involved in the operation of an AC drive?

Review of Basic Principles

Introduction

To understand the operating principles of an electronic drive, it is necessary to understand the basic principles of electricity, electronics, and mechanical devices. In this chapter, we will review the required basic concepts, and relate them to AC- and DC-drive systems. This section is by no means a complete digest of electronics and mechanics but will provide for a baseline of understanding. Consult the Appendix when more information is needed. This will be a review for some readers and a basic introduction into the electrical and mechanical world for others.

Electrical Principles

Resistance, Voltage, and Current

Electricity comes in two forms: alternating current (AC) and direct current (DC). We will first consider the effects of DC on various electrical components and identify the three main characteristics of any electrical circuit. Figure 2-1 illustrates the basic atomic structure—where it all begins.

When we take a close look at nature, we find that all matter is composed of atoms. In the basic structure of an atom, we find that the nucleus is at the center, surrounded by one or more orbiting electrons. This structure is replicated many times for any material. If the material is an insulator, the orbiting electrons do not move from place to place or from atom to atom.

For the purposes of discussion, we will consider a conductor as an atom with three or less orbiting electrons in the outer shell. An atom with five or more orbiting electrons will be considered an insulator. An atom with four orbiting electrons is considered a semiconductor and will be discussed later in this chapter.

Electrons in the outer orbiting rings find it easy to move from atom to atom whenever they are forced to do so. The force that tends to move

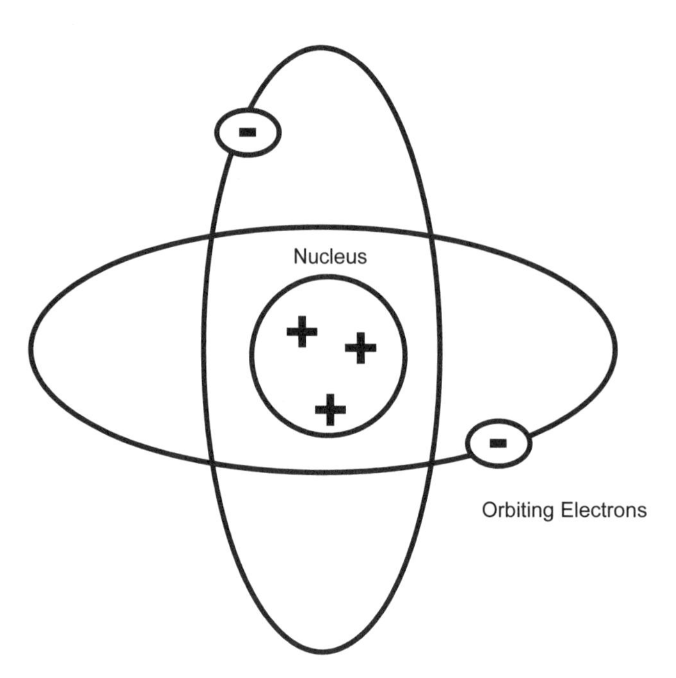

Figure 2-1. Basic atomic structure

electrons is called *voltage* (electrical pressure in a circuit). Voltage is basically the force that causes electrons to travel from atom to atom. As you would expect, the higher the voltage, the more force that is available to move electrons. Some textbooks use the term electromotive force (EMF) when describing voltage. Figure 2-2 shows how voltage "forces" electrons to move from atom to atom.

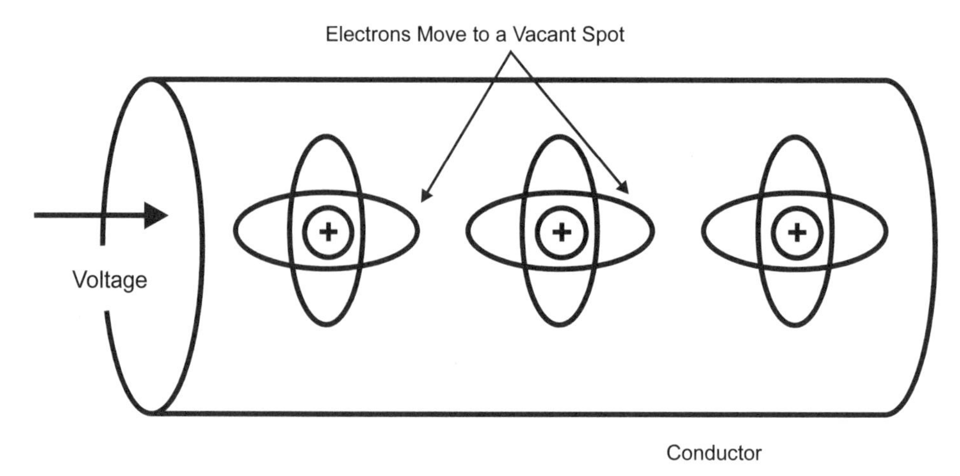

Figure 2-2. The movement of electrons in a conductor

As shown in Figure 2-2, electrons move from atom to atom to take up a spot vacated by the previous electron. Electrons flow in an orderly manner through a conductor. A typical comparison is to compare water flow in a pipe with that of electron flow in a conductor (Figure 2-3).

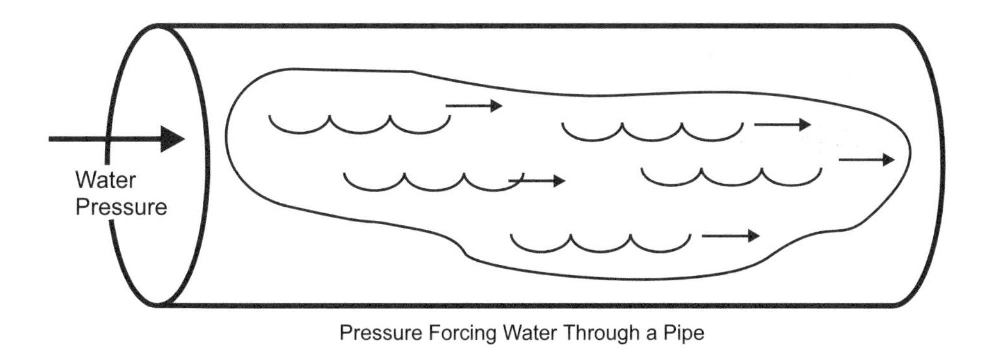

Pressure Forcing Water Through a Pipe

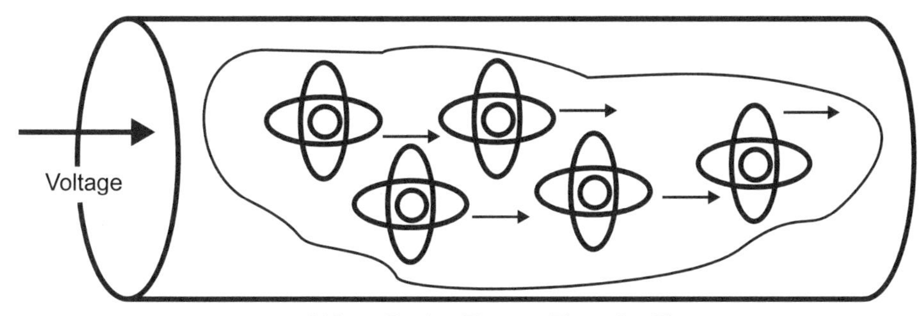

Voltage Forcing Electrons Through a Pipe

Figure 2-3. Water flow in a pipe vs. electron flow in a conductor

When you turn on a water faucet, a certain amount of water pressure forces water through the pipe and out the end of the faucet. The exact same phenomena holds true for electricity.

When you turn on a light, you allow voltage (force) to push electrons (current) through the wire and cause the light to illuminate. At this point, the obvious question is, Why is it necessary to move electrons in the first place?

The reason is fundamental: every electrical user (light bulb, TV, toaster, etc.) has resistance, measured in ohms (Ω). The user of electricity is called an electrical *load*. Figure 2-4 shows a simple fluid and electrical circuit and illustrates the relationship of voltage, current, and resistance.

As seen in the figure, a simple fluid circuit consists of a pump to supply the source of water pressure. The water fountain is considered the load. The pipes provide the path for the water to flow and also provide a certain amount of resistance to flow.

A simple electrical circuit consists of a source of electrons (battery), a load (light bulb), and conductors (wires) to complete the circuit.

Several devices have been added to measure what is happening in the fluid and electrical circuits. In the fluid circuit, a flow meter is measuring how many gallons per minute are being pumped. A pressure meter is also used to measure water pressure is in the system.

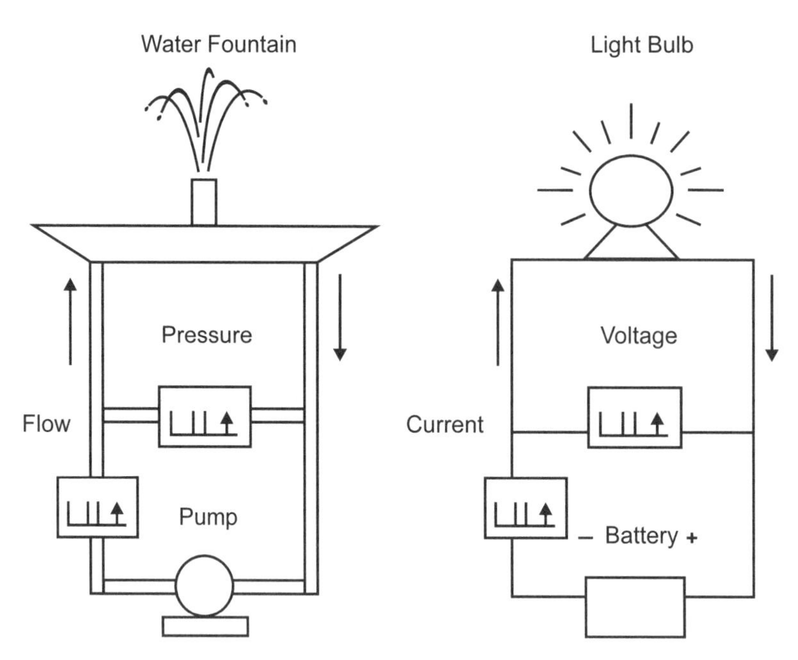

Figure 2-4. Fluid circuit vs. a simple electrical circuit

In the electrical circuit, an *ammeter* is used to measure the rate of electron flow (ampere flow per second or how many electrons are used). A *voltmeter* is used to measure the electrical pressure available in the circuit. The basic principle is that it takes voltage (electrical pressure) to force current (electrons) to overcome resistance. Essentially, the more the restriction in the water nozzle of the fountain, the more water pressure is needed to overcome the resistance. Similarly, the more electrical resistance in the circuit, the more electrical pressure (voltage) is needed to overcome the resistance and light the bulb.

With this general background, we will now look at a DC voltage waveform and review magnetic properties in a circuit. Later in this chapter, we will review the principles of alternating current.

Figure 2-5 shows a DC waveform from the battery shown in Figure 2-4.

DC Waveform

A typical means of demonstrating the characteristics of a circuit is by showing voltage or current versus time. In reviewing the circuit in Figure 2-4, we find that voltage would be flowing continuously unless there is a way of breaking the circuit. The pushbutton switch in Figure 2-5 allows the circuit to be broken when the button is not pressed.

As we see in Figure 2-5, whenever the switch is closed, the voltage rises to a maximum level. The voltage remains constant until the battery loses its ability to supply the rated level (e.g., 6 volts, 12 volts). Notice that the horizontal line with seconds indication is actually labeled *negative*. This point could also be labeled as *0*, but in electrical terms, the zero point is more

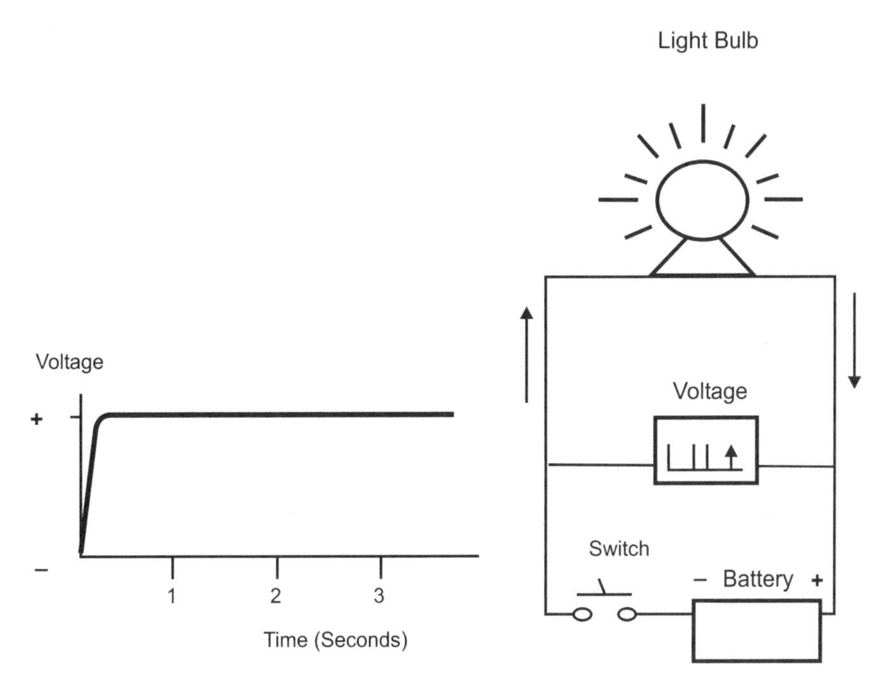

Figure 2-5. DC and a simple circuit

negative than positive. The positive point gives us a reference point. Therefore, if one point in a circuit is positive, then the other reference point will be negative.

As seen in the figure, electrons flow out of the negative terminal of the battery, through the load, and back to the positive terminal of the battery. As we have previously seen, this electron flow is due to the electrical pressure (voltage) that is present in the circuit. It should be noted that in a DC circuit, electrons flow in only one direction.

Magnetic Flux

A magnet is a material that attracts pieces of iron or items made of iron. Figure 2-6 is a common figure shown in many science books and shows the relationship between the north and south poles of a magnet, and the magnetic field, *flux*.

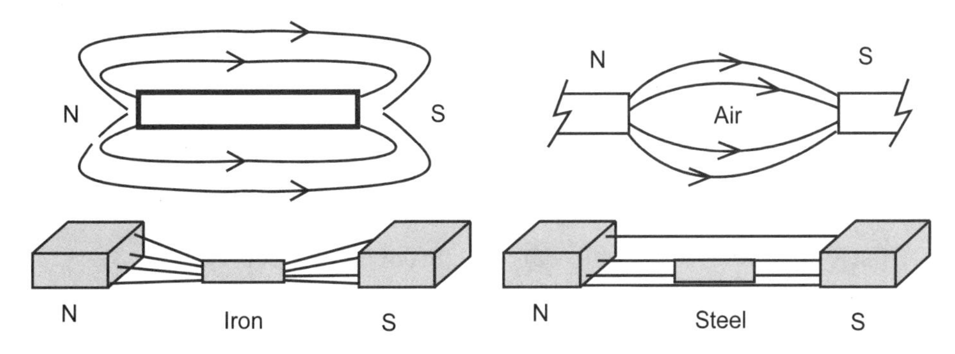

Figure 2-6. Magnetic poles and flux

The invisible lines of force (flux) travel from the north to south poles of a magnet. We can also assume that the basic principles of magnetism apply: north poles attract south poles and south poles attract north poles. It should also be noted that a material such as iron tends to concentrate or conduct the magnetic flux. Magnetic flux can pass through most materials, even those not having magnetic properties (e.g., plastic, rubber, or glass). But as seen in Figure 2-6, iron tends to strengthen the effects of magnetic flux. Typically, the more iron in a material, the better its magnetic attracting capabilities.

Electromagnetism

Electromagnetism is the production of a magnetic field though the use of a voltage and a coil. When an electric current passes through a conductor, a magnetic field is created around the conductor. Figure 2-7 shows the principle of magnetic field created current in a conductor.

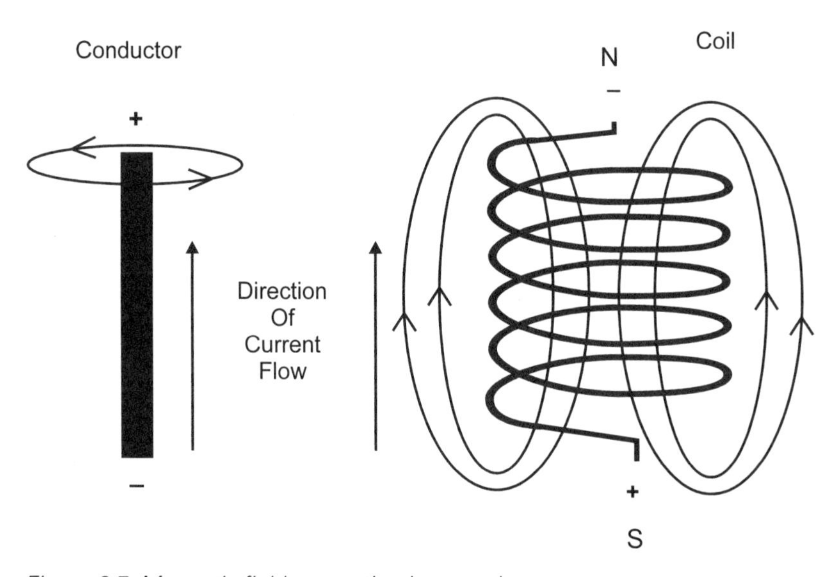

Figure 2-7. Magnetic field generation in a conductor

The magnetic strength can be increased by adding a material such as iron. A common practice is to manufacture electromagnetic products with some type of iron core around or inside the coil. It should be noted that changing the direction of current flow also changes the direction of the magnetic field. In addition, the direction of current flow in a coil dictates which end is north and which is south.

There are several important characteristics that are worth mentioning at this point:

A scientist named Michael Faraday discovered that a voltage was generated by motion between a magnetic field and a conductor. This voltage was called *induced* voltage because there was no physical contact between the conductor and the device generating the magnetic field. Faraday discovered that the faster the motion between the conductor and the magnetic field, the stronger the induced voltage. Today, we know this characteristic of induced voltage as Faraday's Law. Induced voltage due to magnetic flux crossing the path of a conductor is one of the key reasons why motors develop torque. The generation of *rotor flux* is a result of the rotor conductors cutting though *stator flux*. This characteristic is vitally important to the motor's ability to generate torque.

Lenz's Law indicates that a phenomenon occurs whereby an induced electromotive force (EMF) is caused in a direction as to oppose the effect that is causing it. That is, since the stator contains many interconnected *inductors*, EMF tries to keep the stator magnetic field at a constant state. (The inductor opposes changes or a drop in current. It also opposes the collapsing of the magnetic flux due to AC being applied.) This characteristic is of prime consideration when design engineers consider motor performance.

Another characteristic of magnetic fields and conductors lies with how the magnetic field is produced and which direction mechanical movement develops. A discovery called Fleming's Right Hand Rule indicates which direction a conductor (rotor) will move in relation to current flow and magnetic flux direction (stator flux direction).

The right middle finger points in the direction of current flow in the conductor. The index finger points in the direction of the magnetic field. The thumb points in the direction the conduct will move, given the above flux and current flow direction.

Magnetic flux moves from the north to the south pole. If conventional current flow is the method of tracing current, then current travels from positive to negative. With this in mind, we can predict the direction of rotor movement, with an induced current and magnetic field in the stator. Thus it is possible to predict the direction of rotation, given the wiring characteristics of the motor poles.

Note: *The above "Right Hand Rule" is valid if the reader accepts current flow as conventional flow—from positive to negative. If electron flow is accepted by the reader, then current flow is from negative to positive, with the rule now being considered the Left Hand Rule. (The same finger designations apply.)*

We have now reviewed the basic principles of current, resistance, voltage, and magnetic fields. To understand how these principles apply to drive technology and rotating machines, we must review the other type of current available in our power system—alternating current.

Alternating Current

As stated earlier, current flow has been described as electron flow through a conductor. You will recall the fact that DC (direct current) flows only in one direction (stated as electron flow from minus (–) to plus (+). The difference between DC and AC is that AC flows in one direction, reverses, and then flows in the opposite direction. In essence, the flow of electrons continuously changes direction. Figure 2-8 shows this principle.

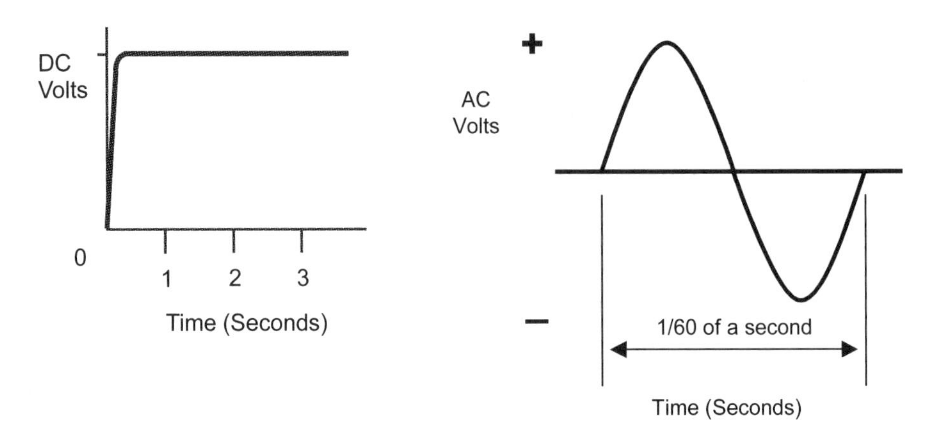

Figure 2-8. AC vs. DC waveforms

As seen earlier in this chapter, DC rises to a specific maximum value and stays at that point, until the power source is removed or drops to zero (e.g., the battery goes dead). AC, on the other hand, goes positive to a maximum level, then to zero, and then to maximum level in the negative direction, and then back to zero.

Useful work is accomplished by AC waveforms as well as DC. In AC, you may think that the work done during the positive half of the waveform is erased by the negative half. However, electrons have the same effects on a load, no matter which direction they flow. Therefore, useful work is accomplished during both the positive and negative halves of the waveform.

Current and Voltage Waveforms (AC)

We are now at the point where we need to review the concepts of voltage and current. When showing AC waveforms, many times you will see both voltage and current shown on the same graph. The graph will be similar to the one in Figure 2-9.

As seen in Figure 2-9, the voltage waveform rises to a higher maximum positive and negative value than the current waveform. Also, both the voltage and current waveforms cross the zero point at the same time. These waveforms are considered to be *in-phase*.

Single- and Three-Phase AC

Alternating current is divided into two forms: one-phase (1ϕ) and three-phase (3ϕ). Single phase is a series of continuous single AC waveforms. This type of AC consists of one voltage and current component that crosses the zero point at the same time (Figure 2-10).

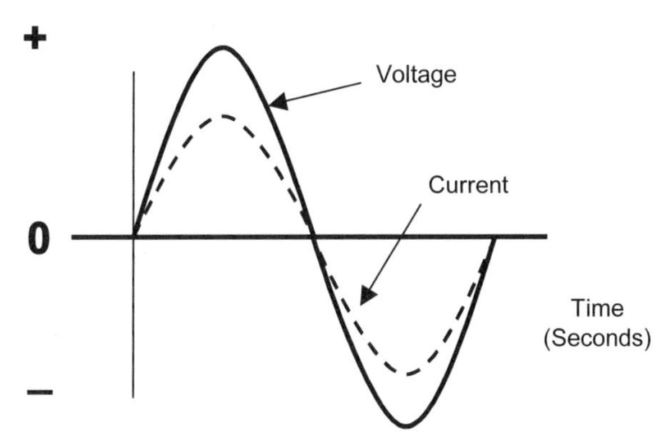

Figure 2-9. AC voltage and current waveforms

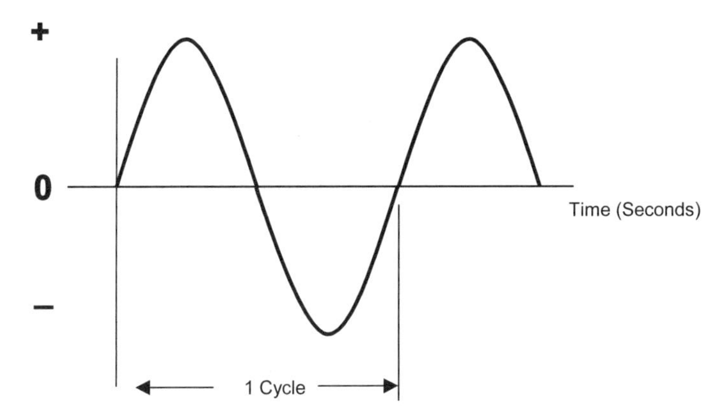

Figure 2-10. Single-phase AC waveform

Three-phase AC is a series of continuous overlapping single-phase AC waveforms. Essentially, three phase is single-phase waves that are offset from each other by 1/3 of a cycle (Figure 2-11).

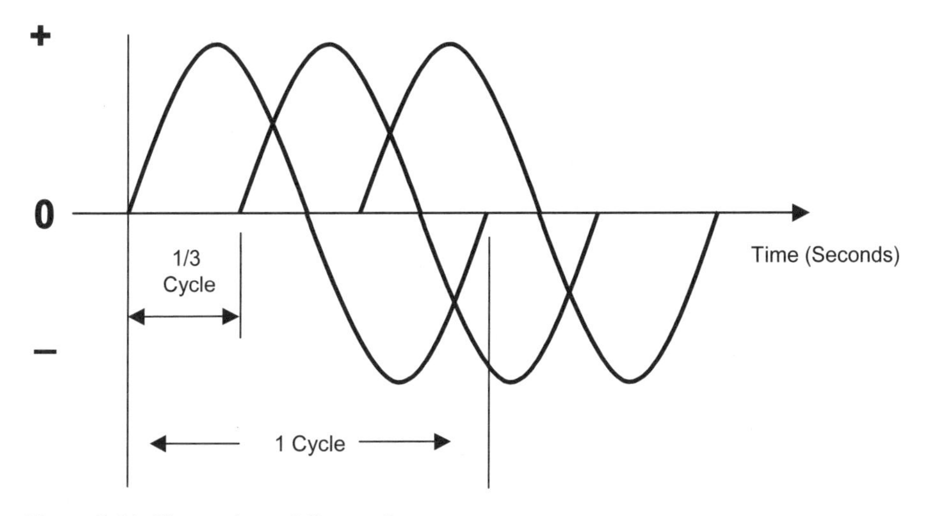

Figure 2-11. Three-phase AC waveform

The reader is probably most familiar with single-phase power, since that is the type that is typical in residential environments to operate toasters, TVs, VCRs, etc. Single phase is most recognizable by two wires and a safety ground (three conductors), with typical voltages of 120 and 240 V.

Three phase is typically used in industrial environments to operate drill presses, packaging lines, machining centers, etc. Three phase is most recognizable by three wires and a safety ground (four conductors), with typical voltages of 240 and 460 V.

Commercial and industrial electrical users mainly use three phase in their processes. Three phase is more efficient to generate and use (less current or amperes draw per horsepower). Three phase is also fairly easy to transmit, though the initial wiring and installation cost is greater than single phase. In a simplistic explanation, three phase would have three times the average usable power, compared with single phase (three positive and negative half waveforms per unit of time). The drawback of using three phase for residential power is the initial installation cost of power and the availability of three-phase consumer electronic equipment. The most energy savings is achieved when rotating machinery of significant horsepower is used in a multitude of industrial processes.

Frequency

A familiar term listed on any electrical device nameplate is hertz (Hz). In the United States, alternating current changes direction 60 times per second—60 Hz. In European countries, AC changes 50 times per second, which translates to 50 Hz. Essentially, the AC waveforms in Figures 2-8 and 2-9 would indicate 1/60 of a second. Sixty of those waveforms would occur every second in U.S. power systems.

As you might expect, electrical equipment that is designed for 50-Hz operation may not effectively operate in the United States on 60-Hz power and vice versa. However, many of the AC- and DC-drive products of today are designed for dual frequency (Hz) operation.

In electrical generation terms, one complete rotation of the generator shaft is 360°. In single-phase generation, one complete cycle is 360 electrical degrees. This one cycle also equals ~16 ms of time (0.016 s). Three-phase waveforms are therefore 120° out of phase with each other—1/3 of 360°. In later chapters, we will discuss the effects of frequency on AC motor speed. A motor designed for, or operated at, 50 Hz will run at a slower speed than if operated at 60 Hz (e.g., 1500 rpm or 1750 rpm, respectively).

Capacitance and Inductance

Capacitance

All electrical circuits have a certain amount of resistance. As we have learned, resistance is an opposition to current flow. Resistance has primarily the same effects on an AC or DC circuit. Capacitance, on the other hand, is the ability to block DC, but appears to allow AC to flow in a circuit. The device that accomplishes this task is known as the *capacitor* and is shown in Figure 2-12.

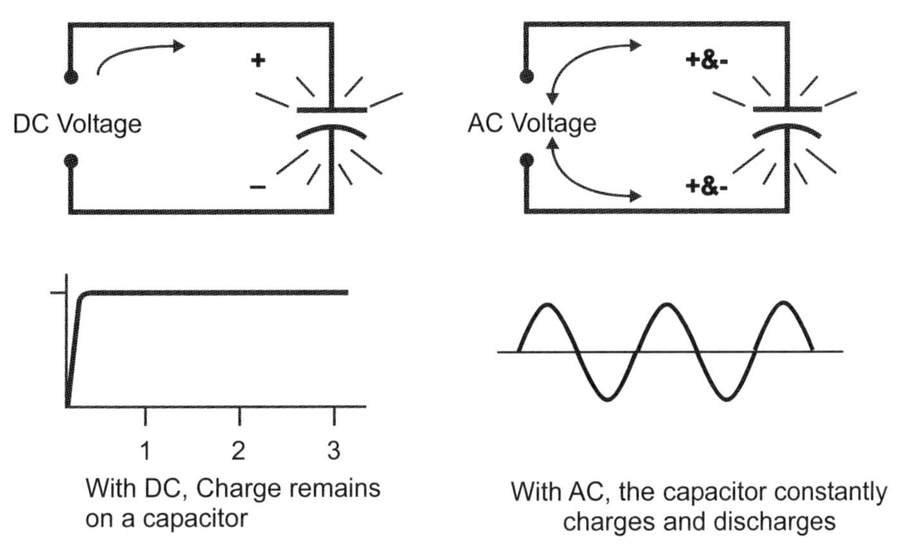

Figure 2-12. Capacitors and their effects on a circuit

If the power applied to a capacitor is DC, then the capacitor tends to charge to whatever voltage is applied. It should also be noted that the DC voltage level remains on a capacitor for a period of time (up to several hours or days for some large capacitor values—50 μF or higher). The capacitor will slowly discharge into the atmosphere over time. It will discharge rapidly when connected to a load, such as a resistor that will quickly absorb the energy.

If the power applied to the capacitor is AC, it appears that AC is flowing through. In reality, the capacitor charges and discharges so rapidly that it is common practice to refer to AC as "flowing through a capacitor."

Drive manufacturers install what are called *bleeder resistors* across large capacitor circuits to bring the voltage down to a safe level after power-down (e.g., discharge 680 VDC down to less than 50 VDC in 1 minute). The ability of a capacitor to store and discharge energy allows improvement in DC drive output voltage regulation (consistency).

In an AC drive, this charging effect also comes in quite handy. The capacitor circuit charges and discharges, keeping the flow of voltage constant and improving the quality of the AC output waveform.

The main purpose of a capacitor is to oppose any change in voltage. As expected, the more capacitance in a circuit, the longer the time required for charging and discharging to occur. Figure 2-13 shows the effects of higher capacitance on a rectified AC waveform.

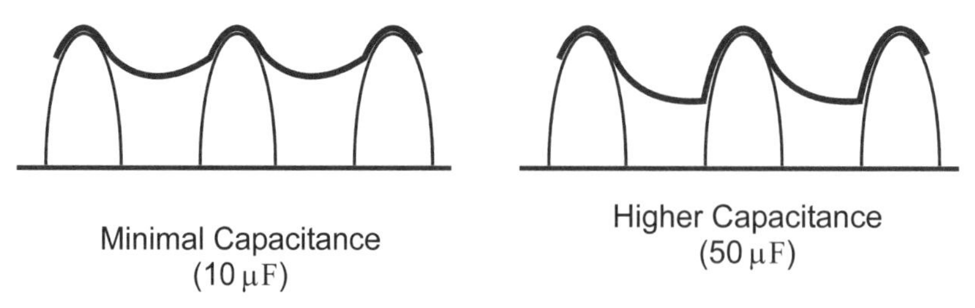

Figure 2-13. Effects of capacitance on an AC waveform

Note: *For illustration purposes, a half-wave rectifier waveform is shown in Figure 2-13. A typical AC drive rectifier output would be "full-wave," which would double the number of positive half waves and increase the DC voltage output.*

Inductance

Inductance is the ability to block AC but allow DC to flow in a circuit. The device that accomplishes this, is known as an *inductor* and is shown electrically in Figure 2-14.

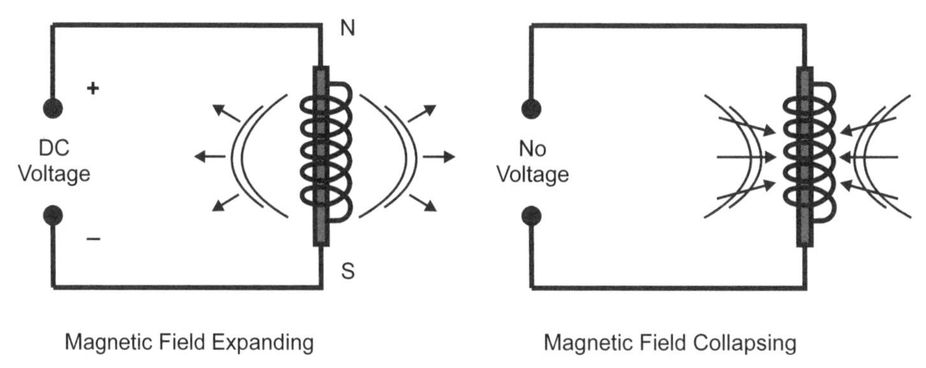

Figure 2-14. Inductance and the effects on a circuit

As shown earlier, an inductor produces a definite polarity when connected to DC voltage. The inductor will be an electromagnet with a specific north and south pole.

The main purpose of an inductor is to oppose any change in current. As you recall, any coil of wire will generate a magnetic field. The inductor works by controlling the expanding and collapsing of the magnetic field. When there is a presence of DC voltage, the magnetic field expands. When DC voltage is removed, the magnetic field collapses and creates a surge of energy. It would not be uncommon for an inductor to produce a short burst of 70 volts, after removal from a 6 volt battery. With this principle in mind, it is easy to see why there is an electrical arc at the contacts of any circuit, whenever a voltage is removed from an inductor.

The magnetic field strength is stronger, with larger amounts of inductance, commonly referred to as *henries*. Typical values would be μh (microhenries) or mh (millihenries). Figure 2-15 shows the effects of higher inductance on an AC waveform.

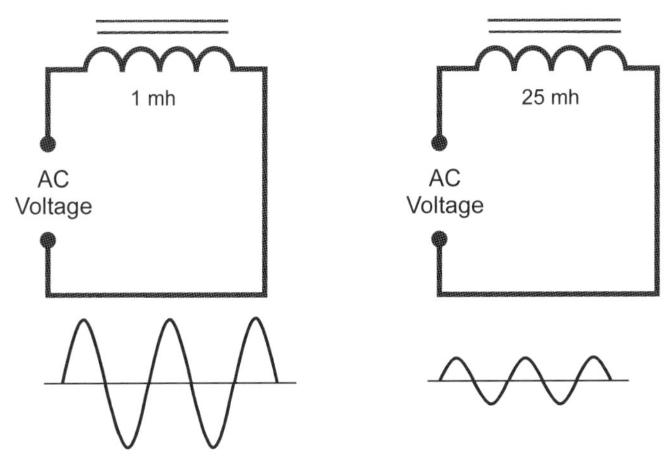

Figure 2-15. Effects of inductance on an AC waveform

As to be expected, the more inductance in a circuit, the more time that is needed to expand and contract the magnetic field around the inductor. In addition, inductors have higher amounts of resistance to AC voltage as compared with DC. An inductor may only have 15 Ω of resistance to DC, but 1000-Ω resistance to AC. AC resistance is call *impedance* and is signified by the letter Z.

Inductors are used in the DC bus Bus circuit of some AC drives to reduce the amount of AC voltage in that circuit. This tends to "purify" the DC, which in turn provides a cleaner output waveform from the drive. Because of the process of reducing or blocking AC, inductors are sometimes called *chokes.*

Power Factor

By strict definition, power factor is a measure of the time phase difference between voltage and current in an AC circuit. When an inductor is used in an AC power system, the current waveform tends to lag behind the voltage waveform. Figure 2-16 shows *in-phase* and *out-of-phase* voltage and current waveforms.

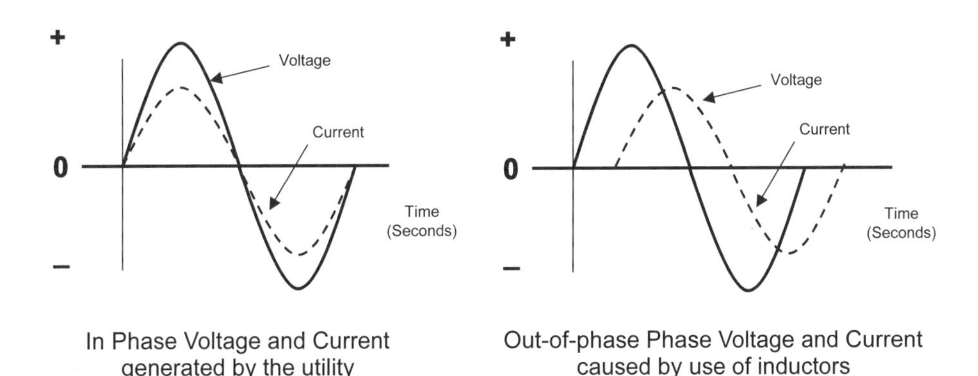

Figure 2-16. Power factor—voltage and current waveforms

In a purely resistive electrical circuit, the voltage and current waveforms would be synchronized or in-phase. In-phase voltage and current has a unity power factor of 1.0. Unity power is transmitted to customers by the utility. However, inductive loads such as motors cause the current to lag behind the voltage waveform. Once this occurs, the current being consumed is out-of-phase with the voltage waveform.

The power factor is calculated by taking the ratio of true power divided by the apparent power in a circuit. True power is the actual power converted to another form of energy by a circuit, and is expressed in watts (W). Apparent power is the power delivered to an AC circuit and is usually expressed in kilovoltamperes (KVA).

Apparent power is the power obtained by taking volts × amperes. Figure 2-17 shows the formula for power factor and unity versus 50% power factor.

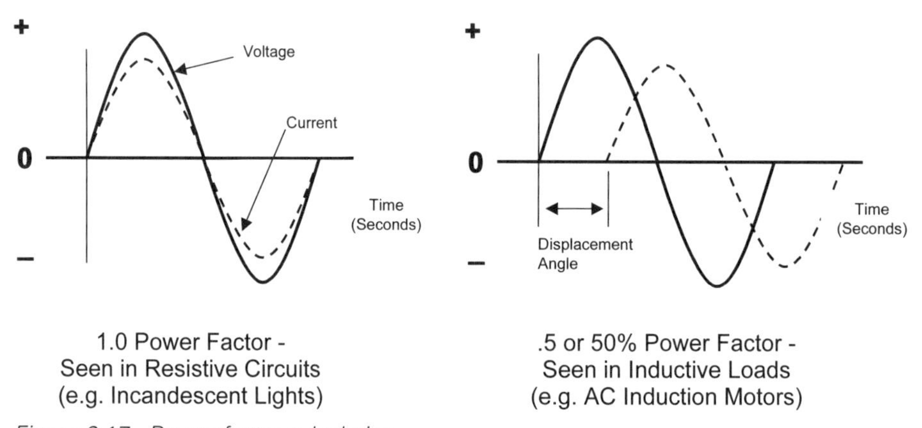

Figure 2-17. Power factor calculation

The deviation between the voltage and current waveform is called the phase angle or displacement angle. If voltage and current were 90° out-of-phase, the result would be a power factor of zero.

The utility generates power that is 100% or unity. If the operating equipment in a factory, such as AC motors, causes less than 100% power factor, the factory will be assessed a penalty by the utility. Essentially, the factory uses devices that cause current to lag voltage, meaning that the factory is wasting energy generated by the utility. The utility must generate more energy to make up for the energy wasted by the factory. If we use this analogy, the graph to the right in Figure 2-17 would indicate wasting 50% of the utility's energy.

In recent years, the utilities have promoted the use of high-efficiency motors. A high-efficiency motor wastes less energy. Typically, high efficiency motors have a higher power factor compared with motors of standard efficiency. However, manufacturers have to make trade-offs between high efficiency and high power factor because of magnetic and electrical characteristics of the motor.

Utilities require customers to correct for poor power factor, or at the very least, assess a penalty for inadequate power factor ratings. The power factor of motors can be improved by installing devices such as power factor correction capacitors. Capacitance counteracts the effects of inductance. With capacitors used in connection with AC motors, the results are a higher power factor and less waste of power. The voltage and current waveform are approaching the in-phase power generated by the utility.

Electrical/Electronic Devices

Introduction

In this section, we will review the major components that comprise an AC- or DC-drive unit. Drive units are built using components in addition to those discussed here.

Inductors, Relays, Transformers and Contactors

Inductors

As discussed in an earlier section, inductance is the ability to block AC and allow DC to flow in a circuit. The main device that accomplishes this phenomenon is the *inductor* with the electrical symbol shown in Figure 2-18.

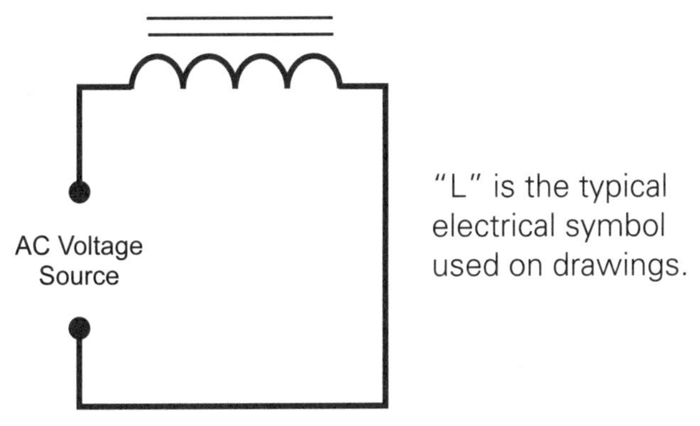

Figure 2-18. Inductor electrical symbol

As seen earlier, an inductor is basically an iron core, with a coil of wire wrapped around it. Inductors are found in many sizes and, as in resistors, the higher the value of an inductor, the greater the opposition to AC flow. Inductors are rated in units called *henries,* with typical values in millihenries (mH) due to the large unit of measure. (**Note:** a millihenry is 1/1000 of a henry.)

Inductors are found in various types of drives, both AC and DC, and will be covered in a later section. When inductors are placed in front of drives, they act as a protective device. In the discussion of electromagnetism, it was stated that Lenz's Law applies to a conductor moving through a magnetic field. An EMF is generated that tries to oppose change in the induced voltage that created it. An inductor would therefore oppose any surge (instantaneous energy increase) if it would occur on the input of a drive.

As shown in Figure 2-19, the three-phase inductor reduces any surge current that could enter the input section of the drive.

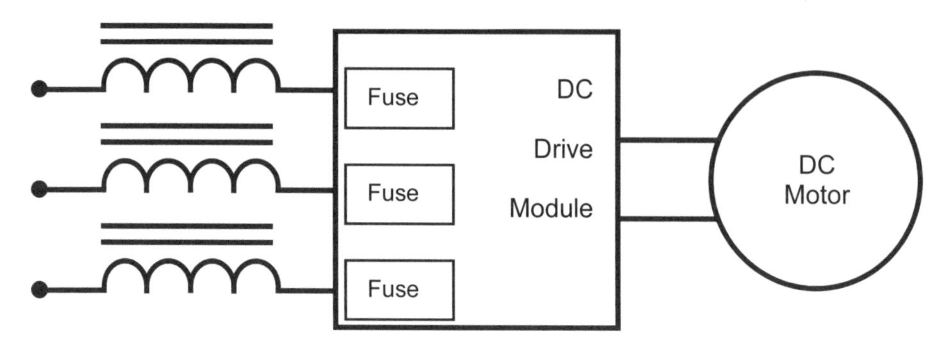

Figure 2-19. AC inductor (line reactor)

DC drives use power components called thyristors (SCRs- Silicon Controlled Rectifiers). If an output short to ground condition exists, tremendous inrush current into the drive would result. This inrush current would result in severe damage to the drive's power conversion and logic sections. When inductors are placed ahead of the drive unit, the input and protective sections of the drive see a limit and delay of short-circuit current. The delay allows time for incoming line fuses to clear and protect the expensive power components.

Relays

Relays are considered an electromagnetic device. Basically, a magnetic field is used to energize a coil, which in turn causes an electrical contact to close. Relays consist of two separate circuits—a *control circuit* and a *power circuit.* The control circuit contains the magnetic coil and can be operated by DC or AC voltage, depending on the coil make-up. The power circuit is where the electrical connection is made that allows current to flow. Power circuits can make single contact (SPST—single pole single throw) or are multi-contact (e.g., DPDT—double pole double throw). Power circuits are sometimes considered *Form C* because of the nature of their operation, which look like the letter C. They are also considered "dry" contacts, since they do not source voltage themselves (Figure 2-20).

Figure 2-20a shows the relay is energized. Figure 2-20b shows the relay power circuit when "de-energized."

As shown, the relay coil is operated from a 120-VAC power source. Typical relay coil voltages are 120 VAC, 240 VAC, 24 VDC, and 12 VDC. The power circuit contacts are typically rated in both DC and AC voltages and

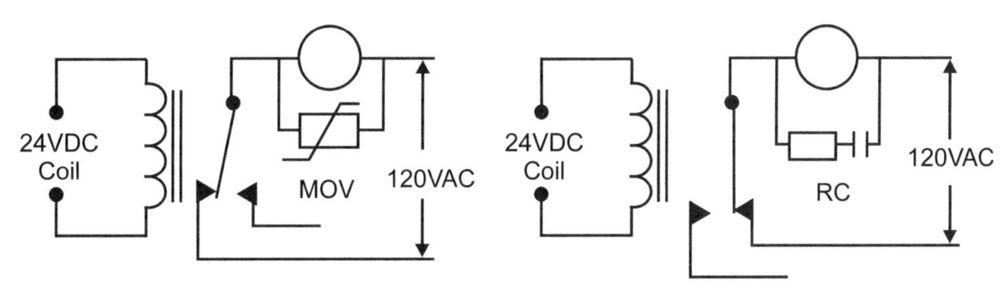

Figure 2-20. Relay symbol and electrical connections

currents. The relay may indicate a maximum switching voltage of 300 VDC/250 VAC. It would also indicate a maximum switching current rating (e.g., 8A @ 24 VDC, 0.4A @ 250 VDC, or 2000 VA @ 250 VAC).

As the power circuit contacts open, a small amount of *arcing* occurs. To help preserve and increase the life of the contacts, some type of noise suppression is normally used. A MOV (metal oxide varistor) or RC (resistor/ capacitor) network is installed in series with the incoming power circuit. As shown in Figure 2-20, suppression would be installed if the incoming power circuit is controlling the coil of a main contactor (discussed in the next section).

Contactors

Contactors are essentially higher power relays. They use the same two circuits that a relay uses: the control circuit and power circuit. It is a common practice to indicate the contactor control circuit (coil) separate from the power circuit. Figure 2-21 shows the contactor coil symbol and the separate power circuit.

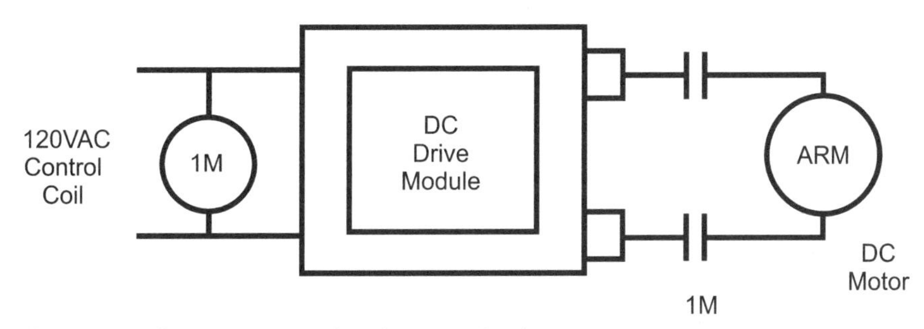

Figure 2-21. Contactor control and power circuits

As with relays, the coil (control circuit) is designed for various voltages. Coil voltages of 115 VAC, 230 VAC, and 460 VAC, single phase are common because of their easy connection to incoming line power. The power circuit is designed to handle DC or AC voltage, at a specific current rating.

In the case of DC drives, a main *DC Loop* contactor is often used to energize the armature circuit of the DC motor. When control-coil voltage is removed, a positive disconnect is accomplished, completely disengaging DC voltage from the motor.

Transformers

Transformers are essentially two inductors separated by an iron core. The iron core increases the electromagnetic characteristics and efficiency of the transformer.

The transformer transfers energy from the *primary* side (input) to the *secondary* side (output). Figure 2-22 shows the construction of a transformer and its symbol.

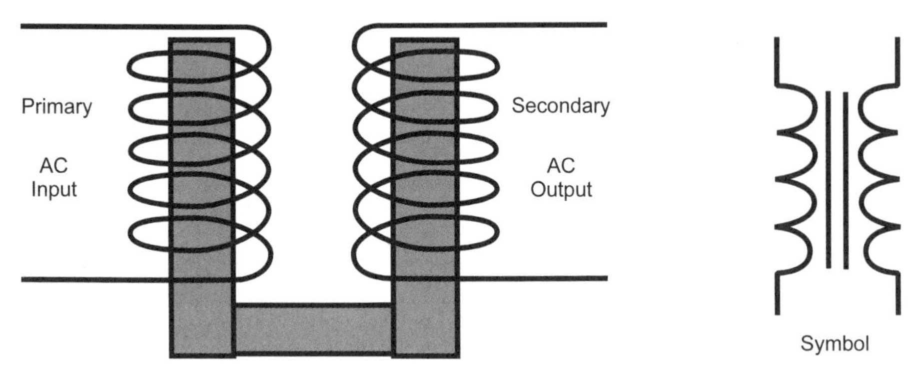

Figure 2-22. Transformer and symbol

There is no physical connection between the coils. Therefore, the transformer has an inherent capability of isolating the primary side from the secondary side. A transformer that merely transfers the same voltage from the primary to the secondary (e.g., 460 VAC to 460 VAC) is termed an *isolation transformer*. Because of the design, the transformer isolates the secondary from the primary, in the event of a short circuit or line interference. In this way, a shock hazard will not exist—protecting the equipment and personnel.

Another feature of the isolation transformer is its ability to step up or step down voltage. For example, common three-phase industrial voltages are 240 VAC or 460 VAC. When an isolation transformer is used, the secondary can step down voltages to 208 VAC or 415 VAC.

One note of importance should be stated here. If voltage is stepped down, the available current is stepped up. For example, if the input voltage is stepped down two times, then the output current will be stepped up two times. The reverse is also true. If the voltage is stepped up two times, then the output current will be stepped down two times. This is because of the fact that *power in = power out* minus any losses.

The transformer is a very efficient device, with losses due only to heat.

Note: *$P = I \times E$, where power (watts), I = intensity of current, and E = electromotive force (voltage). If power in = power out, then input $I \times E$ = output $I \times E$.*

If the voltage is doubled in the output, then the current must be half, in order for the equation to be equal.

Transformers are rated in kVA (kilovolt amps). A transformer with a large kVA or current rating (200 kVA) will be physically larger than one of a smaller rating (2.0 kVA). For example, on a 150-HP, 460-VAC DC drive, a 175-kVA input isolation transformer would be required. A 7-1/2 HP DC drive at 460 VAC would require only an 11 kVA input isolation transformer.

Current Transformers

Another type of transformer used in conjunction with drive technology is termed a *current transformer.* Basically, this transformer is a *sensing* circuit that identifies the amount of current flowing through an incoming power line. The basic characteristics of a transformer apply. Current flowing through a conductor induces a corresponding current into the coil around the conductor. Figure 2-23 shows a current transformer (CT) used to sense input current to an AC drive.

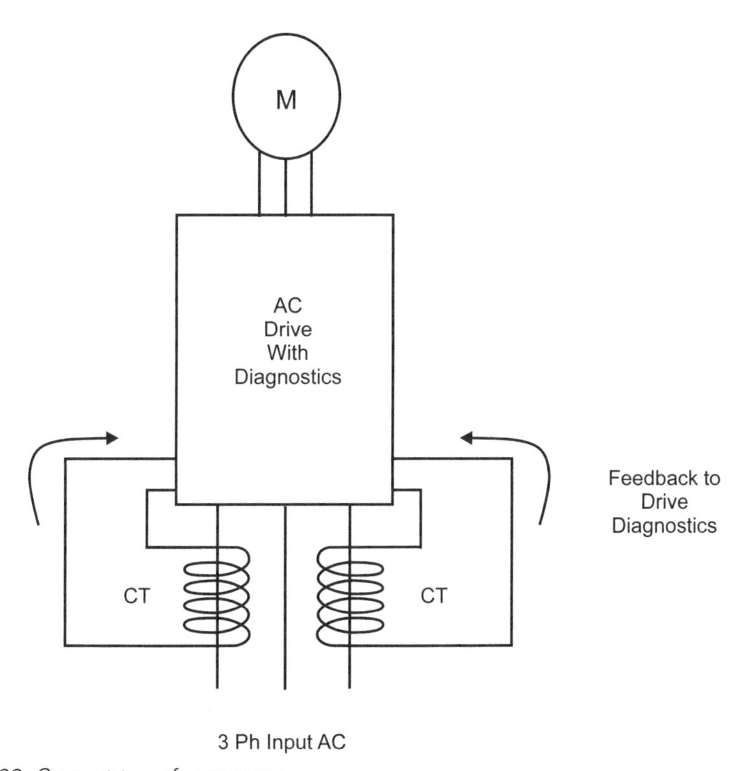

Figure 2-23. Current transformer use

If an extremely high amount of current is detected by the CT and corresponding protective circuitry, the drive is shut down to protect itself and the motor. Drive diagnostics and protective features will be explored in the AC- and DC-drive sections.

Capacitors

As discussed in an earlier section, capacitance is the ability to block DC and allow AC to flow in a circuit. The main device that accomplishes this phenomenon is the *capacitor* with the electrical symbol shown in Figure 2-24.

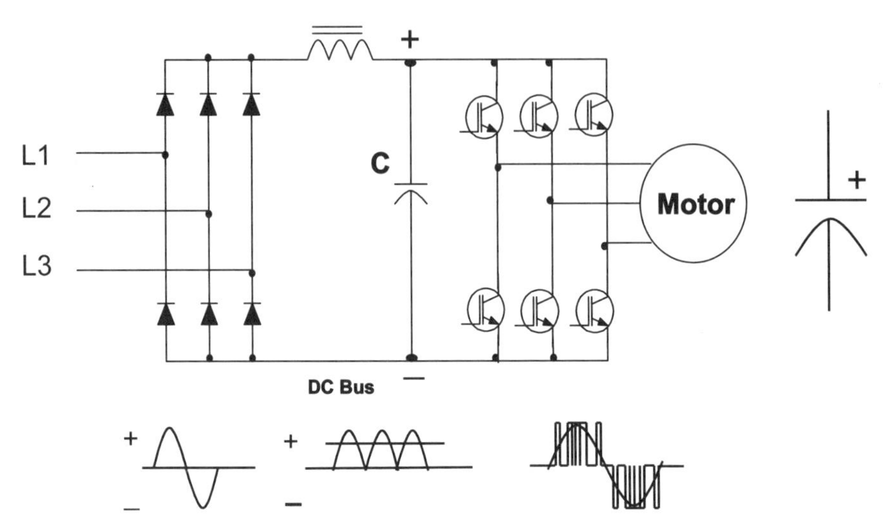

Figure 2-24. Capacitor symbol and use

As seen earlier, a capacitor is basically two plates of conducting material, separated by an insulator. The insulator is usually plastic, mica, or even air, and is called a *dielectric*. Capacitors are found in many sizes and just as in resistors, the higher the value of a capacitor, the greater the opposition to DC flow. Capacitors are rated in units called *farads*, with typical values in microfarads (μF) due to the large unit of measure. (**Note:** a μF is 1/ 1,000,000 of a farad.)

Capacitors also have another rating—working voltage. WVDC (Working Voltage DC) is the maximum voltage a capacitor can handle without being damaged. In drive power circuits, 800 or 1000 WVDC are typical values.

As mentioned earlier, one of the main uses of capacitors in drive circuitry is to filter out AC waveforms in a DC circuit. Figure 2-24 shows this function, using an *electrolytic* capacitor in the DC bus circuit. The capacitor's charging and discharging capability make it a perfect candidate for smoothing out the DC waveform, which in turn, creates a purer output voltage waveform.

Semiconductors

To understand the theory of regulation and power conversion in adjustable speed drives, it is essential that semiconductor basics be discussed. Semiconductors are poor conductors under normal conditions. However, once impurity elements are added to semiconductor materials, their atomic structure changes. Semiconductor materials can be P (positive) or

N (negative), depending on the impurity added at the time of manufacture.

Silicon or germanium provide the base material for electronic components such as SCRs (silicon-controlled rectifiers), GTOs (gate turn-off devices), and ICs (integrated circuits). They also form the base for many of the recently developed logic components such as ASICs (application-specific integrated circuits) and DSPs (digital signal processors).

In an earlier section of this chapter we discussed basic electrical principles, with electrons flowing from negative to positive. This is a common description when discussing the basics of electricity. However, because of the nature of semiconductor circuits, it is conventional to trace current flow from *positive* to *negative*. This is termed *conventional current flow* and will allow for easier understanding of circuit operation. Therefore, for the remainder of this book, we will consider the current flowing in a drive circuit from positive to negative.

A continuing concept throughout discussions of electronics is that electrons tend to seek a point of zero potential. This is similar to the concept that water will tend to seek its lowest point. Voltage will cause current to flow from the highest potential (supply) down to the lowest potential (ground). Voltage will continue to force current flow to ground until no difference of potential exists or until the supply is cut off.

Diodes

Diodes may be considered the simplest semiconductor device. As shown in Figure 2-25, current flow follows in the direction of the triangle.

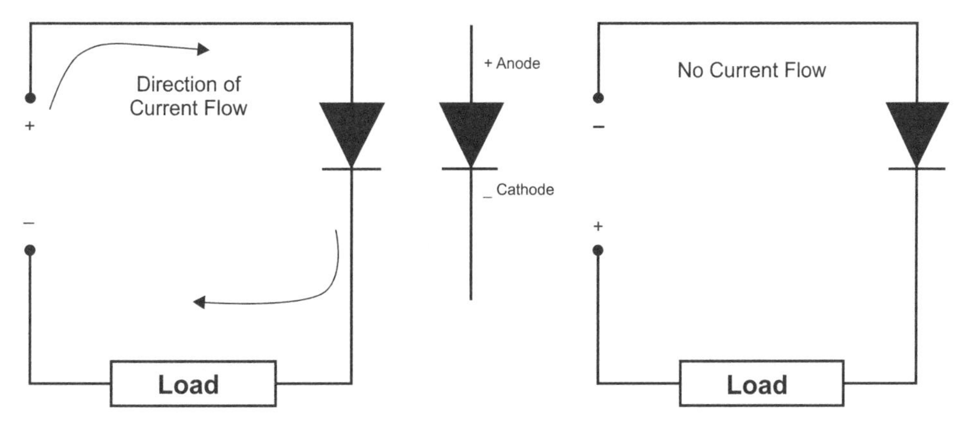

Figure 2-25. Diode symbol and circuit operation

As shown in the figure, current flow would be from positive to negative. A diode allows current flow only in one direction, much like a check valve would allow water to flow in only one direction. If the direction of current flow is from negative to positive, no current will flow. This condition would exist when the power source is AC, which changes direction 60 times/second. A diode has the effect of cutting off the bottom portion of the AC waveform. In doing so, a diode can basically change AC to DC, as shown in Figure 2-26. The circuit on the right (Figure 2-26) is commonly referred to as a *switch mode power supply.*

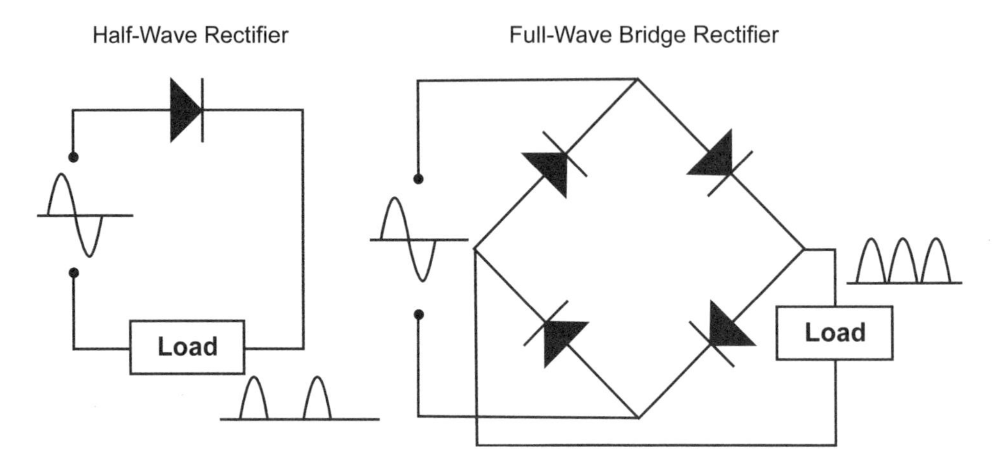

Figure 2-26. Changing AC to DC, using diodes

Many modern three-phase AC drives use a six-diode bridge rectifier circuit that changes AC to DC, which is supplied to the DC bus circuit.

This type of rectifier circuit is the most common in use by today's drive manufacturers and is shown in Figure 2-27.

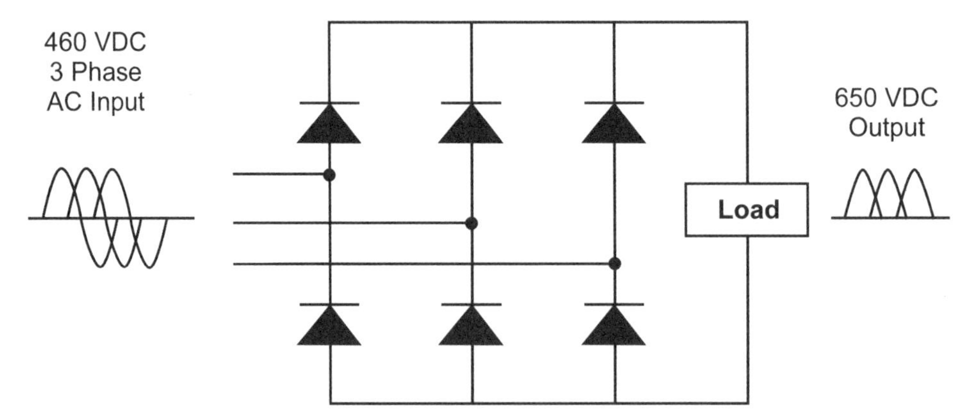

Figure 2-27. Three-phase diode bridge rectifier circuit

This diode bridge circuit works continuously to change AC to DC. There is no control of the output voltage value. As shown in the Figure 2-27, a 460-VAC 3-phase input will yield a 650-VDC output (line voltage × 1.414).

If the drive input voltage is 230 VAC, the diode bridge output would be half (e.g., 325 VDC).

Thyristors (SCRs—Silicon-Controlled Rectifiers)

Diodes provide continuous, fixed-voltage output. However, there are many times when a variable-voltage output is needed. When this is the case, SCRs are typically used. SCRs are essentially two diodes connected back-to-back, with a controlling element called a *gate*. Figure 2-28 shows the schematic symbol for an SCR.

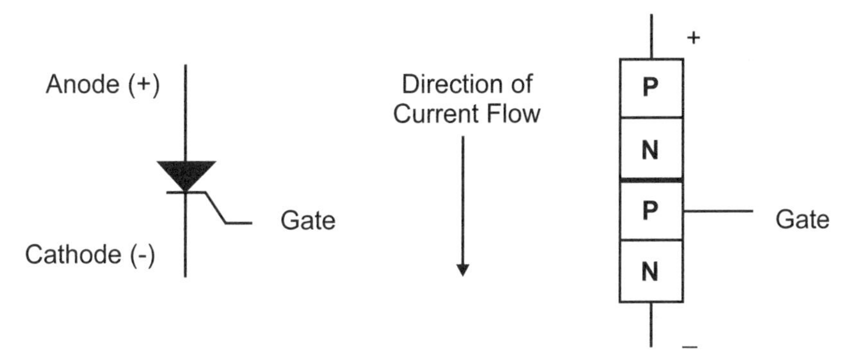

Figure 2-28. Silicon-controlled rectifier (SCR)

When the gate voltage is positive, with respect to the cathode, current is allowed to flow from the anode (+) to the cathode (-). This operation is commonly referred to as *gating on the SCR* or in other terms, *firing the SCR, full-on*. The circuitry associated with SCR gating is called a *pulse generator*. Current flow is limited only by the resistance of the circuit, external to the SCR. As with a diode, an SCR does not allow current to flow in the reverse direction (from cathode to anode).

The SCR is made up of positive (P) and negative (N) junctions—actually two P-N junctions back-to-back. When no gate voltage is applied, at least one of the P-N junctions is *reversed biased* (polarity in the opposite direction). When a junction is reversed biased, no current will flow. When a signal is applied to the gate, both P-N junctions are *forward biased* (polarity in the direction of current flow). Current then flows in the forward direction.

When the positive gate signal is removed, the SCR still remains in a conducting state. The SCR can be "turned off" by cutting off the flow of forward current, by applying a negative polarity to the gate, or by reversing the polarity of the voltage on the anode. When polarity to the SCR is reversed, the SCR will block current flow from the anode to the cathode—basically shut off.

The ability of the SCR to handle high voltages, its small size, and adequate switching speed make it a prime candidate for use in DC as well as AC drives. Switching speed is the ability to quickly turn on and off the device. SCRs can be "turned on" in 1 to 5 μs. However, it may take as much as 100 μs to turn off the SCR.

The basic purpose of the SCR is to control current flow. Figure 2-29 shows how that is accomplished.

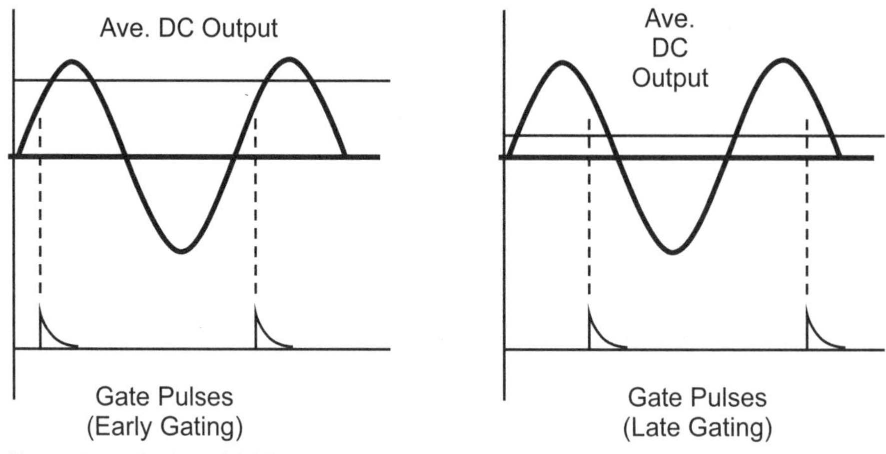

Figure 2-29. Gating of SCR's

The amount of current output from the SCR depends on when the device is *gated on*. If the SCR is gated on early in the AC cycle, a higher average output voltage is seen, compared with a late gating during the AC cycle.

Many DC drives use SCRs in the power section. The basic purpose of a DC drive is to generate DC output from an AC input. The DC output must be variable to allow the DC motor speed to change.

GTOs (Gate Turn-Off) Devices

A GTO is basically an SCR with a bit more capability. The GTO is a switching device that provides the *latching* function (turn-on) capability of an SCR and the controlling function (self turn-off) of a transistor. Turning a GTO on and off is accomplished by simply changing the polarity of the gate current. The GTOs switching time and high current capability is very similar to that of the normal SCR. The GTO features a good short-circuit overload rating, when used in conjunction with overload fuses. Figure 2-30 shows the schematic symbol for a GTO.

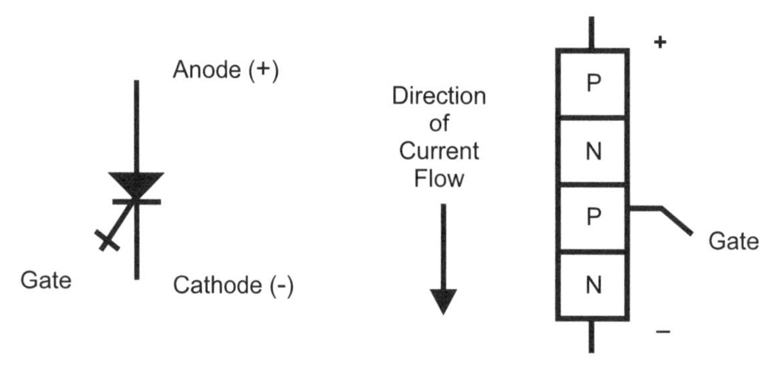

Figure 2-30. GTO (gate turn off) device

GTOs have been successfully applied in AC-drive technology for many years. GTOs can withstand high voltages, between 600–800 V, and have high current capability. Some drive manufacturers still use the GTO for horsepower ranging from 5–1500 HP. The GTO has the ability to be switched on with a positive gate pulse and off with a negative gate pulse without the use of power commutating (switch-off) circuits. A disadvantage of GTOs over SCRs is that GTOs have two to three times the power loss because of the voltage drop across the device.

Transistors

A transistor is a connection of three sections of positive and negative semiconductor material. The *P* and *N* materials are connected so that one of the materials are joined or sandwiched between the other two sections.

There are two basis styles of transistors—NPN and PNP. The style is determined by which material is in the middle, between the other two materials. All transistors contain three leads: emitter, base, and collector. Figure 2-31 shows the two basic styles of transistors and the schematic symbols for each.

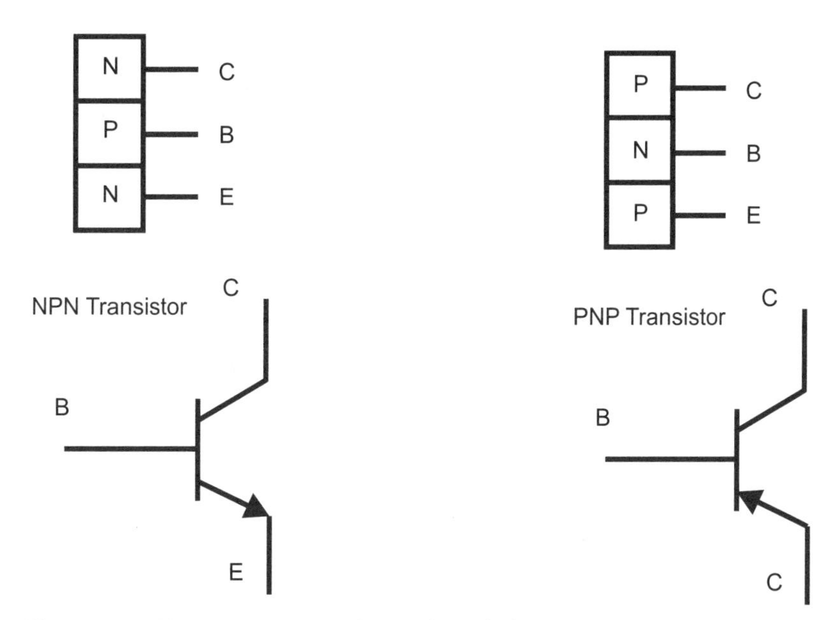

Figure 2-31. Transistor construction and symbols

How the transistor is biased will determine the amount of current flow. The majority of the current flows through the emitter and base to the collector junction. Very little current (2–8%) flows through the base itself. In a transistor, the voltage applied to the base–emitter junction controls the amount of current in the collector. In this way, we can use the transistor as a switching device—allowing large amounts of current output to flow, with only a small amount of controlling voltage applied to the base. When the control current is removed from the base circuit, the transistor stops conducting and *turns off.*

Darlington Bipolar Transistors

A transistor, is a true switch—it can be turned on and turned off by use of a command signal. The power Darlington transistors are essentially two or more bipolar transistors, internally connected in one package. Figure 2-32 shows the schematic symbol for the power Darlington transistor.

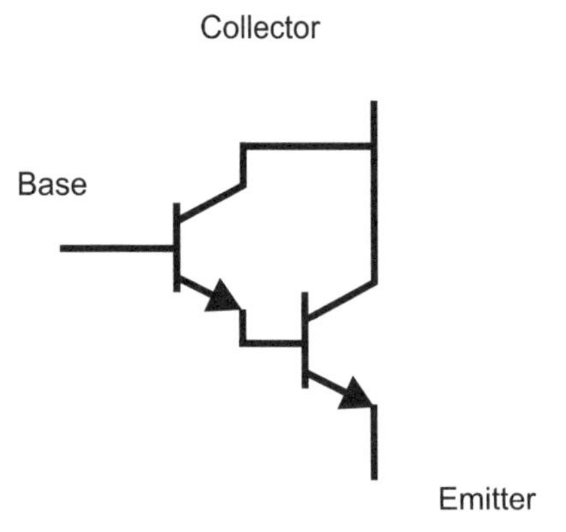

Figure 2-32. Power Darlington transistor

The power Darlington transistor has the advantages of the bipolar transistor, but provides high gain circuitry, much higher than a normal bipolar transistor. The bipolar and power Darlington transistors both have an advantage over SCR and GTO devices. Circuitry that needed to turn on the transistors are much less intensive than that of SCRs and GTOs. In many cases, base driver circuits can be included on existing drive circuit cards, rather than require separate, more complex cards.

IGBTs (Insulated Gate Bipolar Transistors)

IGBTs have fast become the power semiconductor of choice with drive manufacturers from fractional to well over 1000 HP. The IGBT carries all of the advantages of the bipolar and Darlington transistors, but offers one additional feature—increased switching time.

As you will learn in later sections, the switching time of the power semiconductors will have a major role in shaping the output waveform. The faster the switching time, the more exact, electrically, the drive output, compared with pure sine wave power from the utility. An additional benefit of faster switching times is the reduction of audible noise generated by the motor. IGBTs can switch in the 12–16 kHz range, compared with standard transistors of 1–3 kHz.

Higher switching frequencies mean the audible noise is moved out of the normal hearing range. The motor appears to be quieter, compared with a motor operated on a transistor drive. Figure 2-33 traces power device switch times and the number of circuit cards required to operate the devices.

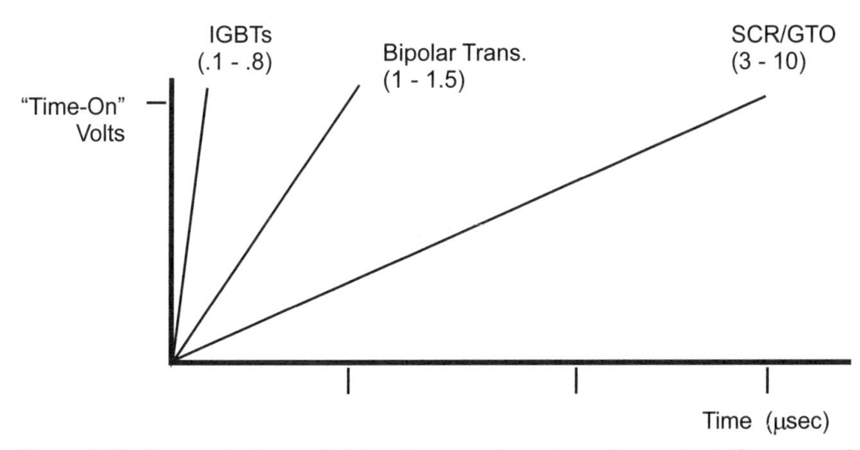

Figure 2-33. Power device switching times and circuit cards required (Courtesy of ABB Inc.)

As seen in Figure 2-33, switching times of the SCR or GTO are in the 3- to10-μs range (500 Hz–1 kHz). On the other hand, switching times of the bipolar transistor are in the 1- to 1.5-μs range (1–4 kHz). The IGBT has the fastest switching time of all: 0.1 to 0.8 μs (5–16 kHz).

The SCR and GTO gained popularity in the early 1960s, and superseded thermionic power devices such as vacuum tubes. AC drives of that era required 12–20 circuit cards to gate on the power devices, turn them off, and verify they were off.

In the early 1980s, bipolar and power Darlington transistors gained popularity because of the switching times as well as the need for only 3–7 circuit cards (the base driver circuitry that caused the transistor to conduct was smaller, therefore requiring less circuit card space).

The currently used IGBT gained acceptance in the early 1990s and caused a further decrease in circuit card requirements. In many cases, hybrid circuitry is included on a power control card, which means the total circuit card count can be down to 2.

The circuitry needed for power semiconductor switching will be examined in greater detail in a later chapter.

Mechanical Principles

Load Types

There are literally hundreds of applications for AC and DC drives. Though it would be almost impossible to cover all possible types, we will review some of the more common applications.

When we look at applications, it is important to consider the load connected to the motor. The load is the determining factor in what type, style, size, and power producing device the motor should be. The drive is the device that will control the motor. In simple terms, it is best to start with the application (load), work backward to the motor (prime mover), then to the drive (controller), and then to the automated or manual control (speed control or PLC).

There are three major categories of mechanical loads - Constant Torque, Constant Horsepower and Variable Torque. Any drive application will fall into one of these three categories. When reviewing the following application types, keep in mind that the drive's primary responsibility it to control the application, protect the motor, and protect itself.

Constant Torque Applications

These types of applications will make up the majority of what we would consider to be industrial applications. Figure 2-34 shows a graph of the characteristics of a constant torque application.

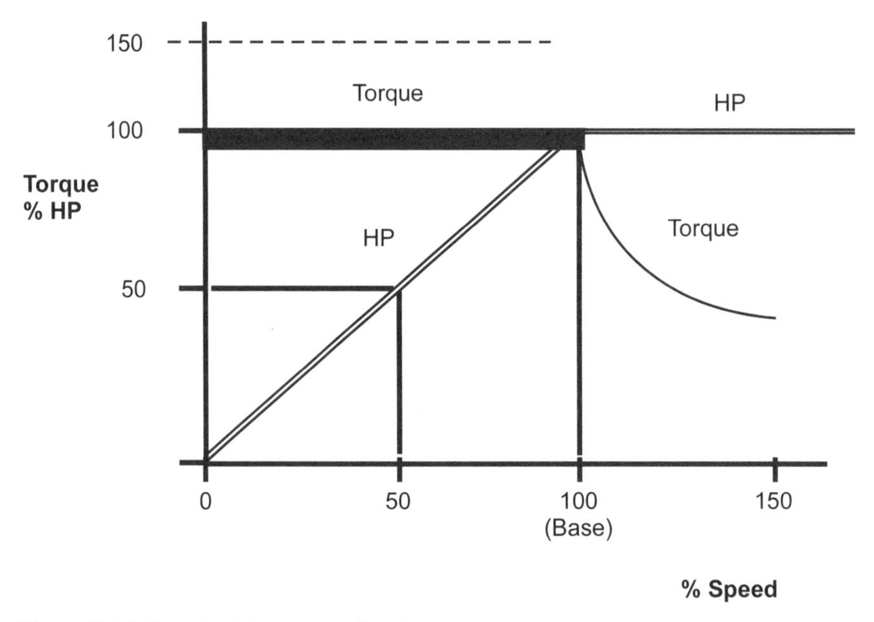

Figure 2-34. Constant torque application

As shown in Figure 2-34, we can see that torque required in this application is 100% and remains constant from zero to base speed (100%). In other words, the rated torque (100%) is required to operate this application, no matter what the speed. In most cases, this application will be operated from only zero to base speed.

It is also evident that this type of application possesses a *variable horsepower* characteristic. In a constant torque application, horsepower is directly proportional to the speed (i.e., at 50% speed, 50% HP is required, etc.). While the horsepower consumed by the motor varies directly with speed, the torque required to power the load remains constant.

In reality, the load may vary from above rated torque (100%) to below rated level and anywhere in between, until the motor attains full speed (in many cases, base speed). In many cases, as much as 150% torque is required to break the load away from a stand-still. The 150% dashed line indicates a possible overload requirement from a motor and drive, if connected to this type of load.

Many applications fall into the constant torque category. The standard belt conveyor shown in Chapter 1 (Figure 1-1) is a prime example. A ball mill in a cement plant is another example. Figure 2-35 shows this process of grinding aggregate into powder for cement.

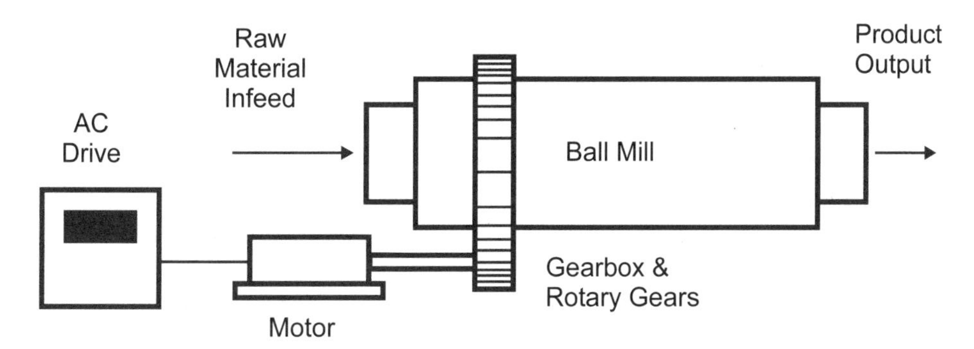

Figure 2-35. Ball mill in a cement plant

In Figure 2-35, the degree of grinding is controlled by the speed of the AC drive. Speeds of less than 120 rpm cause the ball mill cylinder to internally grind the large raw material into smaller particles and eventually into fine granulated powder. The torque required from the motor can be constant from zero to the maximum speed. Overload torque is needed to initially start the mill rotating—with the amount of overload dictated by the amount of material inside the mill at start-up.

Extruders also fall into the constant torque category. A typical extruder, such as a screw extruder for plastic, often requires overload capability, especially when the raw plastic has cooled somewhat and is less than fluid. Figure 2-36 shows a plastic screw extruder.

In Figure 2-36, the AC drive provides variable speed motor operation. It drives the screw vanes at speeds regulated by the temperature of the plastic or the rate of production and die size (output extrusion hole). AC drives provide a high degree of efficiency, while maintaining a constant rate of production accuracy.

Another application combines the use of a rotating feed turntable and a conveyor. Figure 2-37 shows a Rotating Feed Table, which combines both liner motion (conveyor) and rotating motion of a turntable.

As seen in Figure 2-37, the flow rate of the granules can be controlled by the motor speed that is dictated by the AC drive. This type of AC-drive application is highly efficient because of the ability of the drive to accurately regulate motor speed. With accurate motor-speed control, an opti-

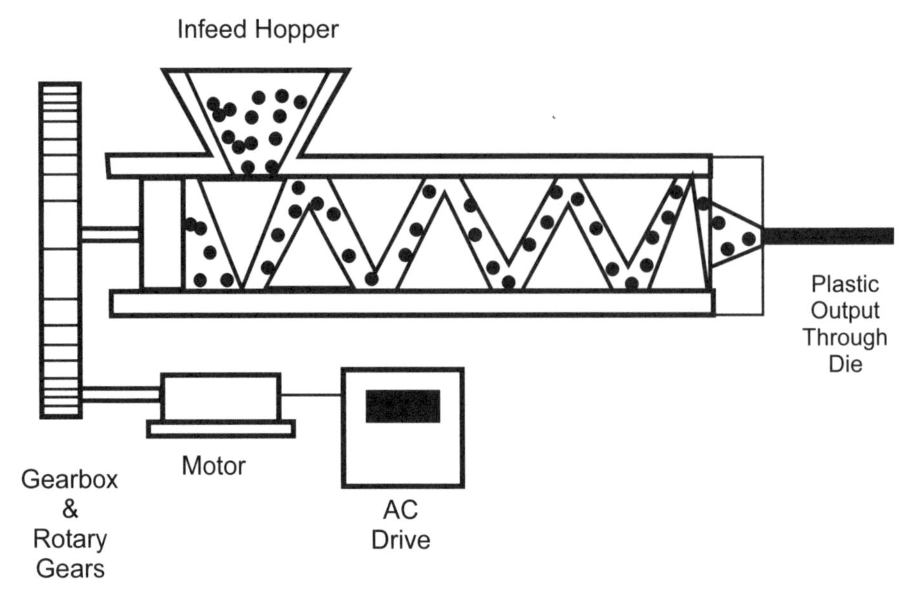

Figure 2-36. Plastic screw extruder

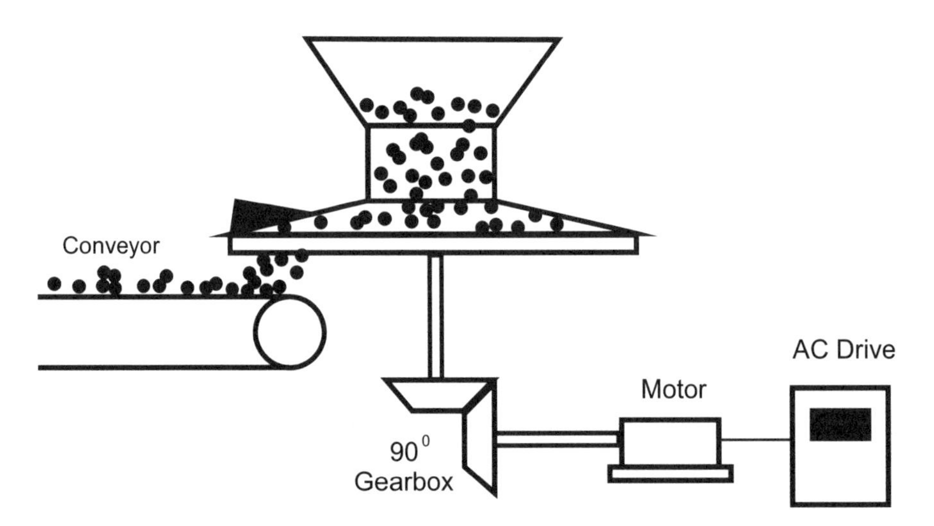

Figure 2-37. Rotating feed table

mum amount of granules can be distributed to the conveyor, which may then be fed to another process, such as heating or coating.

Constant Horsepower Applications

In this type of application, the horsepower required remains constant, while the torque drops off as a ratio of $1/\text{speed}^2$. Figure 2-38 shows the constant horsepower type of load.

Applications of this type operate in the above base speed and below base speed area. The fact that torque drops off as $1/\text{speed}^2$ is an advantage in applications of this type. Figure 2-39 shows a typical constant horsepower application—machine tools.

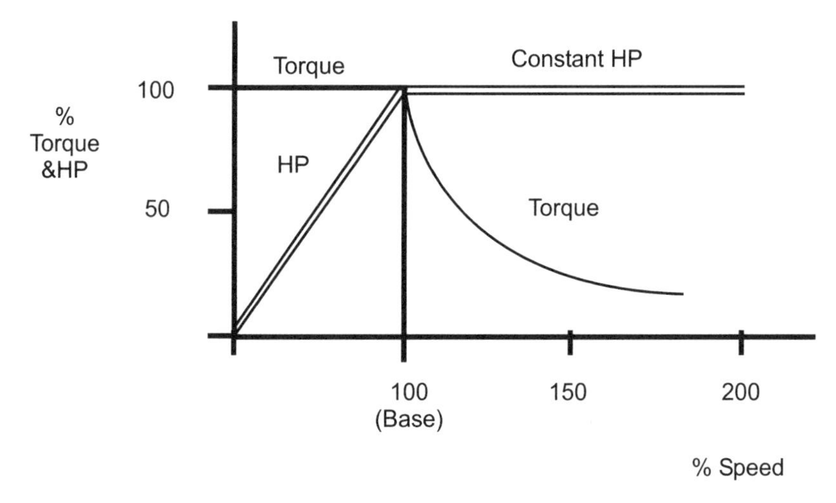

Figure 2-38. Constant horsepower load

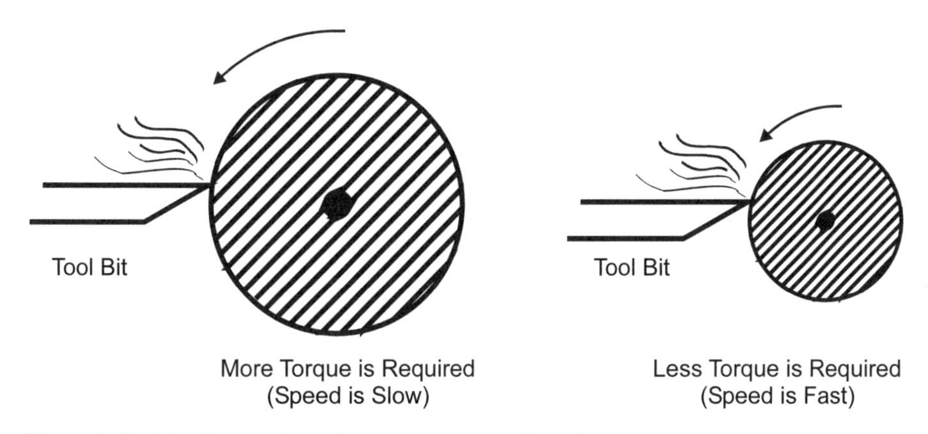

Figure 2-39. Machine tool application (cross section of work piece)

As seen in Figure 2-39, a slow speed is required when the tool bit is taking off large amounts of material. In doing so, a greater amount of torque is required (operating in the "Below Base Speed" section of Figure 2-38). Once the work piece is at the approximate diameter, the speed is increased, and the tool bit is required to take off minimal amounts of material. This process produces a fine, smooth surface (operating in the "Above Base Speed" section of Figure 2-38).

Another example of a constant horsepower application is a center driven winder. Figure 2-40 shows another use of above and below base speed operation.

As seen in Figure 2-40, basically the same scenario exits as with machine tool applications (above and below base speed operation). Very low inertia exists when the take-up roll is first started. This translates to little torque required to start the winding process, thereby allowing a high speed. Once the winding process is started, increasing amounts of inertia are seen at

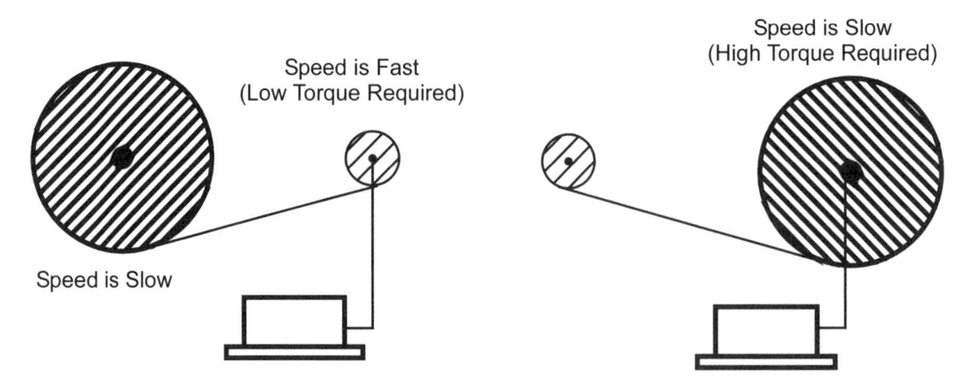

Figure 2-40. Center driven winder (cross section of web roll)

the take-up roll, translating into more torque required, thereby causing the need for a slower speed.

The key to a proper winding process is to have adequate control of torque and speed on the web at all times. If little torque is available at the take-up roll, "telescoping" or bunching of the material is a result. This would be like that of a window shade that is let-go from only one corner. If too much torque is available on the take-up roll, stretching of the material could result, or even worse, a complete break in the web.

Since speed and torque are interactive in this application, it is not necessarily an application for a simple speed-controlled drive. DC drives have found their use in these types of winding applications because of the ease of controlling speed and torque simultaneously. Newer types of AC drives (vector or torque controllers) have also found their way into the control of this type of application in recent years. A more complete discussion of drives specifics in winder applications will be covered in later chapters.

Variable Torque Applications

In this type of application, below base speed, torque required varies as $speed^2$. It should also be noted that the horsepower required varies as $speed^3$. Because of this relationship, this type of application is sometimes referred to as the *cubed exponential* application. Figure 2-41 shows the characteristics of this type of application.

This type of application is a prime candidate for energy savings using AC drives. As seen in the example, to obtain 50% flow rate, only 1/8 or 12.5% horsepower, is required (½ × ½ × ½). It should also be noted that the torque and horsepower curves normally end at the 100% spot (100% speed and 100% torque, flow, and horsepower). Because it is easy to overspeed a motor using a drive, users may have a tendency to increase speed above base, to obtain more CFM output. This is not normally recommended because of the mechanical limitations of the motor and the characteristics of the application.

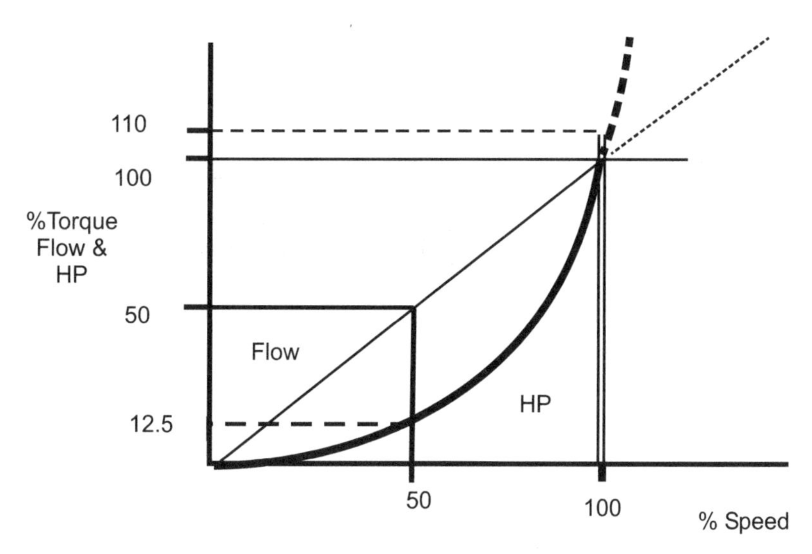

Figure 2-41. Variable torque application

To obtain increased speed above base, a higher output frequency (Hz) must be supplied by the drive. With several Hz output above base, the torque and horsepower curves would follow the natural path indicated by the dashed lines. As shown in the figure, just a few hertz increase in output frequency would cause a much greater demand for motor torque and horsepower. However, flow would continue to increase in a somewhat "linear" manner.

This tremendous increase in torque and horsepower from the motor is now coupled with the fact that decreased motor torque is a natural result of above base speed operation. (Details on this characteristic will be discussed in Chapter 3 – General Principles of Operation.)

The end result is a slight increase in drive output frequency, causing a very large requirement for torque and horsepower, at the same time motor torque is dropping rapidly. Nearly all of the fan systems engineered today take this phenomenon into account. It is rare to need to over-speed a fan, unless the above characteristics are addressed (duct work changes or oversizing the motor, or both).

Because HVAC fan systems are engineered for below base speed operation, typical overload requirements are set at 10%. AC drives that are rated to NEMA standards, will allow 110% current for 1 minute as an overload capability.

As shown in the discussion above, this type of application has two main examples: centrifugal fans and pumps. Figure 2-42 shows a standard HVAC fan application.

In this example, we see that the centrifugal fan is coupled to the motor by means of a belt. The air inlet allows air to enter the fan assembly. Depending on the status of the outlet damper (open, part open, closed), the fan

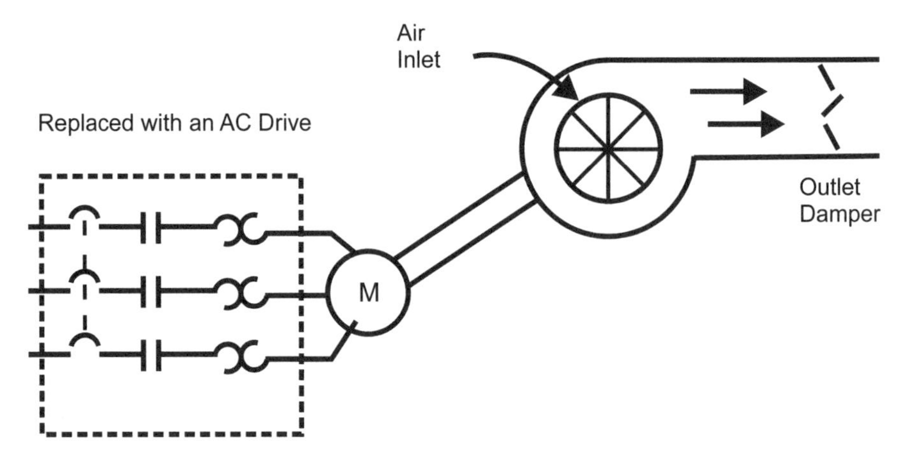

Figure 2-42. HVAC fan application

will blow the amount of air dictated by some control system, typically an actuator. The area in the dashed box indicates a three-phase start contactor and motor overloads to protect the motor, in case of an over-current condition. Also shown is the fact that what's inside the dashed box can be replaced by an AC drive.

As can be imagined, the fan continues to run at full speed, 24 hours a day. This is required, regardless of the status of the outlet damper, because there is no device controlling the speed of the motor. The device that controls airflow has no effect on the speed of the motor and fan.

This method of variable flow control is quite inefficient. Figure 2-43 shows a graph of how the fan actually operates on the basis of the system shown in Figure 2-42. The fan curve indicates the fixed speed fan. The system curve indicates the status of the outlet damper and also the size and shape of the sheet metal duct work.

To reduce the airflow in this fixed-speed system, the actuator must close down the outlet damper, thereby restricting air output. If 50% airflow is desired, the position of the outlet damper must be modified by the actuator, which changes the system curve (indicated by the dashed curve). The air output is reduced; however, the pressure in the system duct work has increased, placing additional load on the motor. This additional load translates to more horsepower required to operate with less airflow.

If the start contactor assembly were replaced by a variable-frequency AC drive, the outlet damper would be locked in full open position (indicated by the existing system curve). For every output frequency of the AC drive, a new fan curve occurs (indicated by the dashed curves).

As seen, where the new fan curves cross the fixed system curve, a different percentage of flow output is achieved. It can also be seen that the amount of pressure in the duct work never exceeds 100%. In essence, if there is

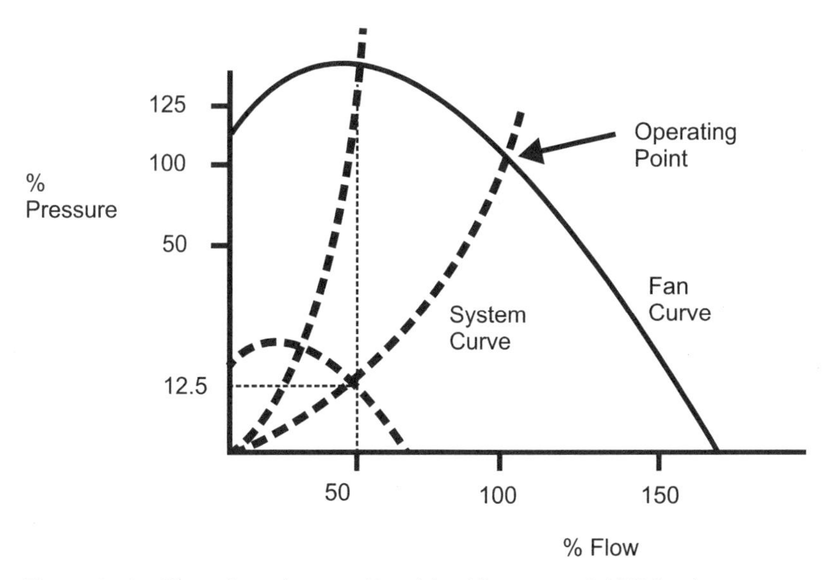

Figure 2-43. Operation of a centrifugal fan (Courtesy of ABB Inc.)

less pressure, the motor doesn't work as hard and energy is saved, compared with full-speed operation.

This same principle works for centrifugal pumps. Reduced speed is a definite advantage when operating a pump, which leads to reduced energy use. However, when speed reduction is contemplated, the optimum efficiency of the pump must be taken into consideration. Pumps have "efficiency islands" around the crossing of the pump and system curves. Any energy savings gained can be lost if operation is done outside these efficiency islands because of greater pump inefficiency.

Speed, Torque, and Horsepower

Understanding speed, torque, and horsepower is essential to understanding mechanical systems. The following discussion will help you gain a basic insight into these relationships, and will help prepare you for a discussion of inertia.

Torque and horsepower are two very important characteristics that determine the size of the motor required for a particular drive application. The difference between the two can be explained using the illustration in the next section.

Torque

Torque is basically a turning effort. Suppose we have a worker that is required to raise a construction elevator by hand. Figure 2-44 shows this example and demonstrates the process of applying torque.

This worker must supply the required torque to raise the elevator from the first floor to the second floor (Figure 2-44).

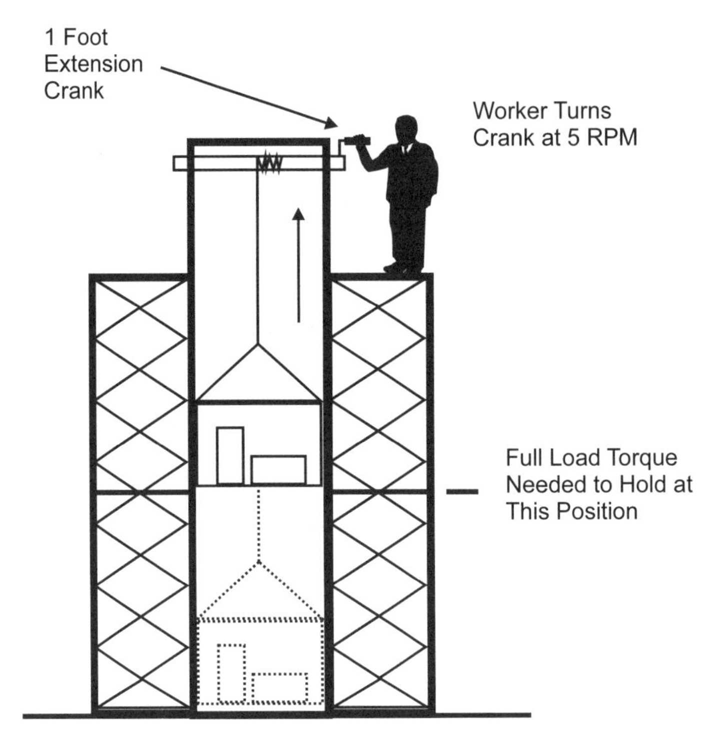

Figure 2-44. Using torque to turn a hand crank

In this example, the worker cannot raise the elevator even though he applies 1 lb-ft of torque.

Note: *Torque = Force × Distance. In this case, the worker applies 1 lb of force on the crank, which is 1 foot in length. We say the torque is one pound times one foot or one lb-ft.*

If the worker wants to raise the elevator, more torque must be applied to the hand crank. The worker has two choices: either place more force on the crank or increase the length of the crank. The worker chooses to increase the length of the extension on the hand crank. The elevator now moves, even though the worker does not apply any more force. Figure 2-45 shows this procedure.

In this case, the worker has developed 5 lb-ft of torque, more than enough torque to turn the crank and raise the elevator.

If the worker turns the crank twice as fast, the torque remains the same. Regardless of how fast the worker turns the crank, as long as the worker is turning it at a steady rate, the torque is unchanged.

Horsepower (HP)

Horsepower takes into account the speed at which the worker turns the crank. Turning the crank faster takes more *horsepower* than turning it slowly. Horsepower is a rate of doing work.

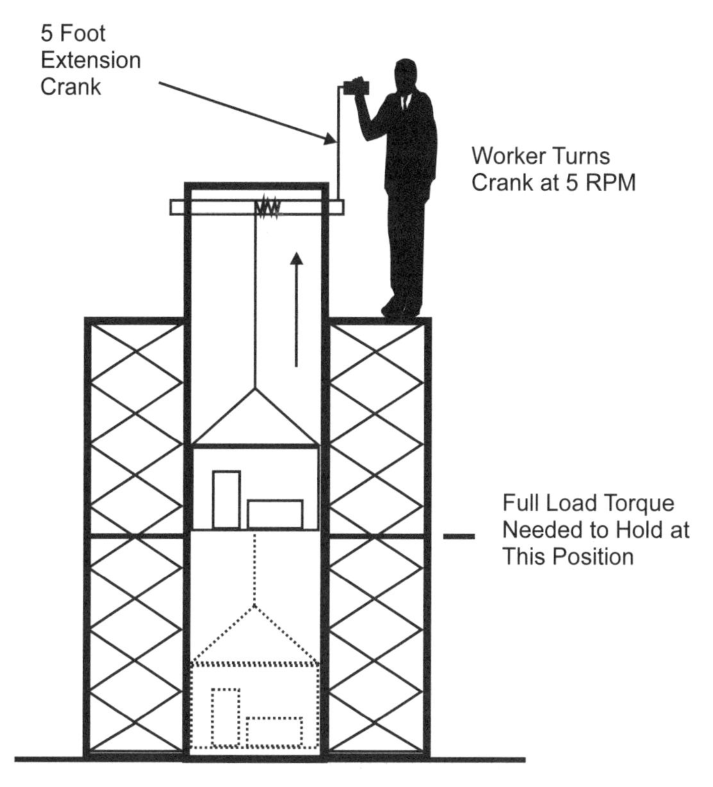

Figure 2-45. Increased length of the hand crank

Note: *By definition, 1 horsepower equals 33,000 ft-lb per minute. In other words, to lift a 33,000-lb weight 1 ft in 1 minute would take 1 HP.*

By using the formula below, we can determine the horsepower developed by the worker. We know the system in Figure 2-44 is developing 5 lb-ft of torque.

Formula:

$$HP = \frac{T \times N}{5252}$$

T = torque in lb-ft

N = speed in rpm

The worker turns the crank at 5 rpm as shown in Figure 2-44. By inserting the known information into the formula, we find that the worker is developing approximately .005 HP ($5 \times 5 \div 5252 = .0047$). As seen by the formula, horsepower is directly related to the speed of turning the crank. If the worker turns the crank twice as fast (10 rpm), he will develop almost .010 HP.

Inertia

Inertia is the measurement of an object's resistance to change in velocity (speed). The measurement holds true whether the object is at a stop or moving at a constant velocity. By definition, inertia deals with the presence of mechanical "resistance." Inertia is resistant to changes in speed or direction.

Note: *In electrical terms, an inductor opposes changes in current, due to resistance. In mechanical terms, inertia opposes changes in speed, also due to resistance.*

Inertia is the reason why your auto can't immediately accelerate from 0–65 mph. As logic would dictate, a 4.5-L engine would be needed to power a large luxury auto, and only a 2.5-L engine would be needed for a small auto. If we apply previously learned concepts of speed, torque, and horsepower, the larger the auto, more horsepower is needed to accelerate from 0–65 mph in 15 seconds. Figure 2-46 shows a comparison of horsepower and speed, in relation to inertia.

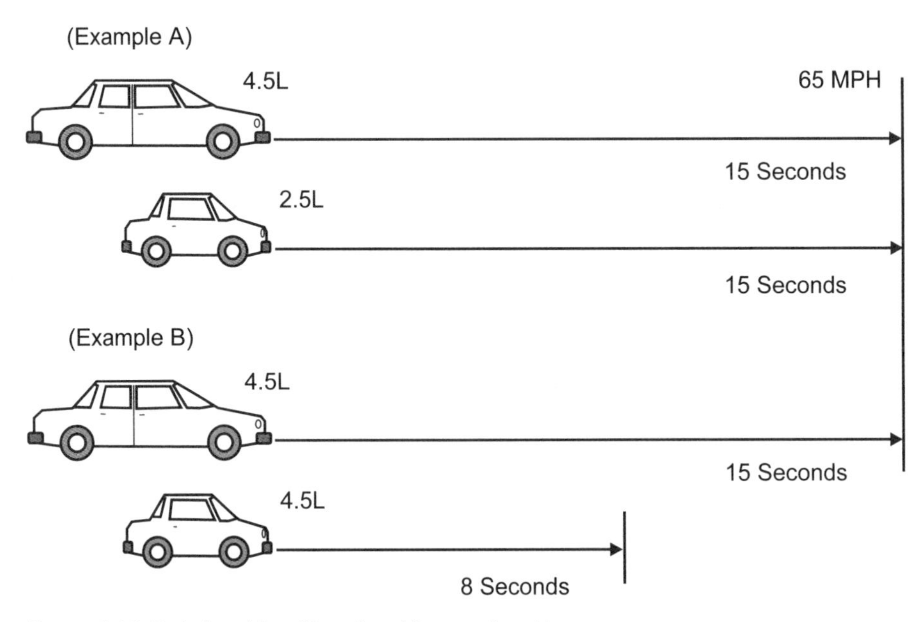

Figure 2-46. Relationship of inertia with speed and horsepower

As seen in Figure 2-46, a higher amount of horsepower is needed to overcome inertia and accelerate the auto, to achieve a speed of 65 mph in 15 s (example A of the figure). The previous would be true if the engines were sized properly in both the large and small autos. However, if the small car needed quicker acceleration capability, we would use the same 4.5-liter engine as in the large auto. The small auto would achieve quicker acceleration because of its oversized engine (example B of the figure).

It should be noted here that the principles of inertia, torque, horsepower, and speed apply to an electromechanical motor. With that in mind, it should also be noted that the extra horsepower of the 4.5-L engine would be needed only on acceleration. A large amount of horsepower is needed for quick acceleration, but only a small amount is needed to keep the auto moving at a constant speed.

This principle is similar to pushing someone on a swing. A large amount of effort is needed to get the person started in a swinging motion, but only a small tap every cycle is needed to keep the person going. The amount of inertia is greater when at a standstill, than when the swing is already in motion.

In relation to rotating machinery, a flywheel would be termed a *high-inertia load*. It would take a large amount of energy to quickly bring the flywheel up and back down in speed. The main reason is that high inertia loads have high resistance to change (in this case, change in speed).

Inertia has a significant impact on which size of drive is chosen to accelerate a high inertia load. We will take a brief look at some commonly used formulas to calculate acceleration and inertia.

The following information will assist you in your general understanding of inertia-related calculations. The logical place to start is to label terms and units of measure. When looking at inertia, two different ways of labeling are commonly used: WK^2 and WR^2. Both terms relate the formula to inertia.

WR^2 refers to the inertia of a rotating object that was calculated by assuming the weight of the object was concentrated around the rim—at a certain distance. That distance is termed R and is the distance from the center of the object. (By strict definition, WR^2 is the weight of an object [W] times its radius [R] squared.) In this definition, inertia is that property by which an object in motion will stay in motion, until acted upon by another force. An example of an inertia calculation of this type is a flywheel.

WK^2 refers to the inertia of a rotating object that was calculated by assuming the weight of the object is concentrated at some smaller distance. The smaller distance is termed K. (By strict definition, WK^2 is the weight of an object times its radius of gyration value squared.) Examples of this type of inertia calculation would be cylinders, pulleys, or gears.

The units of measurement for inertia is the lb-ft^2 (pronounced pound-feet squared). Another unit sometimes found in inertia calculations is in-lb-sec^2, used in calculations for the moment of inertia (motion control applications using servos). Initially, calculations using lb-ft^2 will be used to demonstrate calculations of inertia.

The next section will present some commonly used formulas using torque, horsepower, inertia, and time. These formulas will be used as examples for calculations based on rotating machinery, which need to be considered before drive selection can begin.

Accelerating Torque

The following formula calculates the torque required for rotating motion to begin:

$$T = \frac{WK^2 \times \Delta N}{308 \times t}$$

where:

T = acceleration torque in lb-ft

WK^2= total reflected inertia (total of motor, gear reducer, and load) in lb-ft^2

ΔN = change in speed required in seconds

t = time to accelerate the total system load

A term above that may not be familiar, is the term *reflected inertia*. Basically, this term is used to describe the inertia found at the motor shaft, and is a standard term found throughout the rotating machinery industry. A speed reducer (gear box or belt coupler) changes the inertia that the motor shaft actually sees. More on this subject will be discussed later in this chapter.

Acceleration Time

The next formula is a rearranged version of the previous one, only it allows for the calculation of the time needed to accelerate, given a specified amount of torque, inertia, and change in speed.

$$t = \frac{WK^2 \times \Delta N}{308 \times T}$$

where:

t = time to accelerate the total system load

WK^2 = total reflected inertia (total of motor, gear reducer, load) in lb-ft^2

ΔN = change in speed required in seconds

T = acceleration torque in lb-ft

The following are examples of how inertia is calculated and how much time is needed to accelerate a machine with the specified requirements.

One note regarding calculations should be added here. When performing inertia calculations, two measurement units are commonly used: lb-ft^2 and in-lb-sec^2. For the most part, many calculations are defined in lb-ft^2, which is the units of measure for WK^2 or WR^2. However, in many motion control (servo) applications, inertia is defined in terms of in-lb-sec^2, which is the units of measure for the moment of inertia (J). When performing inertia calculations, be consistent with the formulas and units of measure used. For most practical motion-control applications involving inertia given as J, the following conversions can be used to convert lb-ft^2 to in-lb-sec^2 and vice versa.

To convert a calculated answer of lb-ft^2 to in-lb-sec^2, divide the answer by 2.68.

To convert a calculated answer of in-lb-sec^2 to lb-ft^2, multiply the answer by 2.68.

Solid Cylinder Inertia Calculations

To calculate the inertia of a solid cylinder, the following formula is used.

$$WK^2 = .000681 \times \rho \times L \times D^4$$

where:

WK^2 = inertia of a cylinder in lb-ft^2

ρ = density of cylinder material in lb/in^3

L = length of the cylinder in inches

D = diameter of the cylinder in inches

Note: *The units of measure for WK^2 are in lb-ft^2. Refer to Figure 2-47.*

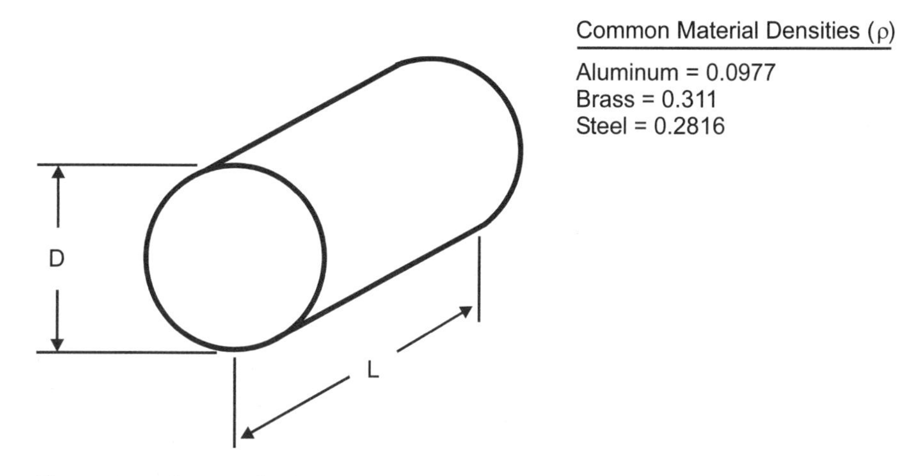

Figure 2-47. Inertia of solid cylinders

For an example of a solid cylinder, let's consider a solid aluminum roll that has a length of 72 inches and a diameter of 18 inches. Its inertia would be:

$$WK^2 = .000681 \times 0.0977 \times 72 \times 18^4$$

$$WK^2 = .000681 \times 0.0977 \times 72 \times 104976$$

$$WK^2 = 502.62 \text{ lb-ft}^2$$

Now that the inertia has been calculated (WK^2), the time it would take to accelerate the system can be determined as follows:

From 0 to 1200 rpm, with an acceleration torque available of 30 lb-ft, the formula for acceleration time will be used:

$$t = \frac{WK^2 \times \Delta N}{308 \times T}$$

Therefore:

$$t = \frac{502.62 \times 1200}{308 \times 30} = \frac{603144}{9240}$$

$$t = 65.27 \text{ s}$$

If the time calculated is too long, then the easiest item to control would be the amount of available acceleration torque—meaning the motor. The motor would have to be upsized to have increased available acceleration torque. Motor torque will again be discussed in the chapter on DC and AC motors.

Hollow Cylinder Inertia Calculations

To calculate the inertia of a hollow cylinder, basically the same formula can be used, but without the inertia of the hollow section. The formula would be:

$$WK^2 = .000681 \times \rho \times L \times (D_2^{\,4} - D_1^{\,4})$$

Figure 2-48 shows a hollow cylinder with the formula parts.

where:

WK^2 = inertia of a cylinder in lb-ft^2

ρ = density of cylinder material in lb/in^3

L = length of the cylinder in inches

D_2 = outside diameter of the cylinder in inches

D_1 = inside diameter of the cylinder in inches.

If we take the previous example and only solve inertia for the hollow cylinder above, we would go through the following calculations. We will assume the same information regarding the cylinder:

Solid aluminum roll has a length of 72 inches, an outside diameter of 18 inches, and an inside hollow diameter of 12 inches. Therefore, we would go through the following calculations:

$$WK^2 = .000681 \times 0.0977 \times 72 \times (18^4 - 12^4)$$

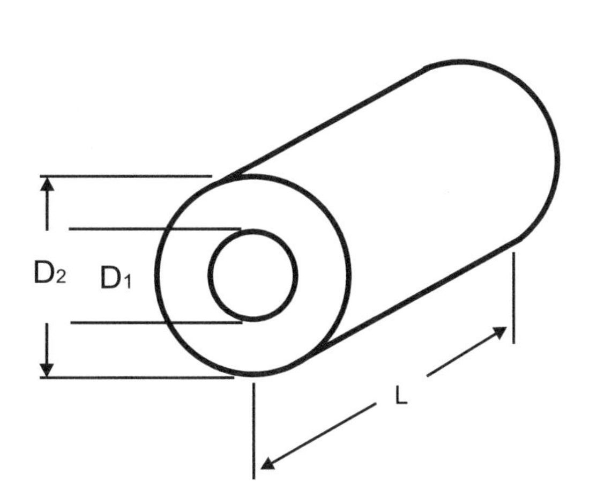

Figure 2-48. Inertia of hollow cylinders

$$WK^2 = .000681 \times 0.0977 \times 72 \times (104976 - 20736)$$

$$WK^2 = .000681 \times 0.0977 \times 72 \times 84240$$

$$WK^2 = 403.34 \text{ lb-ft}^2$$

If we use the above inertia, we can again find the time it would take to accelerate the system. We will use the same example:

From 0 to 1200 rpm, with an acceleration torque available of 30 lb-ft, the formula for acceleration time will be used:

$$t = \frac{WK^2 \times \Delta N}{308 \times T}$$

Therefore:

$$t = \frac{403.403 \times 1200}{308 \times 30} = \frac{484008}{9240}$$

$$t = 52.38 \text{ s}$$

We have determined that the amount of time to accelerate the hollow-cylinder system is definitely less, compared with a solid cylinder. However, it should be noted that the amount of time reduction is not as much as expected. With 66% of the cylinder removed, there was only a reduction of about 13 s of acceleration time. This indicates a characteristic of inertia—the largest amount of inertia is concentrated around the rim, as opposed to the center part of the object.

The same formulas would be used to determine the inertia of pulleys, sheaves, and other rotating objects. Simply break up the objects into solid and hollow cylinders and apply the formulas previously discussed. Then add all the inertia components calculated and determine the time required for acceleration of the system.

Reflected Inertia

One additional note should be stated about inertia. The term *reflected inertia* is the inertia actually found at the motor shaft. This term is standard throughout the industry. A speed reducer (gear box or belt type of coupling device) changes the inertia that the motor actually sees. Figure 2-49 shows this phenomenon.

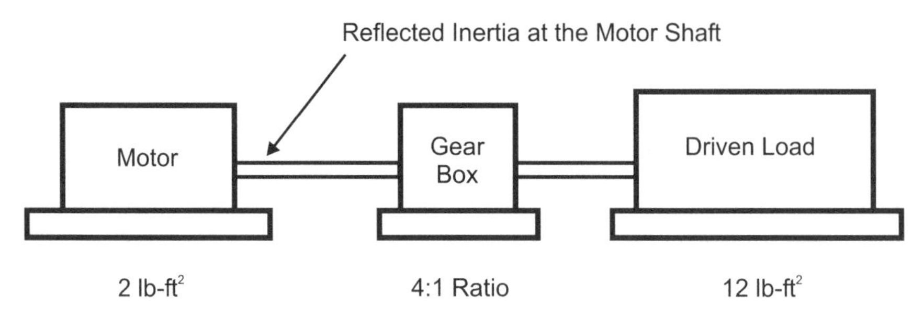

Figure 2-49. Reflected inertia of a system

As seen in Figure 2-49, if an adjustable speed drive was sized for an inertia of 12 lb-ft^2, it may be much larger than actually necessary. Reflected inertia also includes inertia of the actual motor.

Power transmission devices (gear boxes, belts, and pulleys) serve to make the motor's job easier. In our next section, we will look at gear boxes and speed reducers in more detail and determine what relationship exists between speed, torque, and horsepower.

Mechanical Devices

Introduction

As you may recall in an earlier section on horsepower, a worker had to apply a certain amount of torque and horsepower to raise the elevator. The job would have been much easier if some sort of gearing device was applied to the crank, thereby changing the ratio of one revolution of the pulley. Mechanical devices such as belts, sheaves, pulleys, and gear boxes allow this change in ratio.

An easy place to start the discussion of ratios is the common 15-speed bicycle (Figure 2-50).

To get enough torque to start the bicycle in motion, the rider would place the gears into first gear. Notice that the rear wheel sprocket (first gear sprocket) is smaller than the pedal sprocket.

This means that the rear gear sprocket would make five revolutions compared with one revolution of the pedal sprocket. As seen in Figure 2-50,

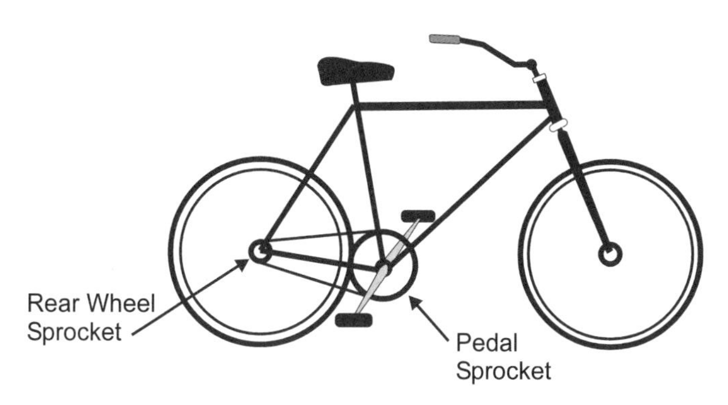

Figure 2-50. Gear ratios—first gear

first gear indicates a 1:5 ratio (one revolution of the driving shaft, in this case the pedal) compared with five revolutions of the output shaft (rear wheel sprocket).

If we assume that the rider did not place the bicycle into first gear and tried to start out in fifteenth gear, we would have a scenario seen in Figure 2-51.

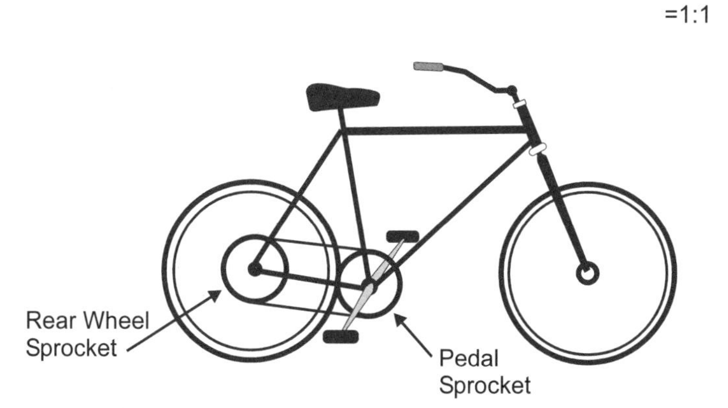

Figure 2-51. Gear ratios—fifteenth gear

As seen in Figure 2-51, the ratio of the rear sprocket to the pedal sprocket has changed to 1:1. Basically there is no mechanical advantage for the rider and therefore no reason to own a 15-speed bicycle. Essentially, the gear arrangement on a bicycle reduces the amount of reflected inertia to the pedal sprocket. This makes the job of starting the bicycle in motion much easier, with less torque applied by the rider. We could consider this action that of breakaway torque required to start the system in motion.

The only item that changed in this example is the amount of inertia reflected back to the pedals, by way of the gears. The weight and inertia of the rider remained constant, no matter what gear was selected. We will use these same principles and apply them to the following power transmission devices.

Belts and Pulleys

Flat and V–Belts

A common arrangement for belt–pulley type transmission systems is the flat belt shown in Figure 2-52. Belt–pulley arrangements are sometimes called belt–sheave, meaning that there is more than one pulley attached together, giving several selections of gear ratios.

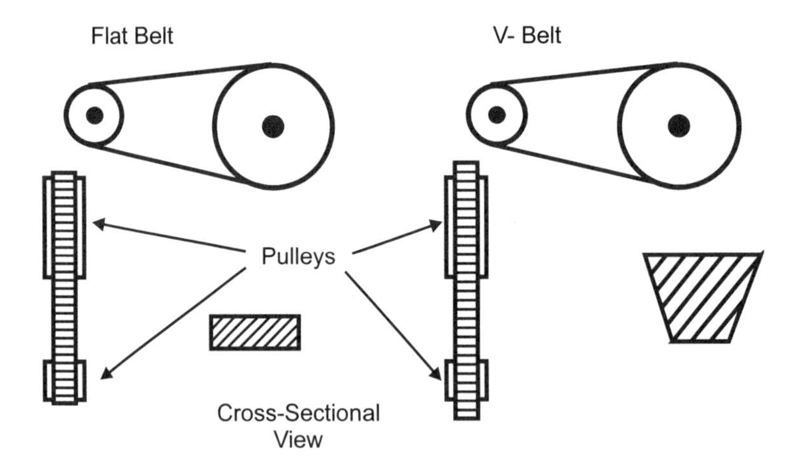

Figure 2-52. Belt–pulley arrangements

For smaller pulley diameters, the flat belt provides low weight and inertia to the power system. A disadvantage of the flat belt is that they rely on maximum friction with minimum slippage to function properly.

The v-belt arrangement allows more surface area with the inside of the pulley, which increases the friction capability (Figure 2-51). V-belts provide shock absorption between the drive and driven shafts due to its inherent v-shaped design. According to some machinery designers, a speed ratio of 7:1 is satisfactory for a v-belt system. Most flat and v-belts are constructed of nylon or durable fibers imbedded in rubber.

Both these types of systems require a certain amount of friction to operate properly. In many cases, some type of tensioning device (spring arrangement) is used to keep the belts tight and efficiency at maximum.

In some applications, a precise belt system is needed. A specific revolution in the driven shaft would produce a specific revolution in the output shaft, with little to no slippage to reduce efficiency. This type of belt system would be the synchronous belt system.

Synchronous Belts

The synchronous belt system is sometimes known as the timing belt system and is shown in Figure 2-53.

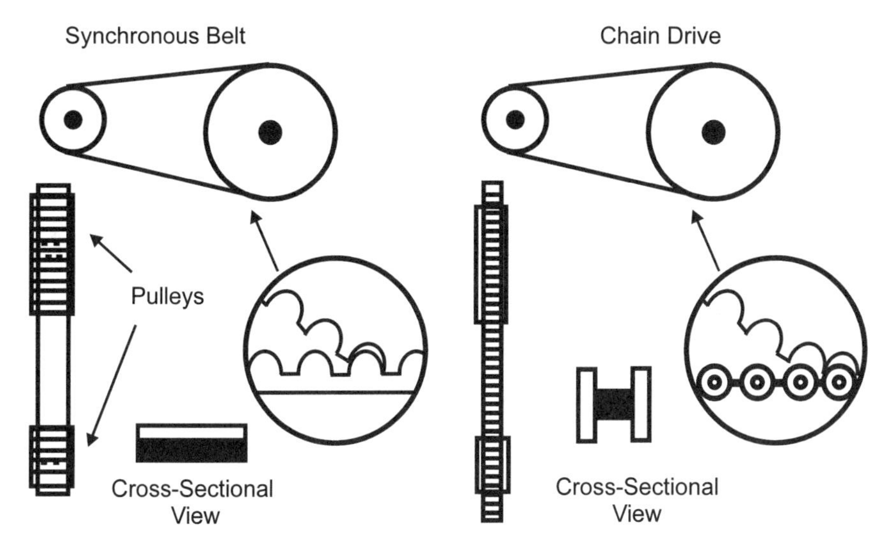

Figure 2-53. Synchronous belts system

The synchronous belt system is basically a flat belt with a series of evenly spaced teeth on the inside of the belt. This system provides the advantages of a belt, with positive grip features and little slip.

Chains and Sprockets

Chain Drive

Chain drives are often used in the same manner as synchronous belts and provide positive synchronization between transmission shafts, especially when large amounts of torque are required (Figure 2-53).

The stretching action of belt systems is not a problem for a chain drive. However, depending on the number of teeth in the drive gear sprockets, slight pulsations (whipping action) could occur in the drive gear sprockets. This can cause a noise or vibration problem if the pulsations are great enough.

Couplings, Gearboxes, and Speed Reducers

In many cases, some positive method of connecting two shafts together is required when the shafts operate along the same centerline. The two most common types of couplings are *rigid* and *flexible* couplings.

The two most common types of rigid coupling are the *flange* and the *sleeve* type.

Flange Coupling

As the name would imply, the flange type uses two metallic flanges slipped over the ends of the two shafts and bolted together. Each individual flange is either pressure fit over the shaft keyway, or locked onto the shaft by some other method such as a set screw (Figure 2-54).

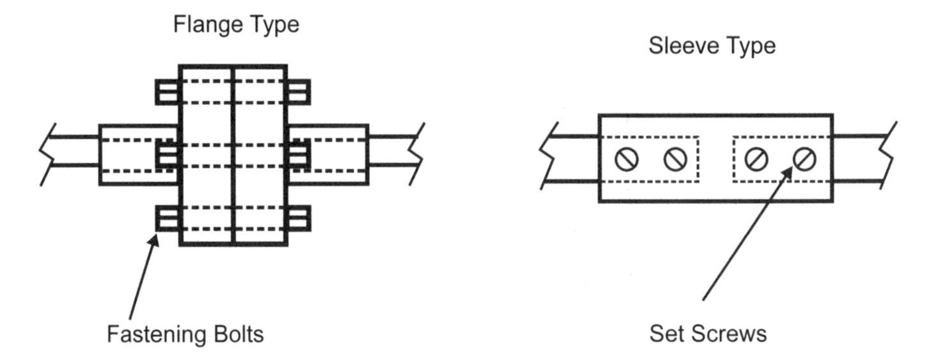

Figure 2-54. Flange and sleeve-type couplings

Flexible Couplings

The function of the flexible coupling is the same as the rigid coupling. The difference between the two is the flexing or twisting capability of the coupling parts (within limits).

A certain amount of flexing is expected with this type of coupling. Flexing may be caused by: misalignment of the shafts, shaft end movement due to insufficient motor and machine mounting, or simple vibration between the connected devices.

The flexible part of the coupling could be considered a "mechanical fuse." If the flexible part fails, it is a sign of mechanical drive trouble in the system. The mechanical system should be thoroughly checked out before the flexible part is replaced, which is the same for an electrical system replacement. We will take a brief look at the two types of flexible couplings: mechanically flexible and elastically flexible.

Mechanically Flexible

These types of couplings obtain their flexibility from the rolling or sliding of the mating parts. As expected, these parts do require some type of periodic lubrication. Typical examples are gear, chain, and sprocket and disc types, shown in Figure 2-55.

Elastically Flexible

This type of coupling (sometimes referred to as elastomeric) obtains its flexibility from the stretching or compressing of a material such as rubber or plastic. The sliding or flexing that takes place is minimal, and lubrication is not required. These types of couplings come in designs such as jaw, clamped, or unclamped donut, and the tire (Figure 2-56).

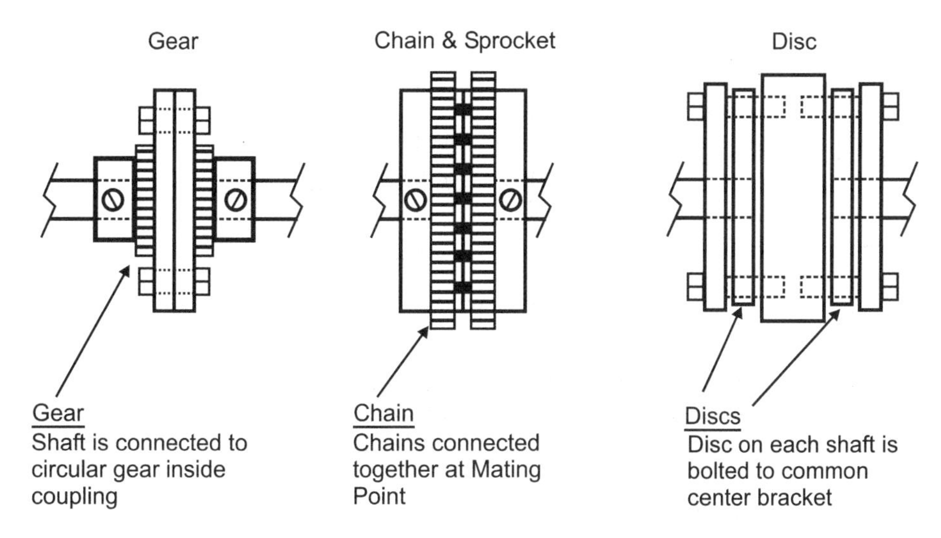

Figure 2-55. Mechanically flexible couplings

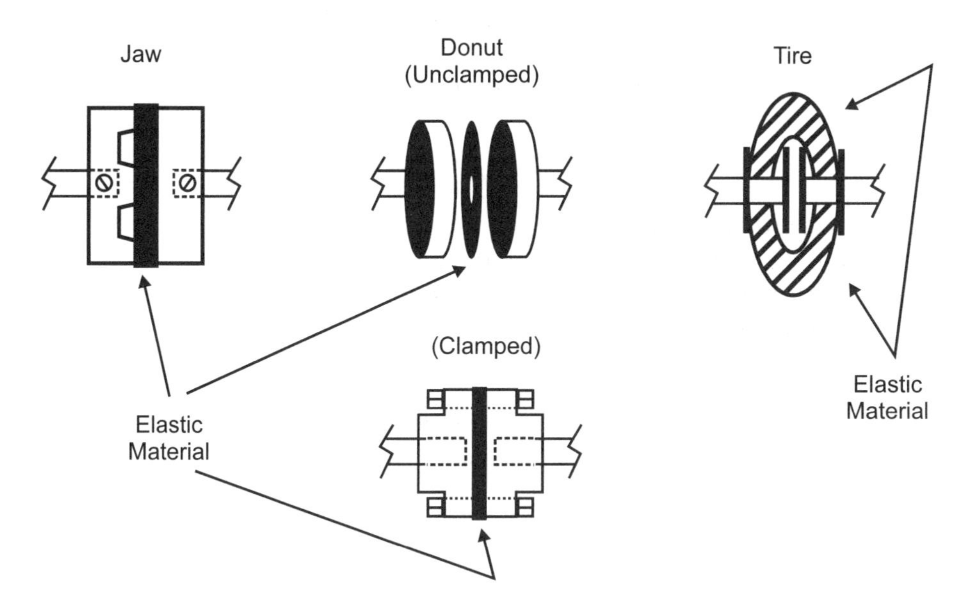

Figure 2-56. Elastically flexible couplings

Gearboxes and Speed Reducers

Gearboxes and speed reducers transmit mechanical power from the motor shaft to the driven load. A simple speed reducer contains two different sized gears, called spur gears. Spur gears are straight teeth cut parallel to the axis of rotation. Speed reducers may have more than two gears, which provide several fixed speed outputs. If that is the case, some type of clutch arrangement will exist to change gears. Figure 2-57 shows the gear relationship within a speed-reducer case.

As seen in Figure 2-57, this type of device provides an efficient means of transmitting positive speed, direction, and torque. In many cases, this device will change speed, with a corresponding change in torque or output

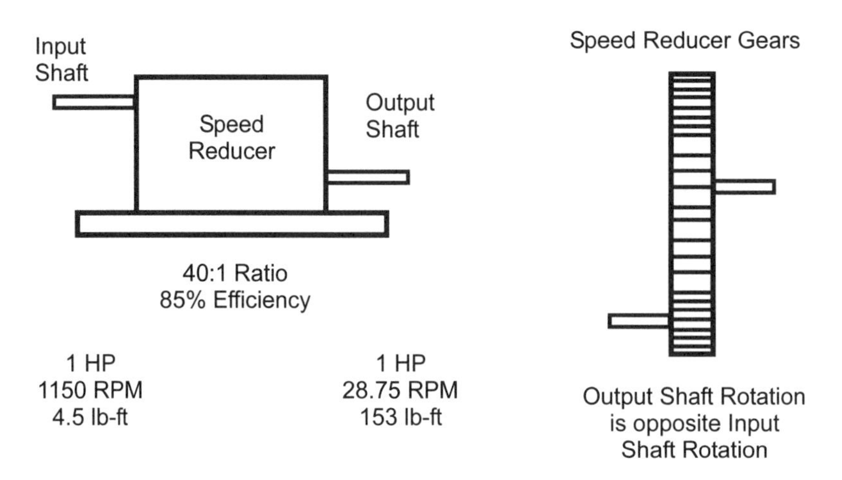

Figure 2-57. Speed-reducer characteristics

direction. The gear reducer acts as a torque amplifier, increasing the torque output by a factor proportional to the ratio, less an efficiency factor.

As seen in Figure 2-57, if a 1150-rpm motor delivers 4.5 lb-ft of torque to the input shaft, then 153 lb-ft of torque is present at the output shaft (given the efficiency of 85%). The formula used is lb-ft × reducer ratio × efficiency of the speed reducer. Therefore, $4.5 \times 40 \times 0.85 = 153$ lb-ft of output torque.

To change the output speed by more than one fixed ratio, more than two gears are required. The same is true if the direction of rotation of the output shaft needs to be identical to that of the input shaft. The type of gear used depends on the application (i.e., horizontal axis of rotation, vertical to horizontal axis of rotation, etc.). Figure 2-58 shows several types of gears used in common speed reducers.

As shown in Figure 2-58, the speed reducer is operating at 85% efficiency. A brief look at mechanical efficiency would be helpful in understanding the actual output of the device. As previously stated, efficiency is the ratio of output power to input power and is expressed in a percent. Therefore the formula for efficiency would be:

$$\text{Efficiency}(\%) = \frac{\text{output} \times 100}{\text{input}}$$

When considering the efficiency of a belt type of device, the more friction available, the less slippage that occurs, and the higher the efficiency. The output shaft turns simultaneously with the input shaft.

In belt systems, several factors aid in decreasing total system efficiency: (1) Losses that occur due to friction of the rubber and cords as the belt stretches and flexes. (2) Friction of the belt as it enters and leaves the pul-

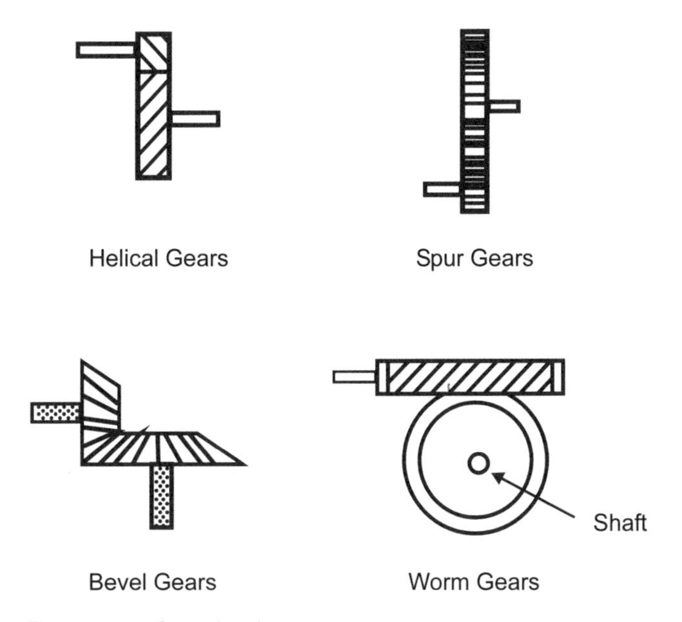

Figure 2-58. Speed reducer gear types

ley or sheave. (3) Bearing friction caused by excessive tension on the pulley (or sheave) causing a high level of drag in the bearings.

Efficiencies of belt transmission systems can be as high as 90–98%. When proper maintenance and belt tension is maintained, these efficiencies can be sustained throughout much of the system's usable life.

Chapter Review

Electrical principles play a major role in understanding how electrical power is modified and controlled in a drive unit. All electrical circuits have three main factors: current, voltage, and resistance. Current is actually the flow of electrons that cause the work to happen in a circuit. Resistance is the opposition to current flow, which is present in any circuit (all matter in almost all modern electrical circuits have some resistance). Voltage is the electrical pressure that tries to overcome resistance.

Two types of voltage are available: direct current and alternating current. Direct current is typically found in battery circuits and its output value does not fluctuate, until the battery goes dead. Alternating current is typically found as a household and industrial power source. The output value fluctuates depending on the time base of transmission (positive to negative to positive output). Frequency is the number of times complete cycles are seen in a power system (e.g., 60 Hz). Two types of AC are available: single phase and three phase.

Electromagnetism is the ability to produce a magnetic field through the use of a voltage and a coil. Electromagnetism plays an important role in the transmission of voltage through inductors, coils, and motor windings.

Devices using this principle are: inductors, relays, contactors, and transformers. Inductance is the ability to block AC voltage and allow DC to flow. Capacitance is the ability to block DC and allow AC to flow. Both inductance and capacitance play a role in the filter circuit in an AC drive. Capacitance in an inductive circuit (motors) tend to improve the power factor of the entire system. The power factor is the measure of the efficient use of the current waveform and is stated as a ratio between the utility generated voltage and current waveform.

Semiconductors are a mix between conductors and insulators; they need an electrical push to drive the device to conduct current. Typical semiconductor devices include diodes (which allow current flow in one direction), thyristors (SCRs that conduct current only when triggered on), GTOs (which can be latched on or off depending on the polarity of the gate signal), transistors (which control the amount of current flow determined by the amount of trigger signal), and IGBTs (specialized transistors that have extremely high speed switch on and off times).

There are three basic types of mechanical loads that are encountered by any AC or DC drive-system: constant torque (e.g., conveyors), variable torque (e.g., centrifugal fans/pumps), and constant horsepower (e.g., machine tools).

Speed, torque, and horsepower play a major role in the operation of any application. Speed affects how much horsepower is required to perform the function—faster speed requires more horsepower. Torque is a turning effort and defines the ability of a system to start and keep moving at a specified rate. Inertia (WK^2 or WR^2) is the measurement of an object's resistance to change in speed. This measurement is needed to determine the acceleration time available from a drive system.

Gears, belts, pulleys (sheaves), chains, and sprockets all work to allow a smooth transmission of mechanical power, and in some cases, change speed and direction. Types of belts and pulleys include flat and v-belts, synchronous belts, and chains and sprockets.

Couplings, gearboxes, and speed reducers offer a positive connection point between the motor and application. Couplings are available in the following designs: flange, sleeve, and flexible (mechanically and elastically).

Speed reducers offer an effective means of changing speed delivered to the application, as well as the torque developed by the motor. If the speed is reduced at the output of the reducer, torque is increased by approximately the same amount. Speed reducers are available in various types such as helical gears, spur gears, worm gears, and bevel gears.

Check Your Knowledge

1. For current to flow, what must be added to overcome resistance?
2. What devices are used to measure current and voltage, respectively?
3. What is DC?
4. What is magnetic flux?
5. What is electromagnetism?
6. What does 60 Hz refer to?
7. Capacitance has the ability to block ____ and let ____ pass.
8. Inductance has the ability to block _____ and let _____pass.
9. Give an example as to where inductance may be helpful.
10. What is power factor?
11. What is one benefit of placing an inductor ahead of the drive?
12. What two circuits make up a relay circuit?
13. How does a transformer conduct output voltage without any physical connection?
14. Indicate a use for capacitors in the DC bus circuit of an AC drive.
15. Explain the operation of a diode.
16. How does an SCR operate?
17. How does a GTO operate?
18. What is a Darlington bipolar transistor?
19. How do IGBTs differ from the common transistor?
20. What are the characteristics of a constant torque load?
21. Indicate two applications that fall into the constant horsepower category.
22. How does an AC drive save the operator money when connected to a centrifugal fan?
23. What is the definition of torque?
24. What is the definition of horsepower?
25. What is the definition of inertia?
26. If a speed reducer has a 10:1 ratio, with 3 lb-ft and 1200-rpm input shaft, what speed and torque would the output shaft be (assume 85% efficiency)?

AC and DC Motors

Introduction

To truly understand the operating principles of an electronic drive, it is first necessary to understand basic direct current (DC) and alternating current (AC) motor theory. As covered previously, the drive is the device that controls the motor. The drive and motor interact to provide the torque, speed, and horsepower necessary to operate the application. Slight differences occur between manufacturers when it comes to motor design, but the basic characteristics apply, no matter what motor is being controlled.

Direct current motors have been the backbone of industrial applications, ever since the Industrial Revolution. This is due to the motor's high starting torque capability and smooth speed control, and its ability to quickly accelerate to speed in the opposite direction.

Consult the Appendix when you need more information on an idea or term. You will also find helpful formulas and conversions related to both DC and AC motors.

DC Motors: General Principles of Operation

Basic Components

Two basic circuits are in any DC motor: the armature (the device that rotates, sometimes referred to as a *rotor*) and the field (the stationary part, sometimes referred to as a *stator*). The two components magnetically interact with one another to produce rotation in the armature. We will take a closer look at each of the parts and how they interact.

Figure 3-1 indicates a very simplistic view of the basic parts of the DC motor.

As seen in Figure 3-1, the armature and the field are two separate circuits and are physically next to each other to promote magnetic interaction.

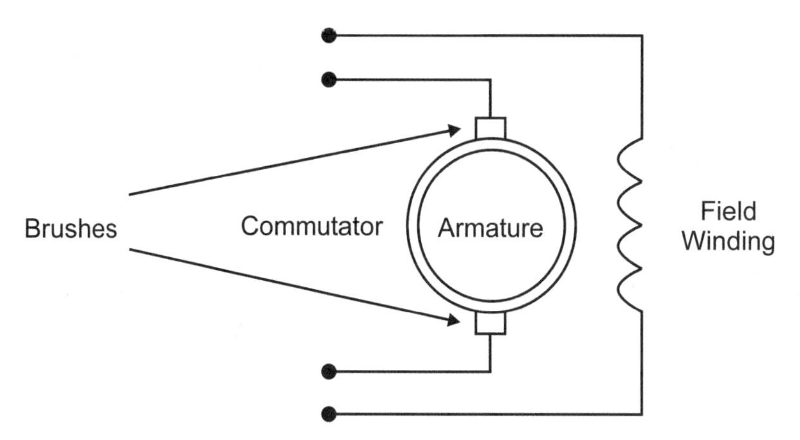

Figure 3-1. DC motor basic parts

The armature has an integral part, called a *commutator*. The commutator acts as an electrical switch, always switching the polarity of the magnetic flux to ensure that a "repelling" force taking place. The armature rotates as a result of the repelling motion created by the magnetic flux of the armature, in opposition to the magnetic flux created by the field winding.

The physical connection of voltage to the armature is accomplished by a device called *brushes*. Brushes are made of a carbon material that is in constant contact with the armature's commutator plates. The brushes are typically spring-loaded to provide constant pressure of the brush to the commutator plates. Figure 3-2 indicates how the armature and field windings are electrically connected.

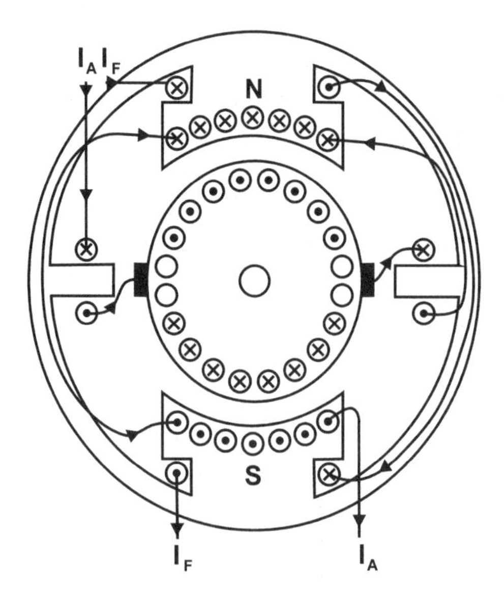

Figure 3-2. Armature and field connections (Courtesy of ABB Inc.)

As seen in Figure 3-2, the leads are brought out away from the windings, and usually are terminated in a conduit box. I_F indicates a field winding connection and I_A indicates an armature connection. (**Note:** "I" indicates current, meaning "intensity of current.")

Figure 3-3. Construction of the armature (Courtesy of ABB Inc.)

The armature device would look like that indicated in Figure 3-3.

The windings are fitted inside slots in the armature. These slots are created by a series of iron "laminations" epoxied together into a long, narrow unit. These slots are actually skewed to allow for smooth rotational action at very low speeds. (Magnetic flux has a tendency to "jump" from field to field. When that occurs, a jerking motion is the result. With the windings at an angle, the magnetic interaction between the armature and field winding is dampened, and the jerking motion is greatly reduced.)

Many manufacturers actually have lengthwise holes around the inside center of the armature. This allows additional cooling air to flow through the armature, reducing overheating. Brushes contact the commutator, which is slightly smaller in diameter, compared with the main body of the device (right side of photo).

There are many coils (windings) around the armature to allow for maximum generation of torque. The polarity of the armature coils must be reversed at the precise time to ensure that the repelling action continues. This action is called *commutation* and takes place when properly aligned brushes are contacting the commutator.

Special windings called *commutation windings* are installed between the magnetic poles to straighten the magnetic field flowing through the armature. If these windings were not installed, a distortion or bending of the magnetic flux would occur, and reduced motor torque would be the result. Figure 3-4 indicates the location of commutation windings.

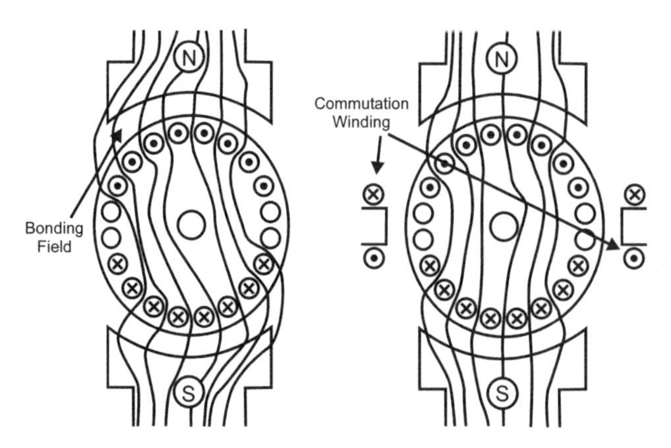

Figure 3-4. Commutation windings

As brushes wear from constant contact with the commutator plates, arcing occurs. Arcing can be reduced by using commutation windings, but some arcing does occur. To reduce arcing, which causes degraded performance, brush replacement is required. The replacement is part of any routine preventative maintenance (PM) program.

The field winding unit is constructed in much the same way, with iron laminations making up the bulk of the device. Windings are inserted lengthwise around the windings. Iron laminations tend to increase the strength of the magnetic flux. Figure 3-5 indicates the typical construction of a motor field winding unit.

There are additional windings that are installed to the magnetic poles of the field windings. These windings are called *compensation windings* and tend to smooth the field flux across the pole. Without the compensation windings, the left side of the north pole would become saturated because of additional magnetic fields generated by the armature. Figure 3-6 indicates the location of these windings.

At this point, it should be noted that there is another type of DC motor that uses permanent magnets instead of field windings. These types of motors, designated "PM" DC motors, do not need a separate exciter or power supply to generate the field magnetic flux. Only a power supply for the armature is needed. If armature supply voltage is available, the PM DC motor includes all the necessary magnetic features to produce shaft rotation.

Figure 3-7 indicates the relationship of the main parts of a DC motor. These parts may look slightly different, depending on manufacturer, but all DC motors will have these components.

Control of Speed and Torque

The speed of a DC motor is a direct result of the voltage applied. As indicated earlier, the DC motor requires two separate circuits to generate motor torque.

Figure 3-5. Motor field winding construction (windings rotated up 90º) (Courtesy of ABB Inc.)

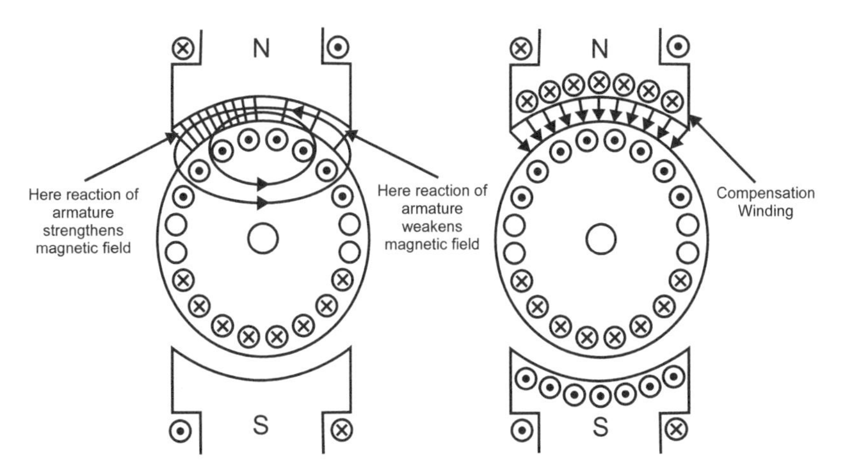

Figure 3-6. Compensation windings (Courtesy of ABB Inc.)

Control of Speed

The field receives voltage from a separate power supply, sometimes referred to as a *field exciter*. This exciter provides power to the field, which in turn generates current and magnetic flux. In a normal operating state, the field is kept at maximum strength, thereby allowing the field winding to develop maximum current and flux. This condition is known as opera-

Figure 3-7. Major components of a DC motor (Courtesy of ABB Inc.)

tion in the armature range. (The only way to control the speed is through change in armature voltage.)

The armature power supply applies voltage to the armature through the brushes and the commutator. Basically, the greater the amount of voltage applied, the faster the speed of the motor. We can see this relationship in the formula below:

$$S = \frac{Va - Ia \times Ra}{K_2\phi}$$

where:

S	=	speed in rpm
Va	=	armature voltage
Ia	=	armature current
Ra	=	resistance of the armature
K_1	=	motor design constant
ϕ	=	strength of the field flux

As seen in the formula, if the load on the motor remains constant, the armature current will stay constant, as well as the resistance of the armature. In addition, the motor design constant will remain the same, as well as the strength of the field flux. When all of these components remain constant, the only determining factor in speed is the amount of armature voltage applied.

The above formula will work in determining speed, when at or below the base speed of the motor. The formula will also indicate speed, when operating above base speed. It is possible to operate in an extended speed range, as long as the motor manufacturer is consulted for the maximum safe operating speed.

As shown in the formula, if armature voltage is at maximum and all the other components remain constant, speed can possibly be increased by reducing the field flux (ϕ). It is necessary to point out, however, that this must be done with caution.

Reduced field flux is the result of reducing the voltage from the field exciter. If voltage is reduced to near zero, the speed of the armature can increase to the point of motor self-destruction. This operation above base speed is known as the *field weakening speed range,* for apparent reasons. The field exciter will have safeguards in place to avoid excessive speed. Most DC drive systems will allow a field weakening range of no less than 1/3 of the normal voltage. If the voltage drops to less than that amount, pre-programmed safety circuits in the drive shut down the armature supply and bring the motor to a safe stop.

Increased speed is made possible by a reduced amount of field flux, when operating above base speed. In essence, less EMF is available to act as holdback magnetic flux. Torque available from the motor is also a function of speed.

Typical armature voltage ratings in the United States are 90, 180, 240, or 500 VDC. Typical U.S. field voltage ratings are 100, 200, 150, or 300 VDC. As stated earlier, the amount of voltage applied to the armature would dictate the output shaft speed. For example, if a 1750-rpm motor with a 240 VDC armature had 120 VDC applied (1/2 voltage), the shaft speed would be approximately 875 rpm (1/2 speed).

Control of Torque

Under certain conditions, motor torque remains constant when operating below base speed. However, when operating in the field weakening range, torque drops off inversely as $1/\text{speed}^2$. The amount of motor torque can also be determined by a formula. The following relationship exists in a DC motor and serves to help determine the motor torque available:

$$T = K_1 \phi I_a$$

where:

T = torque developed by the motor

K_1 = motor design constant

ϕ = strength of the field flux

I_a = armature current

As seen in the formula, if the field flux is held constant, as well as the design constant of the motor, then the torque is proportional to the armature current. The more load the motor sees, the more current is consumed by the armature.

A selling point of DC motors is their ability to provide full torque at zero speed. This is accomplished by the two power supplies, energizing their power structures to supply voltage to the armature and field. When additional load is dropped across the armature, magnetic flux of the armature cuts through the field flux. Once this occurs, more current is drawn through the armature, and the drive's power structure conducts the required amount of current to meet the demand. This phenomenon occurs whether the motor is at any speed, including zero.

Enclosure Types and Cooling Methods

There are various types of enclosures associated with DC motors. The following are the more common configurations found in industry. The system of cooling or ventilation is inherent in the enclosure design. In most cases, to allow the motor to develop full torque at less than 50% speed, an additional blower is required for motor cooling.

DPFG (Drip-Proof Fully Guarded)

The drip-proof fully guarded (DPFG) type of enclosure is self-ventilated and has no external means of cooling. In many cases, these types of motors can be modified to accept additional outside air. Most DPFG designs can generate 100% rated torque down to 50% of base speed. Figure 3-8 shows a DPFG motor.

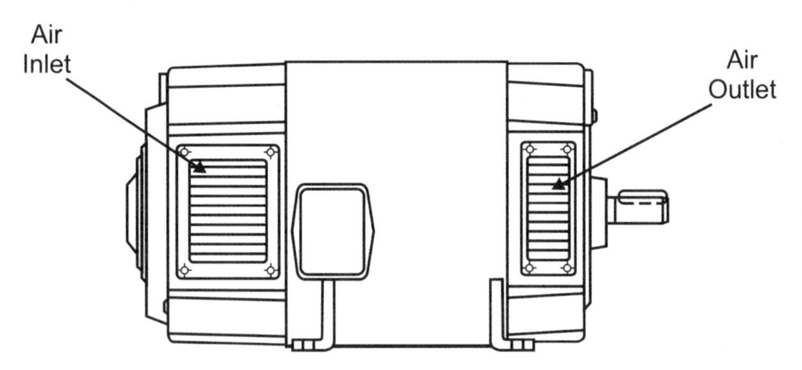

Figure 3-8. DPFG motor (Courtesy of Emerson Motors Technologies™)

DPBV (Drip-Proof Blower Ventilated)

The drip-proof blower ventilated (DPBV) type of enclosure has an integral blower, which may or may not include a filter. The blower is typically mounted on the commutator end to provide constant cooling airflow. It is not uncommon for blower ventilated motors to deliver 100% rated torque down to 10 or 5% of base speed. Figure 3-9 shows a DPBV motor.

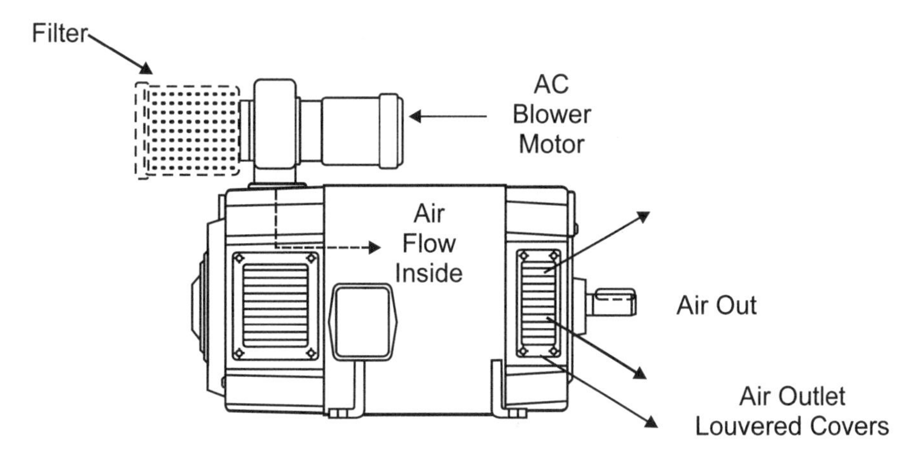

Figure 3-9. DPBV motor (Courtesy of Emerson Motors Technologies™)

DPSV (Drip-Proof Separately Ventilated)

The drip-proof separately ventilated (DPSV) type of enclosure uses ducted air in the CFM amount required to cool the motor. This type of motor is capable of delivering 100% torque down to 10 or 5% of base speed. In many cases, this type is suitable for use in hazardous or contaminated environments. Figure 3-10 indicates a DPSV motor.

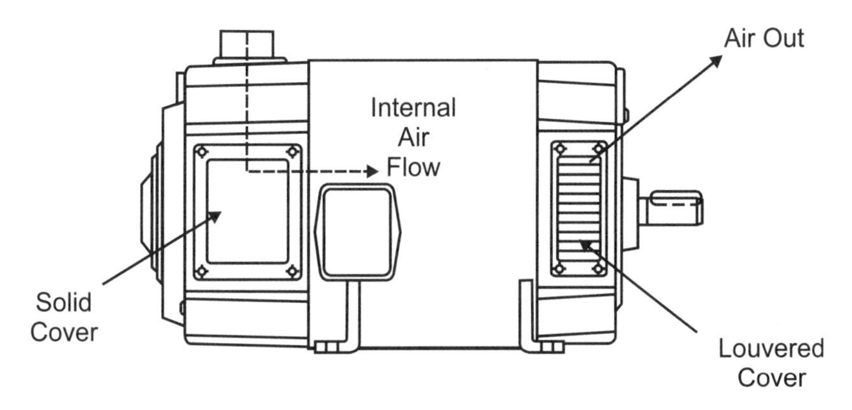

Figure 3-10. DPSV motor (Courtesy of Emerson Motors Technologies™)

TESV (Totally Enclosed Separately Ventilated)

The totally enclosed separately ventilated (TESV) type of enclosure has air flow ducted into and out of the motor in the CFM amount required for cooling. This type of motor is capable of delivering 100% torque down to 10 or 5% of base speed. In many cases, this type is suitable for use in hazardous or contaminated environments. Figure 3-11 indicates a TESV motor.

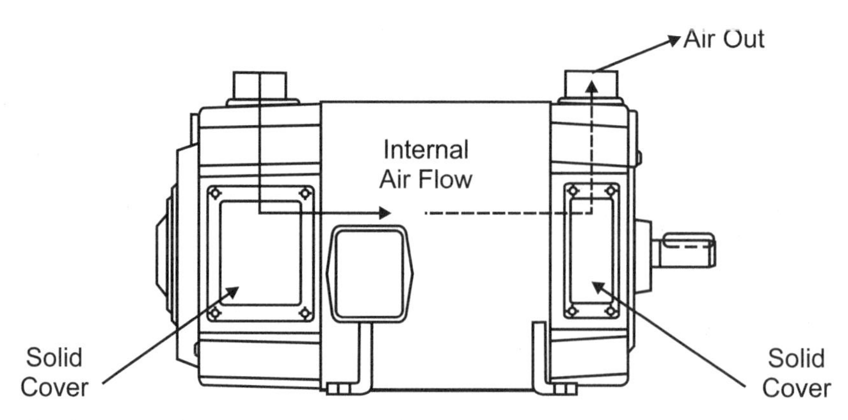

Figure 3-11. TESV motor (Courtesy of Emerson Motors Technologies™)

TENV (Totally Enclosed Non-Ventilated)

The totally enclosed non-ventilated (TENV) type of enclosure has no external cooling, but uses an internal fan to circulate the air within the motor. This type of motor is capable of delivering 100% torque down to 10 or 5% of base speed. Due to the cooling effects, these types of enclosures are not practical for large horsepower ratings. For a comparison, a 100-HP open drip motor would be the approximate equal size of a 30-HP TENV motor. Figure 3-12 indicates a TENV motor.

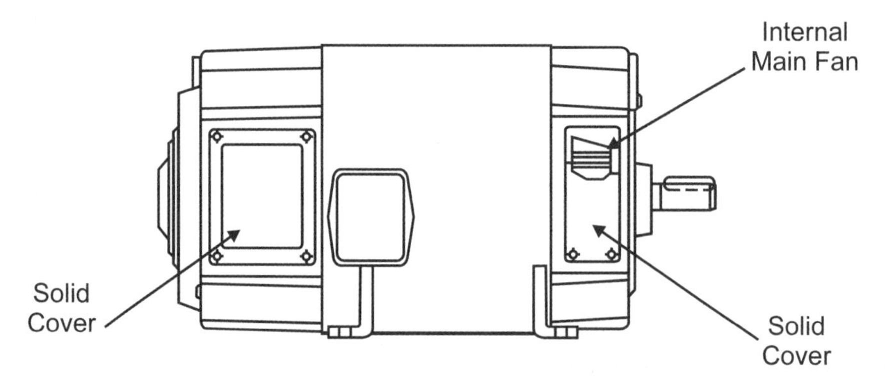

Figure 3-12. TENV motor (Courtesy of Emerson Motors Technologies™)

TEAO (Totally Enclosed Air Over)

The totally enclosed air over (TEAO) type of enclosure has a blower mounted directly on top of the motor. This allows for constant air flow over the external surface of the motor frame. There is no internal cooling effect taking place, only around the outside of the unit. Motors of this type are capable of delivering 100% torque down to approximately 10% of base speed. Figure 3-13 indicates a TEAO motor.

TEFC (Totally Enclosed Fan Cooled)

The totally enclosed fan cooled (TEFC) type of enclosure has an externally mounted fan on the commutator end shaft. Air flow is a direct result of the

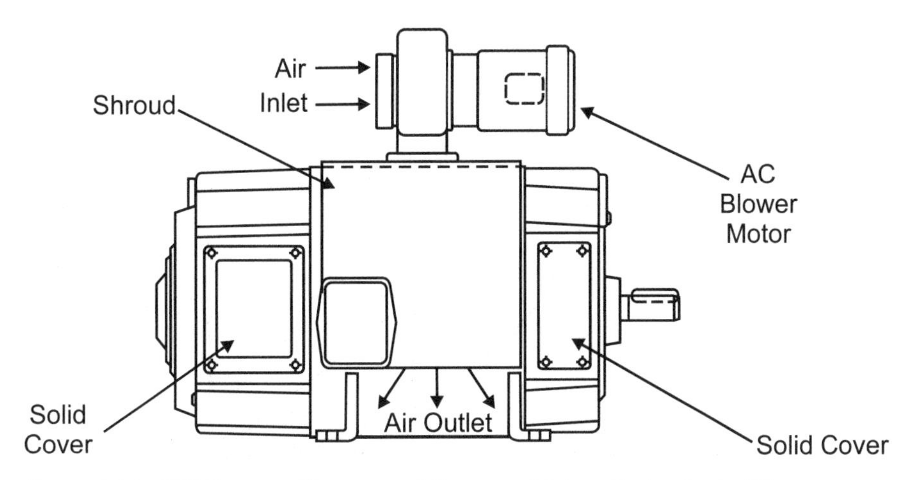

Figure 3-13. TEAO motor (Courtesy of Emerson Motors Technologies™)

speed of the motor. Because of this fact, this type of enclosure is not suitable for low-speed applications. These types of motors are capable of delivering 100% torque down to 60% of base speed. Figure 3-14 indicates a TEFC motor.

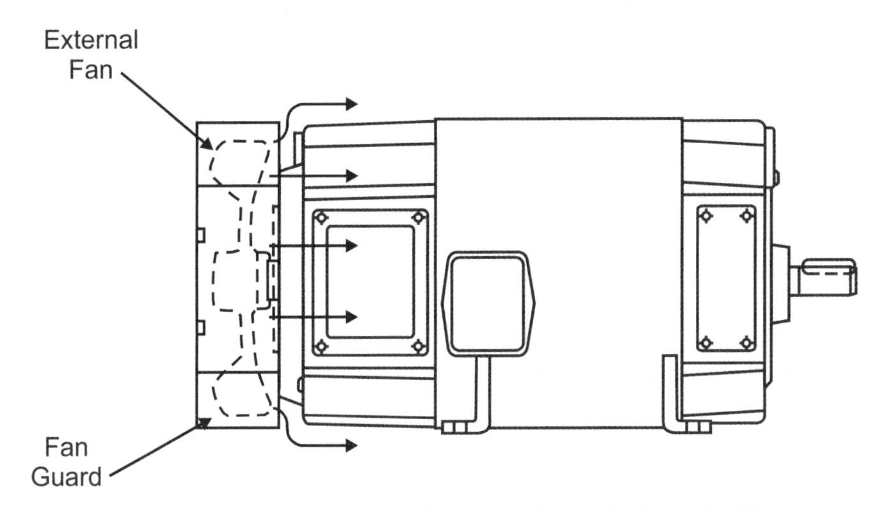

Figure 3-14. TEFC motor (Courtesy of Emerson Motors Technologies™)

TEUC (Totally Enclosed Unit Cooled)

The totally enclosed unit cooled (TEUC) type of enclosure uses an air-to-air heat exchanger and receives its cooling through an external blower. The blower draws air into the heat exchanger through the air inlet. An internal blower circulates the internal cooled air throughout the inside of the motor. The external and internal blowers are in two separate chambers to restrict the mixing of outside and inside air.

These types of motors are able to deliver 100% rated torque down to 3 or 2% of base speed (20:1 constant torque applications). Figure 3-15 indicates a TEUC motor.

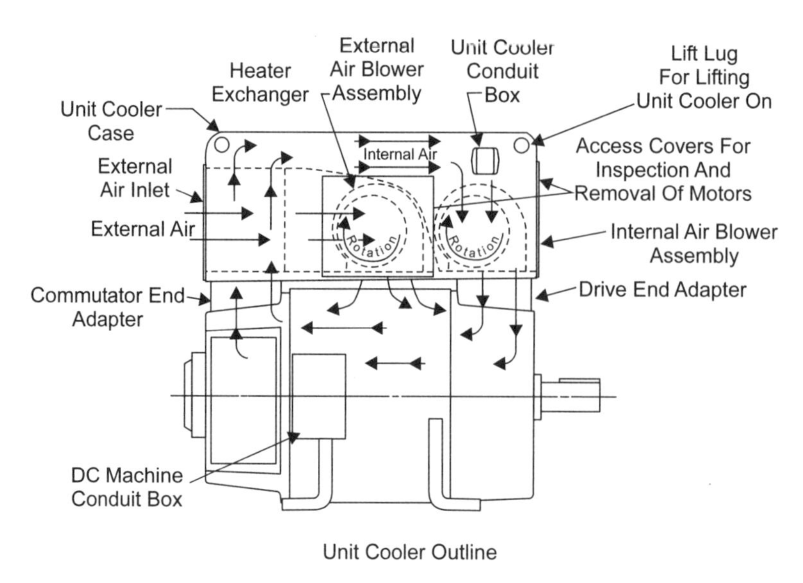

Figure 3-15. TEUC motor (Courtesy of Emerson Motors Technologies™)

Protection and Ratings

As with any electrical device, motors must be kept safe from harmful elements, or their performance and lifespan will be diminished. Elements such as carbon or metal dust particles, and acids and salts, are all excellent conductors. These materials, wet or dry, can conduct current at very low voltages and across very small gaps. Also, water or condensation can seriously degrade the insulation system of a motor. Water with chemicals or minerals is a conductor and can promote leakage currents, causing premature failure.

In many industrial atmospheres, oily compounds are present, which are deposited on all surfaces over a period of time. These surfaces begin to accumulate contaminates, which can develop a short in motor commutators or in brush riggings. Here again, leakage currents can also develop, causing long-term degrading of motor insulation and eventual motor failure.

The following items need to be reviewed periodically to ensure trouble-free operation.

Over Temperature Conditions

Placing the motor into overload conditions is one cause of over-temperature. High ambient temperatures and dirty or clogged air filters on the machine or motor blowers also contribute to over-temperature failures. High temperature inside the motor cause expansion stress in the wire insulation, resulting in cracks, which in turn can cause contamination and eventual wire failure. The shrinking and hardening of the wire lacquer insulation is a cause for loss of insulation strength.

Ambient Temperature

Typical recommendations are for the motor ambient conditions not to exceed 40°C (104°F). Most motors are designed for continuous operation at this ambient temperature. However, motors that will continuously be used in higher temperatures will typically be designed with a lower temperature rise class of insulation.

DC motor insulation must have mechanical and dielectric strength. It must withstand the normal handling necessary in the assembly of the motor, as well as operation thereafter. The major insulation classes are A, B, F, and H, and a brief description is as follows:

- Class A is the lowest grade, suitable for typical household appliances, but not normally industrial applications.
- Class B is general purpose, used in many industrial applications. More demanding duty requires Class F or Class H.
- Class H is the heavy-duty insulation, capable of withstanding high ambient and internal motor temperatures.

Normal life expectancy of an insulation system is 10,000 to 15,000 hours of operation, depending on temperature. Reducing the motor's winding temperature by 10°C will double the insulation life. Conversely, increasing the temperature by 10°C will cut the life expectancy in half.

If you need more information, contact a local motor distributor, NEMA (National Electrical Manufacturers Association) or a local representative of EASA (Electrical Apparatus Service Association).

If the ambient temperature is above 50°C, special consideration must also be made for the bearing and shaft lubricants. The motor manufacturer must always be consulted when continuous temperatures rise above this value.

Vibration

Vibration causes problems such as shaft stress and eventual shorting of conductors between winding turns or between layers of windings. Severe vibration can cause cracks in the lacquer insulation, which exposes the conductors to contamination. Commutation problems may also develop from the "bouncing" of brushes on the commutator. Continuous vibrations tend to cause metal fatigue, which may a cause for premature casting (frame) or bearing failure.

Altitude

Standard motor ratings are based on operation at altitudes of up to 3300 feet (1000 m) ASL (above sea level). Many manufacturers recommend the user to lower the motor rating by 1% for every 330 feet above 3300 feet ASL. The reason is that the air is less dense at higher altitudes (less air molecules to take the heat away from the motor frame). To reduce the need for lowering the rating a motor-mounted blower normally will be sufficient to cool the motor and prevent overheating.

Protection

Most motor manufacturers encourage the purchase and use of a motor thermostat. This device is typically a bi-metallic disk or strip that is sensitive to temperature rise. When the temperature reaches a predetermined level, the thermostat acts as a switch and opens a control circuit, which in turn shuts down the motor. (When a drive is connected to a motor, this thermostat is connected to an auxiliary circuit that shuts down the drive when over-temperature conditions arise.)

The thermostat is mounted on a commutating coil inside the motor, which means the device needs to be installed at the time of manufacture. Standard configuration is a normally closed contact. However, normally open configurations are also available.

This type of device usually retails for about $150 and is very reasonable insurance against motor overheating. Once a motor overheats, insulation damage can occur, causing thousands of dollars in repair costs and additional costs in down time.

Ratings

Typical DC motors have ratings that are found on the nameplate. Figure 3-16 indicates a typical DC motor nameplate.

ABB	
Motor **Sep.**	06-1995 **IEC 34-1-1969**
Type DMP 112-4L	**No** 1124 01659
12.5 **kW**	1500 **r/min**
Duty S1	**Ins. Class** F
Arm. 495 **V**	**Arm.** 29.9 **A**
Exc. 300 **V**	**Exc.** 2.18 **A**
IP 23S **IC** 06	**IM** 1001
Cat. No. FR 159 101-1A	123.5 **kg**
MADE IN FRANCE	**FABRIQUE EN FRANCE**

Figure 3-16. DC motor nameplate (Courtesy of ABB Motors)

- **Frame:** indicating the frame rating per specific horsepower and torque capability.
- **HP:** available horsepower at the designated armature and field voltage and current ratings.

- **Amps/field amps:** designations for armature and field winding amps, respectively. These ratings are needed when programming the protection features in a drive controller.
- **Base/max. speed:** indicates the rated speed in rpm, when operating at rated armature and field amps, as well as rated load. The *max speed* indication is the maximum safe operating rpm possible, while remaining within the limitations of the motor.

Additional ratings include enclosure type, thermostat type, ambient temperature rating, catalog and serial number, and tachometer type and rating. These ratings have been previously discussed. Refer to Chapter 5 "Drive Control and Feedback Devices," for more information on tachometers.

Most DC motors also carry one of three duty ratings:

- **Continuous duty:** rating given to motors that will continuously dissipate all the heat generated by internal losses without exceeding the rated temperature rise.
- **Intermittent duty (definite time):** rating given to a motor that carries a rated load for a specified time without exceeding the rated temperature rise.
- **Intermittent duty (indefinite time):** rating given to a motor that is usually associated with some RMS load of a duty-cycle operation.
- **Peak torque:** the peak torque that a DC motors can deliver is limited by the load point at which damaging commutation begins. Brush and commutator damage depends on the sparking severity and duration. Peak torque is limited by the maximum current that the power supply can deliver.
- **Calculating torque:** An easy means of calculating the available torque from a DC motor is to use the following formula:

$$\text{Torque} = \frac{\text{HP} \times 5252}{\text{Speed}}$$

where:

Torque = torque available from the motor in lb-ft

HP = nameplate horsepower at base speed

Speed = rpm

As an example, assume a 10-HP DC motor has a 240-V armature, 39.2 amp with a speed of 1775/2750. We will insert the needed numbers into the formula and determine the base speed (1775) torque:

$$\text{Torque} = \frac{10 \times 5252}{1775} = \frac{52520}{1775} = 29.5 \text{ lb-ft}$$

The above formula will work for determining torque at any speed up to base speed. (Again, remember that base speed in rated: armature voltage, field current, and load.)

To determine the torque per amp ratio, simply divide 29.5 by 39.2, which equals 0.75 lb-ft of torque per amp. Determining the torque per amp ratio above base speed is also possible by calculating the torque, using the above formula for the speed over base, then using the ratio of the calculated torque and the amp meter reading at that speed. As expected, the amount of torque developed is less, above base speed, compared with below base speed.

DC Motor Types

Introduction

Basically, four different types of DC motors are used in industrial applications: series wound, shunt wound, compound wound, and permanent magnet. Several factors must be considered when selecting a DC motor for a specific application.

First, decide what the allowable variation in speed and torque can be for a given change in load. Each type of motor has benefits that are advantageous for certain applications. The following review will help you decide which motor may provide better performance in a given application. The DC motor and drive specifications should always be consulted to determine the specific speed and torque capabilities of the system. The speed/torque curves listed below are for illustrative purposes.

Series Wound DC Motors

A series wound DC motor has the armature and field windings connected in a series circuit. Figure 3-17 shows a series wound DC motor, with an associated speed/torque curve.

As seen in Figure 3-17, this type of motor configuration features very high breakaway torque. Typical applications for this motor would be printing presses, ski lifts, electric locomotives, cranes, and oil drilling.

The starting torque developed can be as high as 500% of the full load rating. The high starting torque is a result of the fact that the field winding is operated below the saturation point.

An increase in load will cause a corresponding increase in both the armature and field winding current, which means that both armature and field winding flux increase together. As you recall, the torque developed in a DC motor is the result of the interaction of armature and field winding fluxes. Torque in a DC motor increases as the square of the current value.

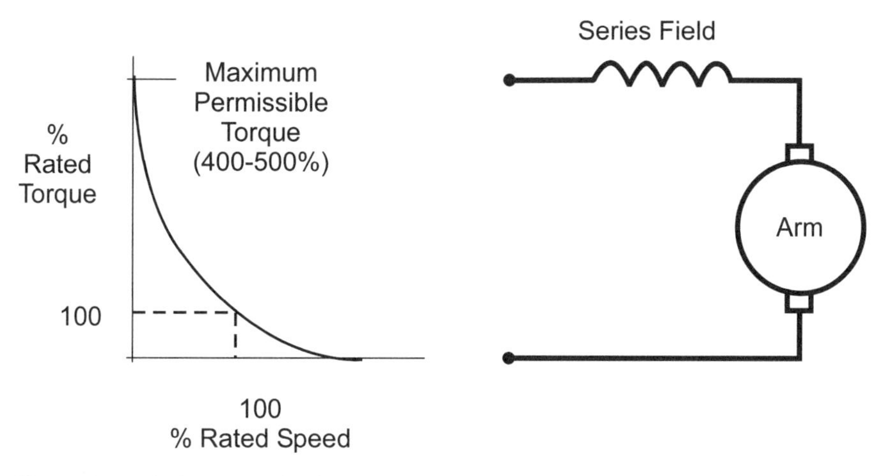

Figure 3-17. Series wound DC motor circuit and curve

A series wound DC motor will generate a larger torque increase compared with a shunt wound DC motor for given increase in current.

Conversely, the speed regulation of a series wound DC motor is poorer than that of a shunt wound motor. As stated above, when the load increases, so does the armature and field winding current. When the load is reduced, so is the current, which causes a corresponding decrease in flux density. As a reminder of DC motor basics, when the field flux is reduced once the motor is running, a decrease in "hold-back" electromotive force (EMF) occurs. Therefore, when the load is reduced, speed increases. If the load were completely removed, the speed of the motor would increase to infinity—basically until the motor destroys itself. As a safety precaution, series wound DC motors should always be connected to a load.

Parallel (Shunt) Wound DC Motors

A shunt wound DC motor has the armature and field windings connected in parallel. Figure 3-18 shows a shunt wound DC motor, with an associated speed/torque curve.

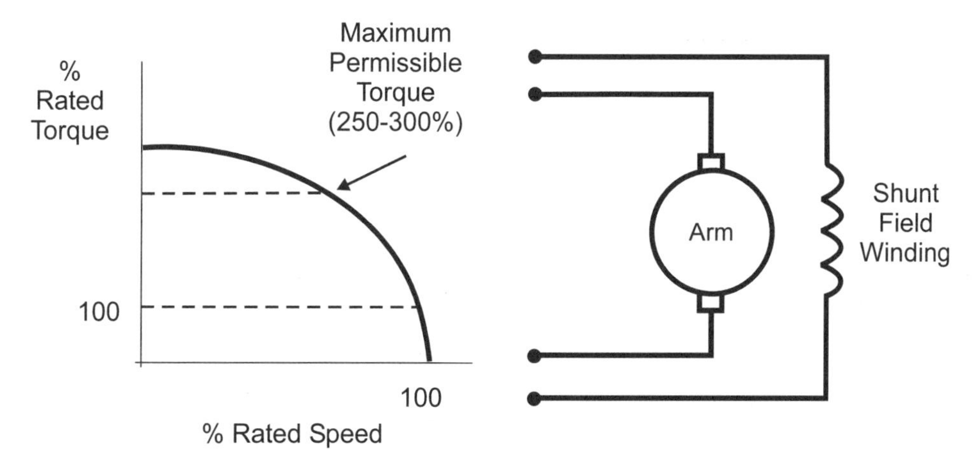

Figure 3-18. Shunt wound DC motor and curve

This type of DC motor is probably the most widely used motor in industrial applications. As indicated in the figure, this type of motor requires two power supplies—one for the armature and one for the field winding.

Typical applications for this motor would be printing presses, ski lifts, plastic extruders, conveyors, and practically any other application where DC motors are used. Because of the need for two power supplies, this type of motor is a prime candidate for a DC drive (converter), which usually includes a low-current field winding exciter (power supply).

With constant armature voltage and field winding excitation, this type of motor offers relatively flat speed/torque characteristics. The starting torque developed can be 250–300% of the full load torque rating for a short period of time. Speed regulation (speed fluctuation due to load) is acceptable in many cases between 5–10% of maximum speed, when operated from a DC drive. Regulation of this amount would be typical when operated from a drive controller, open loop (no electronic feedback device connected to the motor shaft). As discussed in Chapter 5, speed feedback devices such as a tachometer generator can dramatically improve the regulation (down to less than 1%).

Because of the need for two power sources, the shunt wound DC motor offers the use of simplified control for reversing requirements. Direction of any shunt wound motor can be changed by simply reversing the direction of current flow, in either the armature or shunt field winding. The capability of armature or field reversal is standard on many DC drive modules. (In many cases, the reversing of flux and direction is accomplished in the field winding control. The field winding consumes less than one tenth of the current compared with the armature circuit. Smaller components and less stress on circuitry is the result when "field reversal" is used for DC motor control.)

Compound Wound DC Motors

A compound wound DC motor is basically a combination of shunt wound and series wound configurations. This type of motor offers the high starting torque of a series wound motor. In addition, it offers constant speed regulation (speed stability) under a given load. This type of motor is used whenever speed regulation cannot be obtained from either a series or shunt wound motor. Figure 3-19 indicates a compound wound DC motor, with an associated speed/torque curve.

The torque and speed characteristics are the result of placing a portion of the field winding circuit in series with the armature circuit. This additional armature winding circuit is not to be confused with the commutating winding or interpoles. The commutation windings also have a few turns, but have the duty of neutralizing armature reaction.

When a load is applied, there is a corresponding increase in current through the series winding, which also increases the field flux. This in turn increases the torque output of the motor.

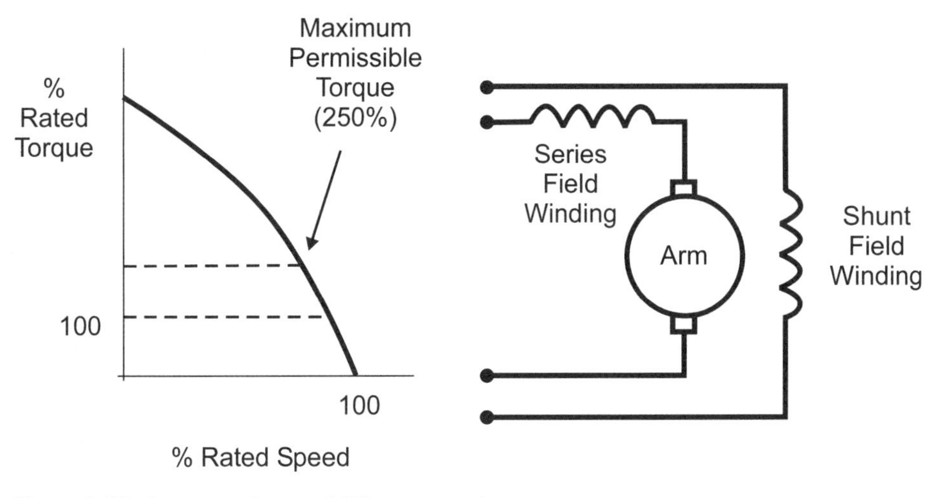

Figure 3-19. Compound wound DC motor and curve

Permanent Magnet DC Motors

A permanent magnet motor is built with a standard armature and brushes, but has permanent magnets in place of the shunt field winding. The speed characteristic is close to that of a shunt wound DC motor. When adding the cost of a DC motor and control system, this type of motor is less expensive to operate, since there is no need for a shunt field winding exciter supply. Figure 3-20 indicates a permanent magnet DC motor, with an associated speed/torque curve.

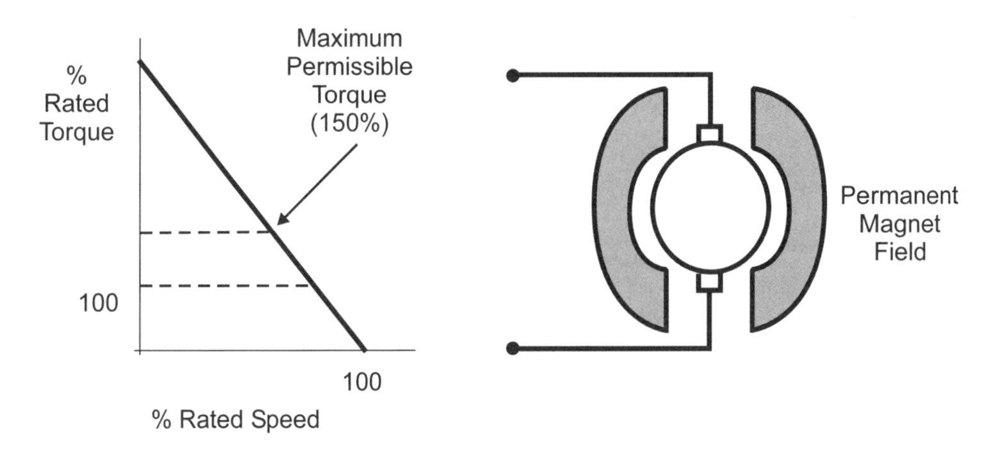

Figure 3-20. Permanent magnet DC motor and curve

Along with less expensive operation, this type of motor is simpler to install, with only the two armature connections needed. This motor type is also simpler to reverse—simply reverse the connections to the armature.

The permanent magnet poles are usually constructed of materials such as ceramic or alnico (aluminum, nickel, and cobalt). The ceramic magnets are used for low-horsepower, slow-speed applications because of their low flux level generation. Though this type of motor has good operational characteristics and lower cost, there are several drawbacks to this type of motor compared with the others.

Materials such as ceramic have a high resistance to demagnetization. However, permanent magnets do have a tendency to lose some of their magnetic strength over use and time. This reduction in magnetic field strength causes a corresponding reduction in torque output. To counteract this possibility, some higher-cost permanent magnet motors include windings built into the field magnets for the purpose of "re-magnetizing" the magnets.

In addition to ceramic or alnico magnets, rare earth magnets are also a cost-effective means of generating magnetic field flux. This type of magnetic group includes the "embedded" magnet, which is only one of nine different magnetic materials available.

Though this type of motor has very good starting torque capability, the speed regulation is slightly less than that of a compound wound motor. The overall torque output makes this motor a prime candidate for low-torque applications. Peak torque is limited to about 150%. This limitation is based on the fact that additional "demagnetizing" of the field poles could occur if more torque was developed.

Specialty DC Motors—PM DC Servomotors

Servomotors are considered "specialty" in that they are used in applications that require very fast speed response and accuracy. In many cases, the shaft speed is accelerated from zero to 6000 rpm in hundredths of a second. The same speed profile could be needed in the deceleration mode, as well as an immediate reversal of direction.

These types of motors must be designed to handle the stress of acceleration, plus not fluctuate in speed, once the desired speed is obtained. Special consideration is given to heat dissipation, since these motors must be small, yet generate enough torque to operate the machine. The small size allows this type motor to fit inside small packaging, palletizing, and processing machines. Typically, these motors are long and narrow, in contrast to a standard shunt wound DC motor. The long, narrow design results in low inertia armature assemblies, which can be accelerated quickly. Servomotor design with permanent magnets affords the smallest space possible. In comparison, shunt field windings must have laminations wide enough to generate the necessary field flux, which adds to the total width of the machine. Figure 3-21 indicates the physical appearance of a typical DC servomotor.

As seen in Figure 3-21, this type of motor is usually of a totally enclosed design to seal out most moisture, dust, and moderate contaminates. The physical frame of the motor acts as a heat sink to dissipate the heat generated.

Figure 3-21. DC servomotor with C face mounting (Courtesy of Baldor Electric Company)

Many servomotors are used expressly for positioning applications. Therefore, the motor design allows for a position feedback device such as an encoder or resolver. Mounting of the servomotor can be easily done by means of a "C" face (no flange, but tapped holes to receive mounting bolts) or "D" flange (outside flange with through-holes).

The principle involved in the PM servomotor is exactly the same as the standard PM DC motor. It has an armature, commutator, and the PM field for magnetic interaction. The difference comes in the physical size and shape of the servomotor, as well as the performance and speed characteristics.

Specialty DC Motors—Brushless Servomotors

Another type of DC servomotor uses the high-torque and acceleration characteristics, but without the use of a commutator or brushes. This type, called the *brushless DC* servomotor, takes input three-phase or single-phase input power and converts it to DC used by the motor windings. The windings create magnetic flux that interacts with the PM field to generate motor speed and torque. Figure 3-22 shows the design of the brushless DC servomotor.

As seen in Figure 3-22, instead of the permanent magnets being mounted as the field, the magnets are actually part of the rotor. (**Note:** Since there are no brushes or commutator, the term "rotor" is used instead of armature, indicating an AC-type machine design.) A typical brushless DC servomotor may have multiple poles, such as three N and three S poles. There would also be corresponding windings in the stator to create the magnetic interaction. (**Note:** Because this is an AC-type machine design, the term "stator" is used instead of "field" or "field windings.")

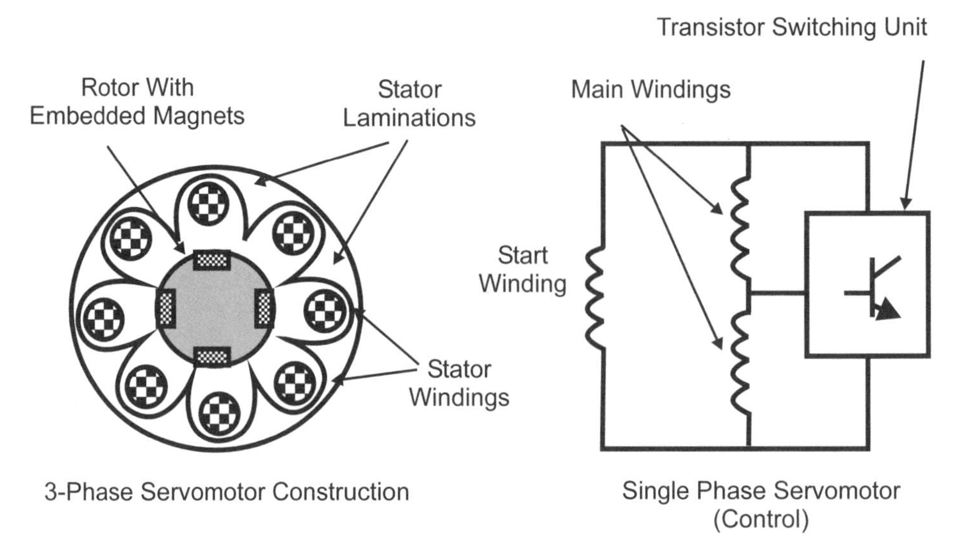

Figure 3-22. Brushless DC servomotor (design and control)

The rotor of the servomotor is usually laminated iron with magnets inserted and "press-fit" or epoxied into position. Special high-speed bearings support the rotor in position. Instead of a standard conduit box, servomotors usually include a military-style connector. This style features all connections on one plug or receptacle, with a screw-on ring to ensure positive contact. This style of connector is resistant to machine vibration and electrical interference.

The servomotor takes input power and converts it to DC for the main windings in the stator. Depending on the design of the servomotor, the control unit may include transistors that are turned on or off to generate voltage. In the case of a three-phase servomotor, an external servo amplifier is connected to generate the control voltage for the stator windings.

The main disadvantage of this motor is the inability to develop high starting torque. In the case of a single-phase servomotor, half of the main windings are used at any given time. This causes the copper losses to be somewhat high. However, since transistor switching is used for control of the brushless DC servomotor, motor life is mainly limited by the bearings, since there are no commutator segments or brushes to wear out.

AC Motors: General Principles of Operation

Introduction

The squirrel cage induction motor is probably the most widely used motor in industry today. Traditional applications for AC induction motors include fans and pumps. The AC induction motor has been widely accepted in many demanding industrial applications, compared with the DC motor, because less maintenance is required. It is quite common to find AC motors in applications such as compressors, machine tools, conveyors, mixers, crushers, ski lifts, and extruders. With its efficient operation and energy savings characteristics, the AC induction motor will increase in prominence throughout the next several decades.

The basic principles of operation of any manufacturer's motor is essentially the same. Specific designs may differ, such as the air gap between the rotating parts, voltage insulation strength, and resistance to high-voltage spikes. However, the main parts in an induction motor are all the same.

It should be noted here that in the world of AC motors, there are basically two languages: NEMA (National Electrical Manufacturers Association) in North America, and IEC (International Electrotechnical Commission) in most of the rest of the world. Until recently, there was little need to be aware of the differences, both subtle and obvious. However, that is all changing as the motor market becomes more global. This trend gained additional fuel in 1992 when the economies of the European Common Market countries became one.

Later in this section, NEMA versus IEC motor ratings will be explored. More companies are shipping their electrical products overseas, and vice versa. In the not-so-distant future, it will be difficult to not come in contact with an IEC-rated motor. Therefore, a review of the comparisons will be useful. In addition, because of industry's wide use of three-phase induction motors, the focus of this section will be on that motor type. However, several other common three-phase motor types will also be explored.

All AC motors can be classified into single-phase and polyphase motors (*poly* meaning many-phase, or three-phase). Because polyphase motors are the most commonly used in industrial applications, we will take a closer look at the construction of these units. Keep in mind that there are also single-phase AC motors in use for applications such as small appliances, residential fans, furnaces, and many other low-horsepower applications.

For industrial applications, however, mainly three-phase induction motors are used. The main advantage of using three-phase motors is efficiency. Three-phase motors are much simpler in construction than other types and require less maintenance. A more powerful motor can be built into a smaller frame compared with a single-phase motor. The three-phase motor will operate at a higher efficiency compared with the single-phase motor.

There are several types of polyphase motors: induction, wound rotor, and synchronous. The most common type of motor in this group is the squirrel cage induction motor. This motor type will be the basis for understanding the general AC motor principles.

AC Induction Motor

The main parts in an AC induction motor is the rotor (rotating element) and the stator (stationary element that generates the magnetic flux). The rotor construction looks like a squirrel cage, hence the traditional name: squirrel cage induction motor. Figure 3-23 indicates the rotor construction.

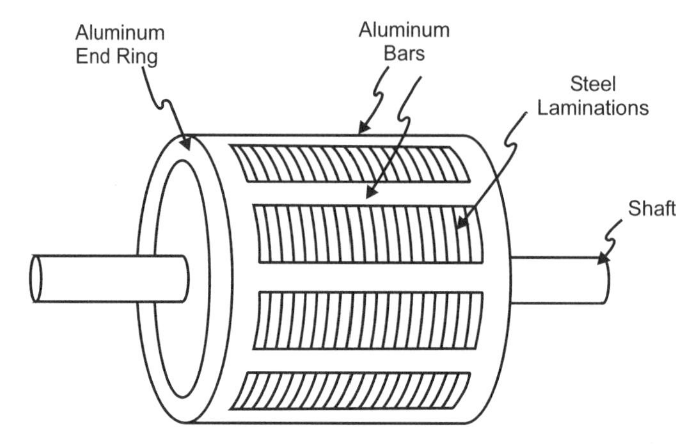

Figure 3-23. Squirrel cage induction motor rotor

The squirrel cage motor is the simplest to manufacture and the easiest to maintain. The operation of the squirrel cage motor is simple. The three-phase current produces a rotating magnetic field in the stator. This rotating magnetic field causes a magnetic field to be set up in the rotor also. The attraction and repulsion between these two magnetic fields causes the rotor to turn. This concept can be seen in Figures 3-24 and 3-25

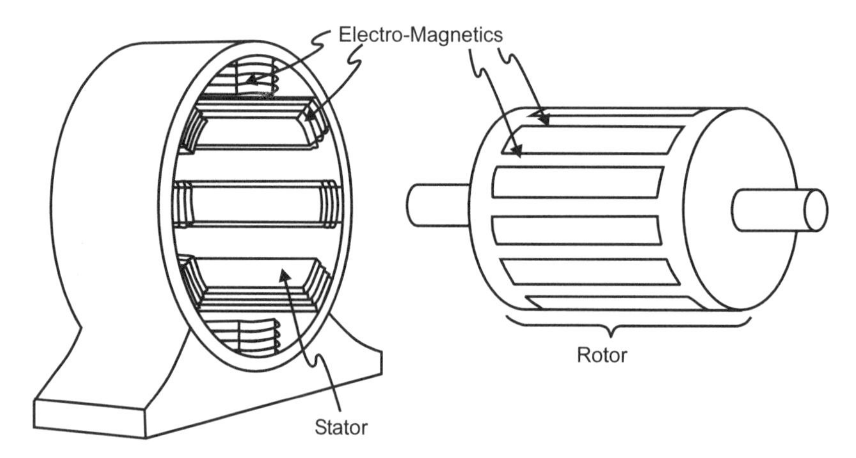

Figure 3-24. Rotor and stator

The squirrel cage motor is a constant-speed motor with either a normal or high starting torque. These characteristics fulfill the requirements of the majority of industrial applications.

The concept of the rotating magnetic field is shown in Figure 3-26. This figure shows the relationship of the three-phases versus pole magnetic fields. Each magnetic pole pair is wound in such a way that allows the sta-

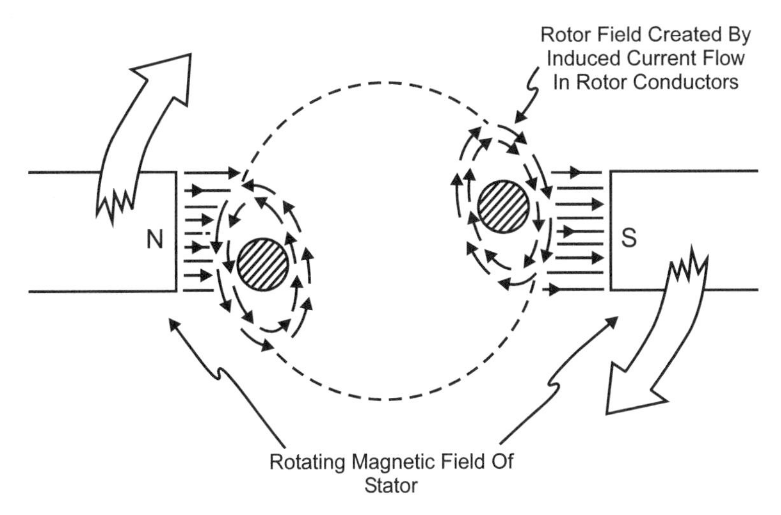

Figure 3-25. End view of two rotor segments (magnetic interaction with stator)

tor magnetic field to "rotate." The stator of the motor consists of groups of coils wound on a core, which are enclosed by a frame. The simple two-pole stator shown in Figure 3-26 has three coils in each pole group. (A two-pole motor would have two poles × three phases = six physical poles.) Each coil in a pole group is connected to one phase of the three-phase power source. One characteristic of three-phase power is that the phase current reaches maximum value at different time intervals. Figure 3-26 also indicates the relationship between maximum and minimum values.

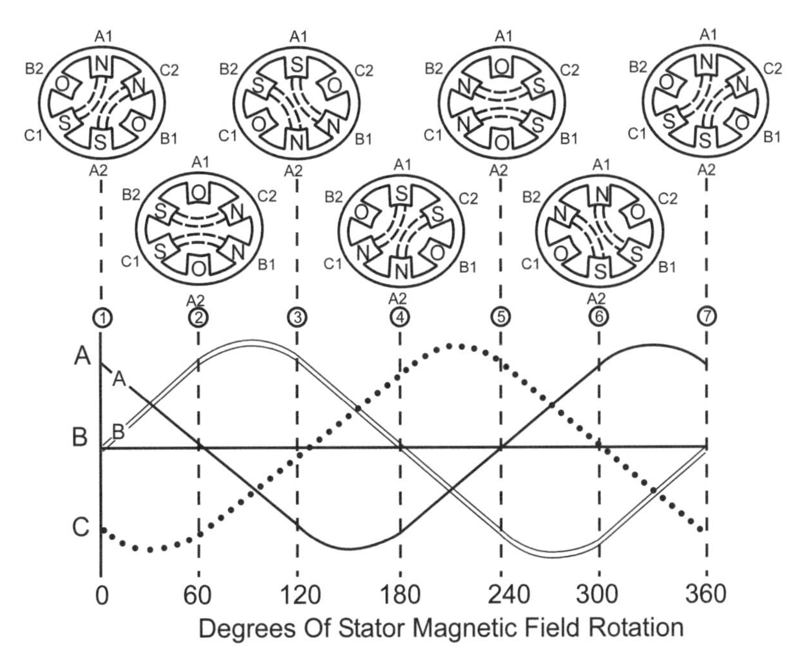

Figure 3-26. Basic two-pole stator

For the sake of example, our focus will be an instant in time when the current is almost at maximum in the "A" coils. (Use the upper left corner of Figure 3-25.) The magnetic fields of these coils will also be at almost maximum value. At this same instant, the currents of phase "B" are at zero and phase "C" currents are slightly more than "A."

At a later instant in time, the current in the "B" coils is close to maximum with consequent maximizing of the magnetic field of the "B" coils. At this same instant, the field of the "C" phase is slightly less than maximum. The "A" coil fields are at zero value.

This same process repeats as the magnetic field of each of the phases reaches maximum, all at different times (different degrees of magnetic field rotation). The maximum field thus sequentially repeats at "A," "C," and "B" continuously around the stator and essentially defines a rotating magnetic field.

The coils of the stator are wound such that they are diametrically opposite coils. This means that they carry the same phase current but are connected so their magnetic fields are of opposite polarity. Again, the motor shown in Figure 3-26 would be a configuration of a two-pole winding.

Magnetic Field (Rotor)

The rotor is the rotating part of the motor. The rotor consists of copper or aluminum bars, connected together at the ends with end rings. Refer to Figure 3-27.

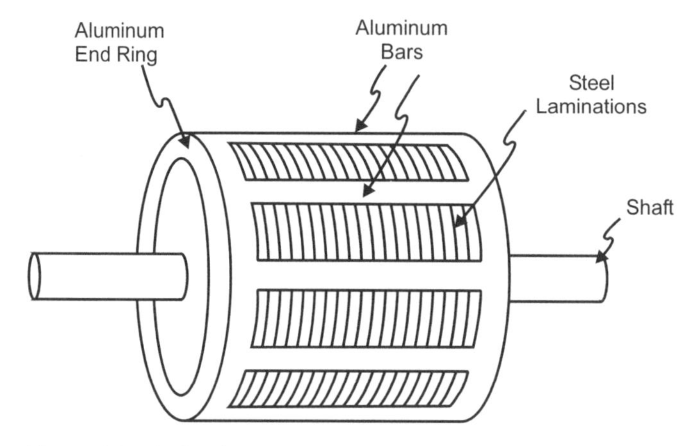

Figure 3-27. Induction motor rotor construction

The inside of the rotor is filled with many individual disks of steel, called *laminations.* The revolving field set up by the stator currents, cut the squirrel cage conducting aluminum bars of the rotor. This causes voltage in these bars, called *induced voltage*. This voltage causes current to flow in the aluminum bars. The current sets up a magnetic field around the bars with corresponding north and south poles in the rotor. Torque is produced from the attraction and repulsion between these poles and the poles of the revolving stator field.

Figure 3-28 shows the assembly of the parts into a complete induction motor unit.

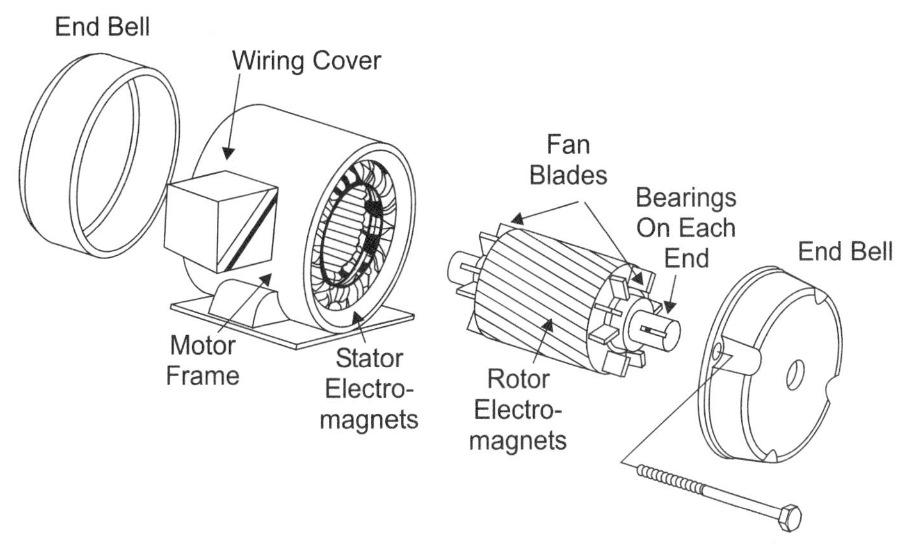

Figure 3-28. Induction motor construction

Eddy Current Generation

The rotating stator magnetic field and induced voltage in the rotor bars also causes voltage in the stator and rotor cores. The voltage in these cores cause small circulating currents to flow. These currents, called *eddy currents,* serve no useful purpose and result only in wasted power. To reduce these currents, the stator and rotor cores are constructed with laminations. (discussed in the previous section). These laminations are coated with insulating varnish and then welded together to form the core. This type of core substantially reduces eddy current losses, but it does not eliminate them entirely.

Induction Motor Design

Engineers can design motors for almost any application by changing the design of the squirrel cage rotor and stator coils. Characteristics such as speed, torque, and voltage are just a few of the features controlled by the designer.

To standardize certain motor features, the National Electrical Manufacturers Association (NEMA) has established standards for a number of motor features. The following section contains many of the features that will be helpful in selecting the right motor for a specific application.

Control of Speed, Torque, and Horsepower

Control of Speed

The speed of a squirrel cage motor depends on the frequency and the number of poles for which the motor is wound. The higher the frequency, the faster the motor operates. The more poles the motor has, the slower it operates. The smallest number of poles ever used in a squirrel cage motor is two. A two-pole 60-Hz motor will run at approximately 3600 rpm. As soon will be seen, the motor will always operate at a speed less than 3600 rpm.

To find the approximate speed of any squirrel cage motor, the formula for synchronous speed can be used, which is actually the speed of the rotating magnetic field:

$$N = \frac{120 \times F}{P}$$

N = synchronous speed (rpm)

F = frequency of the power supply (Hertz)

P = number of stator poles

Squirrel cage induction motors are wound for the synchronous speeds found in Table 3-1.

No. of poles	Sync. speed (at 60 Hz)	Sync. speed (at 50 Hz)
2	3600	3000
4	1800	1500
6	1200	1000
8	900	750
10	720	600
12	600	500

Table 3-1. Motor synchronous speeds vs. number of poles

Most standard induction motors (NEMA 143T through 445T frame sizes) are wound with a maximum of eight poles.

The actual speed of the motor shaft is somewhat less than synchronous speed. This difference between the synchronous and actual speeds is defined as *slip*. If the squirrel cage rotor rotated as fast as the stator field, the rotor bars would be standing still with respect to the rotating magnetic field. No voltage would be induced in the rotor bars, and no magnetic flux would be cut by the rotor bars. The result would be no current set up to produce torque. Since no torque is produced, the rotor will slow down until sufficient current is induced to develop torque. When torque is developed, the rotor will accelerate to a constant speed. Figure 3-29 is a graphical representation of slip.

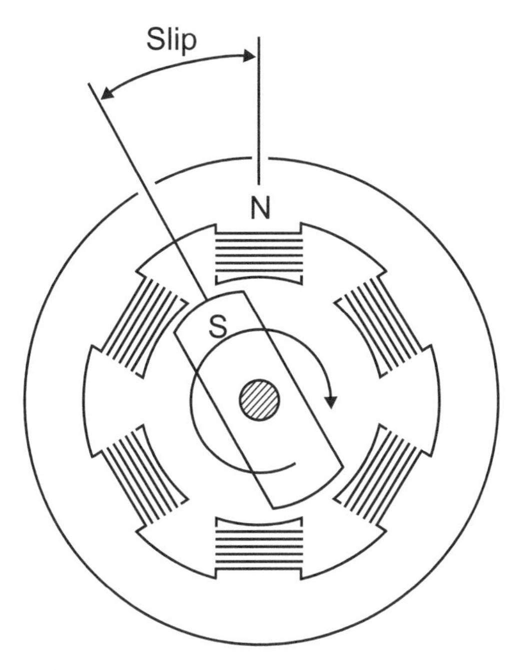

Figure 3-29. Slip in an induction motor

To summarize: There must be a difference between the rotating magnetic stator field and the actual rotor bars' position. This allows the rotor bars to cut through the stator magnetic fields and create a magnetic field in the rotor. The interaction of the stator and rotor magnetic fields produce the attraction needed to develop torque.

When the load on the motor increases, the rotor speed decreases. Then the rotating field cuts the rotor bars at a faster rate than before. This has the effect of increasing the current in the rotor bars and increasing the magnetic pole strength of the rotor. Basically, as the load increases, so does the torque output.

Slip is usually expressed as a percentage and can easily be calculated using the following formula:

$$\text{Percent slip} = \frac{\text{Synchronous speed - Actual speed}}{\text{Synchronous speed}} \times 100$$

Squirrel cage motors are built with the slip ranging from about 3–20%. Motors with a slip of 5% or higher are used for hard-to-start applications. A motor with a slip of 5% or less is called a *normal slip* motor. A normal slip motor is often referred to as a *constant speed* motor because the speed changes very little with variations in load.

In specifying the speed of the motor on the nameplate, most motor manufacturers use the actual speed of the motor at rated load. The term used is *base speed*. Base speed is a speed somewhat lower than the synchronous speed. It is defined as the actual rotor speed at rated voltage, rated hertz, and rated load.

Direction of Rotation

The direction of rotation of a squirrel cage induction motor depends on the motor connection to the power lines. Rotation can easily be reversed by interchanging any two input leads.

Control of Torque and Horsepower

As discussed earlier, horsepower takes into account the speed at which the shaft rotates. It takes more horsepower to rotate the shaft fast, compared with rotating it slowly. Note: Horsepower is a rate of doing work.

By definition, 1 HP equals 33,000 ft-lb per minute. In other words, lifting a 33,000-pound weight 1 foot, in 1 minute would take 1 HP.

By using the familiar formula below, we can determine the horsepower developed by an AC induction motor.

$$HP = \frac{T \times N}{5252}$$

T = torque in lb-ft

N = speed in rpm

For example, a motor shaft turns at 5 rpm and develops 3 lb-ft of torque. By inserting the known information into the formula, we calculate that the motor develops approximately 0.003 HP ($3 \times 5 \div 5252 = .0028$). As the formula shows, horsepower is directly related to the speed of motor shaft. If the shaft turns twice as fast (10 rpm), the motor will develop almost .006 HP, twice as much.

We can see the general rules of thumb for torque developed versus speed by reviewing Table 3-2.

Torque developed will vary slightly on lower HP and rpm motors or non-standard motors.

As seen in Table 3-2, at higher synchronous speeds, the induction motor develops less torque compared with lower speeds. We can also see that the higher the number of poles, the larger the amount of torque developed.

No. of poles	Sync. speed (at 60 Hz)	Torque developed per HP
2	3600	1.5 lb-ft
4	1800	3 lb-ft
6	1200	4.5 lb-ft
8	900	6 lb-ft
10	720	7.5 lb-ft
12	600	8.75 lb-ft

Table 3-2. AC induction motor—speed vs. torque developed

Basically, more poles mean stronger magnetic fields that will be produced. With more magnetic flux interacting with rotor flux, a stronger twisting motion will result, thereby developing more torque.

Regarding the issue of motor torque, there are several areas on the standard speed/torque curve that should be reviewed. An induction motor is built to supply this extra torque needed to start the load. The speed torque curve for a typical induction motor is seen in Figure 3-30.

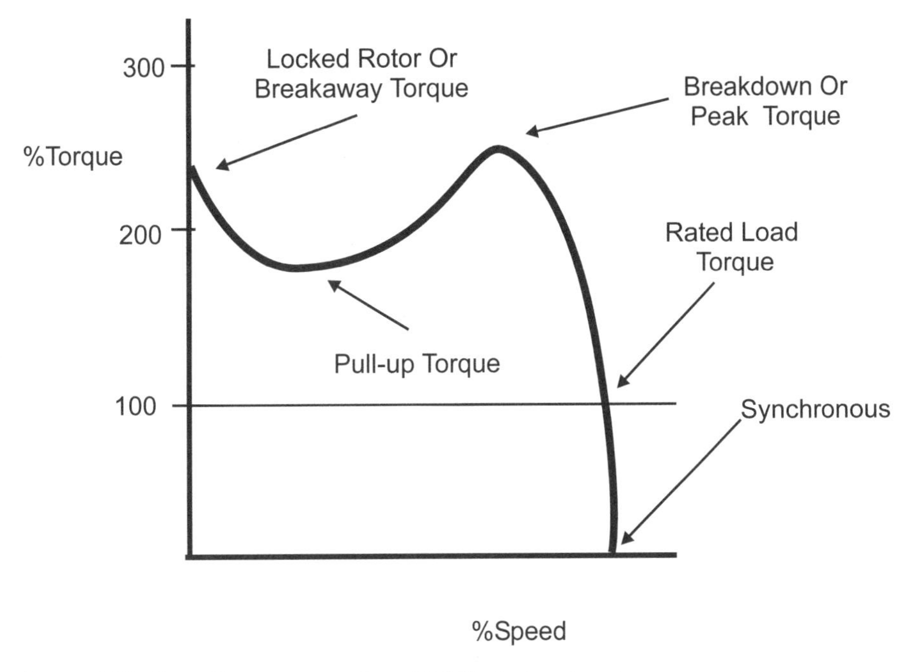

Figure 3-30. Speed/torque curve for a NEMA design B motor

Figure 3-30 shows the starting torque to be about 250% of the rated-load torque.

Peak (Breakdown) Torque

Occasionally a sudden overload will be placed on a motor. To keep the motor from stalling every time an overload occurs, motors have what is called a *breakdown torque*. The breakdown torque point is much higher than the *rated load torque* point. For this reason, it takes quite an overload to stall the motor. The speed/torque curve shown in Figure 3-30 indicates the breakdown torque for a typical induction motor to be about 270% of the rated load torque.

Operating a motor overloaded for an extended period of time will cause an excessive heat buildup in the motor and may eventually burn up the motor windings.

The NEMA definitions and ratings for an induction motor's characteristic torque is given later in this chapter.

Locked Rotor Torque (Starting or Breakaway Torque)
The *locked rotor torque* of a motor is the minimum torque, which it will develop at rest for all angular positions of the rotor. This capability is true with rated voltage and frequency applied.

Pull-Up Torque
The *pull-up torque* of a motor is the minimum torque developed by the motor when accelerating from rest to the breakdown torque point. For motors that do not have a definite breakdown torque, the pull-up torque is the minimum torque developed up to rated speed.

Peak (Breakdown) Torque
The *breakdown torque* of a motor is the maximum torque that it will develop. This capability is true with rated voltage and frequency applied, without an abrupt drop in speed.

Rated Load Torque
The *rated load torque* of a motor is the torque necessary to produce the motor's rated horsepower at rated-load speed. (**Note:** Rated load speed is normally considered base speed. Base speed means actual rotor speed when rated voltage, frequency, and load are applied to the motor.)

The above torque designations are all very important to the motor designer. Essentially, motors can be designed with emphasis on one or more of the above torque characteristics to produce motors for various applications. An improvement in one of these torque characteristics may adversely affect some other motor characteristic.

Enclosure Types and Cooling
Motors are often exposed to damaging atmospheres such as excessive moisture, steam, salt air, abrasive or conducting dust, lint, chemical fumes, and combustible or explosive dust or gases. To protect motors, a certain enclosure or encapsulated windings and special bearing protection may be required.

Motors exposed to the following conditions may require special mountings or protection: damaging mechanical or electrical loading such as unbalanced voltage conditions, abnormal shock or vibration, torsional impact loads, excessive thrust, or overhung loads.

Many types of enclosures are available. A few of the most common types are listed here, many of which are the same designations as for DC motors. It is strongly recommended that personnel actively involved with applying induction motors be familiar with, and adhere to, the contents of NEMA MG2 ("Safety Standard for Construction and Guide for Selection, Installation and Use of Electric motors and Generators").

Open Motor

The open motor enclosure type has ventilation openings that permit passage of external cooling air over and around the windings.

Open Drip-proof Motor

The open drip-proof (ODP) enclosure type is constructed so that drops of liquid or solids falling on the machine from a vertical direction cannot enter the machine. (This vertical direction is not at an angle greater than 15°.)

Guarded Motor

(This could be abbreviated DPFG—drip-proof fully guarded.) The guarded enclosure type has all ventilation openings limited to specified sizes and shapes. This enclosure prevents insertion of fingers or rods and limits accidental contact with rotating or electrical parts.

Splash-proof Motor

The splash-proof enclosure type is so constructed that drops of liquid or solid particles falling on the motor cannot enter. (These liquid or solid particles can be in a straight line or at any angle not greater than 100° from the vertical.)

Totally Enclosed Motor

The totally enclosed enclosure type prevents the free exchange of air between the inside and outside of the case, but is not airtight.

Totally Enclosed Non-Ventilated (TENV) Motor

The totally enclosed non-ventilated enclosure type is not equipped for cooling by external devices.

Totally Enclosed Fan-Cooled (TEFC) Motor

The totally enclosed fan-cooled enclosure type has a shaft-mounted fan to blow cooling air across the external frame. It is a popular motor for use in dusty, dirty, and corrosive atmospheres.

Totally Enclosed Blower-Cooled (TEBC) Motor

The totally enclosed blower-cooled enclosure type is totally enclosed and is equipped with an independently powered fan to blow cooling air across the external frame. A TEBC motor is commonly used in constant torque, variable-speed applications.

Encapsulated Motor

The encapsulated enclosure has windings that are covered with a heavy coating of material to protect them from moisture, dirt, abrasion, etc. Some encapsulated motors have only the coil noses coated. In motors with pressure-embedded windings, the encapsulation material impregnates the windings, even in the coil slots. With this complete protection, the motors can often be used in applications that demand totally enclosed motors.

Explosion-Proof (TEXP) Motor

The explosion-proof enclosure is totally enclosed and built to withstand an explosion of gas or vapor within it. It also prevents ignition of gas or vapor surrounding the machine by sparks, flashes, or explosions that may occur within the machine casing.

Protection and Ratings

Motor Protection

The typical method of starting a three-phase induction motor is by connecting the motor directly across the power line. *Line starting* a motor is done with a three-phase contactor. To adequately protect the motor from prolonged overload conditions, motor overloads are installed, typically in the same enclosure as the three-phase contactor. These overloads (OLs) operate as heater elements—heating to the point of opening the circuit, and mechanically disconnecting the circuit (Figure 3-31).

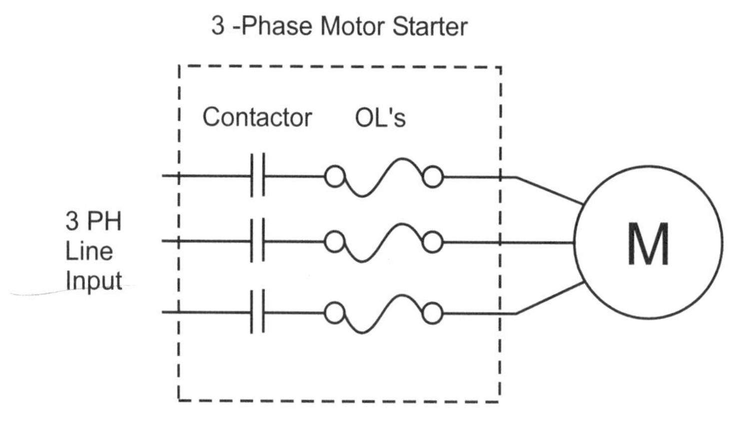

Figure 3-31. Line starting a motor

Overloads can be purchased with a specific time designed into the element. Classes 10, 20, and 30 are the usual ratings for industrial use. A class 10 overload indicates that the overload will allow 600% inrush current for 10 s before opening the circuit. Class 20 overloads would allow 600% inrush current for 20 s, and a class 30 would allow 30 s of operation. The current draw from a typical induction motor, as well as the torque produced can be seen in Figure 3-32.

Line starting an induction motor, as shown in Figure 3-32, would allow the motor to develop rated torque, as soon as the motor starter button is pressed. This is because across the line, the motor has the benefit of full voltage, current, and frequency (Hz). As long as the input power is of rated value, the motor would develop the torque as seen in Figure 3-32, from zero to base speed.

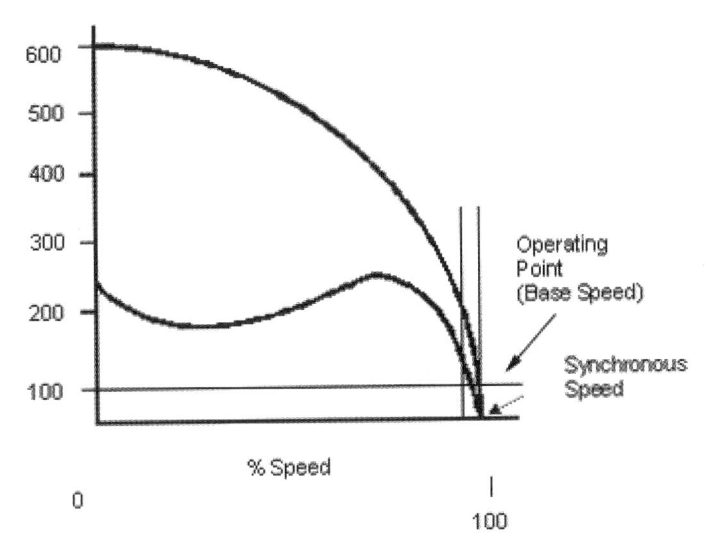

Figure 3-32. Motor torque and inrush current (line starting)

If the ratio of voltage to hertz is maintained, then the motor will develop the rated torque that it was designed to produce. This relationship can be seen in Figure 3-33 and is designated the *volts per hertz* ratio (V/Hz).

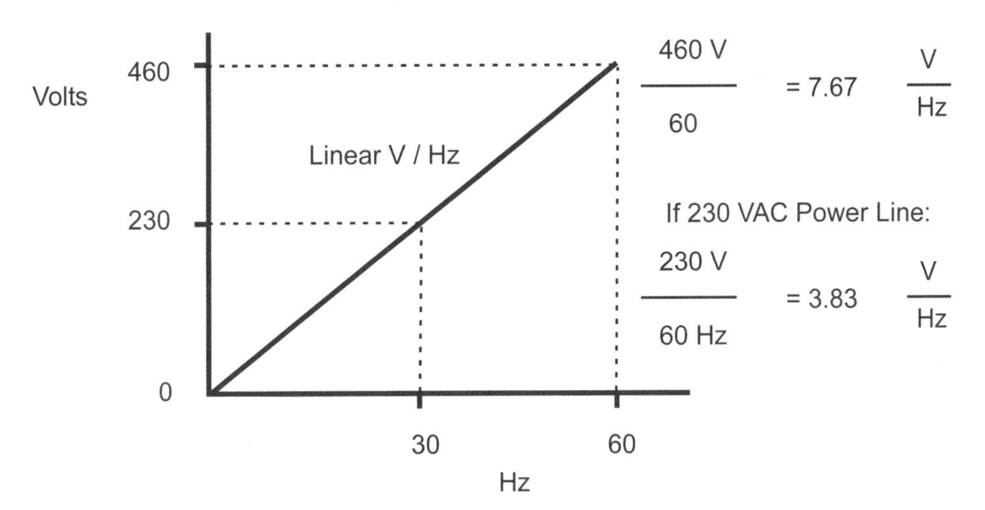

Figure 3-33. Volts per Hz ration (V/Hz)

As seen in Figure 3-33, the V/Hz ratio is calculated by simply dividing the input voltage by the hertz. This characteristic is an important ingredient of AC drive design, which will be covered in the next chapter.

There may be applications where full torque is not desirable when the motor is started: a conveyor application in a bottling line, for example. If the feed conveyor has uncapped full bottles on the conveyor, full torque when the conveyor is started would be a not-so-good situation. (The bottles would spill all of their contents.) In cases like that, a reduced torque type of start would be required. There are also cases where full voltage and hertz, which causes 600% inrush current, would cause a serious power dip on the utility system. High-horsepower motors connected to compressors would be an example. In these cases, a *reduced voltage* start would be required. If the voltage is less than rated value, the motor would not develop rated torque (according to the V/Hz ratio listed in Figure 3-32). Reducing the V/Hz ratio also reduces the starting current, which means there is less of a power dip.

Reducing the starting current may be accomplished in any one of the following ways.

Primary Resistor or Reactance

The primary resistor or reactance method uses series reactance or resistance to reduce the current during the first seconds. After a preset time interval, the motor is connected directly across the line. This method can be used with any standard induction motor.

Auto Transformer

The auto transformer method uses an auto transformer to directly reduce voltage and the current for the first few seconds. After a preset time interval, the motor is connected directly across the line. This method can also be used with any standard induction motor.

Wye–Delta

The wye-delta method applies the voltage across the Y connection to reduce the current during the first few seconds. After a preset time interval, the motor is connected in delta mode permitting full current. This type of induction motor must be constructed with wye-delta winding connections.

Part–Winding

The part-winding method uses a motor design that has two separate winding circuits. Upon starting, only one winding circuit is engaged and current is reduced. After a preset time interval, the full winding of the motor is connected directly across the line. This type of motor must have two separate winding circuits. To avoid winding overheating and damage, the time between first and second winding connections is limited to 4 seconds maximum.

Motor Ratings

When reviewing ratings, it is also necessary to review several design features of the induction motor. Induction motor design classifications, characteristics, and ratings will now be reviewed in detail.

Because of the variety of torque requirements, NEMA has established different "designs" to cover almost every application. These designs take into consideration starting current and slip, as well as torque. These motor design classes should not be confused with the various classes of wire insulation, which are also designated by letter.

Table 3-3 indicates the various NEMA design classifications and suitable applications.

Design class	Starting current	Locked rotor torque	Breakdown torque	% Slip	Suitable Applications Fans, blowers, rotary pumps, unloaded compressors, machine tools, misc. Constant speed load.
A	High	Med. Torque	High	5% Max	Fans, blowers, rotary pumps, unloaded compressors, machine tools, misc. Constant speed load.
B	Medium	Med. torque	High	5% Max	Fans, blowers, rotary pumps, unloaded compressors, machine tools, misc. Constant speed loads.
C	Medium	High torque	Medium	5% Max	High-inertia starting (e.g., centrifugal blowers, flywheels, crushers. Loaded starts (e.g., piston pumps, compressors, conveyors). Constant load speed.
D	Medium	Extra-high torque	Low	5–13%	Very high inertia, loaded starting. Considerable variation in load speed (e.g., punch presses, shears, forming machine tools, cranes, hoists, elevators, oil pump jacks)
E	Medium to high	Medium to high	Medium to high	75%	Pumps, fans, and blowers

Table 3-3. NEMA torque designs for polyphase motors

Figure 3-34 indicates the relative differences in torque, given a specific motor NEMA design class. The motors indicated are all line started.

As seen in Figure 3-34, the major differences are in the starting torque and peak or breakdown torque capabilities.

Efficiency

The efficiency of a motor is simply the ratio of the power "out" to the power "in," expressed in percentage.

$$\text{Efficiency} = \frac{\text{Power out}}{\text{Power in}} \times 100\%$$

Figure 3-35 illustrates the general relationship between current, slip, efficiency, and power factor.

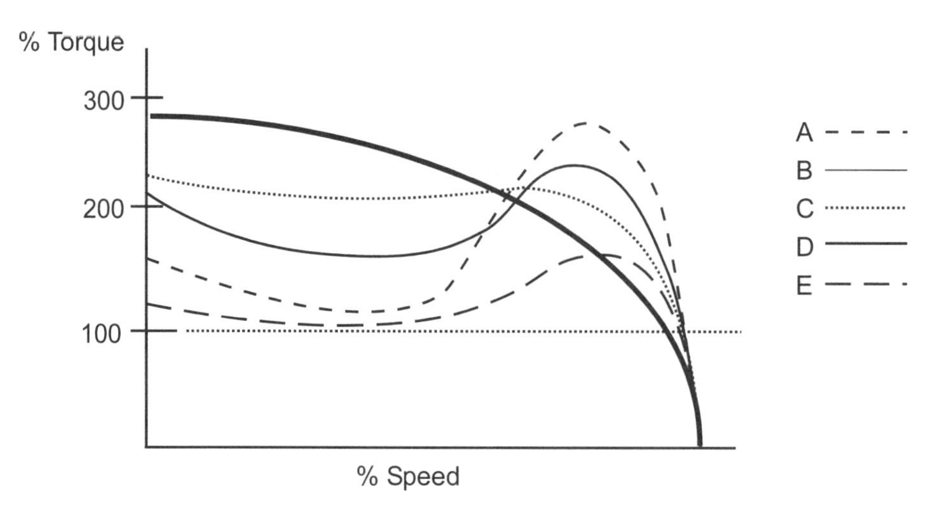

Figure 3-34. Comparison of NEMA Designs (speed/torque characteristics)

Generally, motor efficiency is relatively flat from rated load to 50% of rated load. Some motors exhibit peak efficiency near 75% of rated load.

Power Factor

Power Factor (P.F.) is the ratio of real power to apparent power, or kW/ kVA. Kilowatts (kW) are measured with a wattmeter, and kilovolt-amperes (kVA) are measured with a voltmeter and ammeter. A power factor of one (1.0) or *unity* is ideal. Power factor is highest near rated load, as seen in Figure 3-35. Power factor at 50% load is considerably less and continues to dramatically decrease until zero speed.

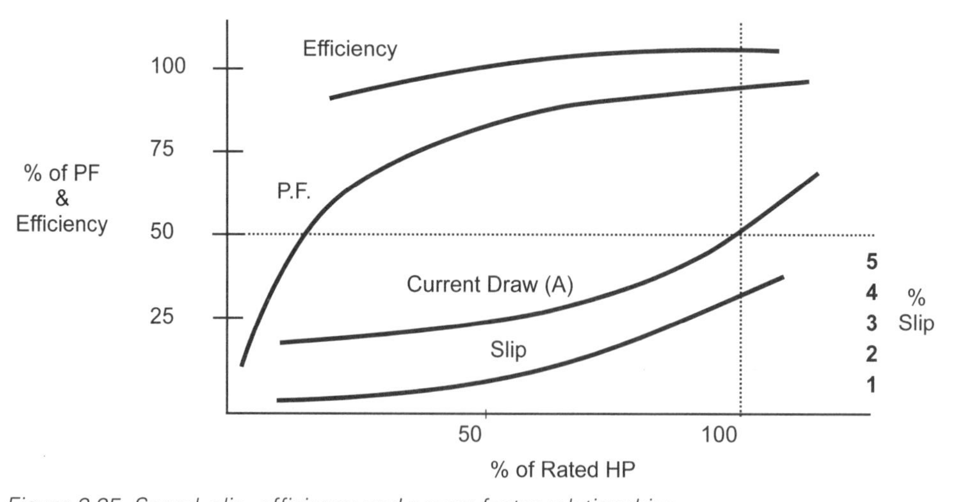

Figure 3-35. Speed, slip, efficiency and power factor relationships

Current Draw

Current draw in amperes is proportional to the actual load on the motor in the area of rated load. At other loads, current draw tends to be more non-linear (Figure 3-35).

Locked Rotor (kVA/HP)

Another rating specified on motor nameplates is *locked rotor kVA per horse-power.* (Some manufacturers use the designation *locked rotor amps.)* A letter appears on the nameplate corresponding to various kVA/HP ratings. Refer to Table 3-4 for letter designations.

Code letter	kVA/HP
A	0–3.14
B	3.15–3.54
C	3.55–3.9
D	4.0–4.4
E	4.5–4.9
F	5.0–5.5
G	5.6–6.2
H	6.3–7.0
J	7.1–7.9
K	8.0–8.9
L	9.0–9.9
M	10.0–11.1
N	11.2–12.4
P	12.5–13.9
R	14.0–15.9
S	16.0–17.9
T	18.0–19.9
U	20.0–22.3
V	22.4 and above

Table 3-4. Locked rotor kVA per HP

The nameplate codes are a good indicator of the starting current in amperes. A lower code letter indicates a low starting current and a high code letter indicates a high starting current for a specific motor horse-power rating. Calculating the starting current can be accomplished using the following formula:

$$\text{Locked rotor amps} = \frac{1000 \times \text{HP} \times \text{KVA/HP}}{1.73 \times \text{volts}}$$

Example: What is the approximate starting current of a 10-HP, 208-V motor with a nameplate code letter of "K" ?

Solution: From Table 3-4, the kVA/HP for a code letter of "K" is 8.0 to 8.9. Taking a number approximately halfway in-between and substituting in the formula, we get:

$$\text{Locked rotor amps} = \frac{1000 \times \text{HP} \times 8.5}{1.73 \times 208} = 236 \text{ amps}$$

Therefore, the starting current is approximately 236 amperes. The starting current is important because the purchaser of the motor must know what kind of protection (overload) to provide. The installation must also include power lines of sufficient size to carry the required currents and properly sized fuses.

Insulation Systems

An insulation system is a group of insulating materials in association with conductors and the supporting structure of a motor. Insulation systems are divided into classes according to the thermal rating of the system. Four classes of insulation systems are used in motors: class A, B, F, and H. Do not confuse these insulation classes with motor designs previously discussed. Those design classes are also designated by letter.

Another confusion factor is the voltage insulation system classes of the stator windings. Those classes are also designated by class B, F, and H, for example. NEMA, standard MG1, part 31 indicates the voltage insulation classes, relative to use on AC drives. More review of motor voltage insulation characteristics will be done in Chapter 4.

At this point, we will review the temperature insulation classes, common in standard industrial induction motors operated across the line.

Class A. Class A insulation is one in which tests have shown suitable thermal endurance exists when operated at a temperature of 105°C. Typical materials used include cotton, paper, cellulous acetate films, enamel-coated wire, and similar organic materials impregnated with suitable substances.

Class B. Class B insulation is one in which tests have shown suitable thermal endurance exists when operated at a temperature of 130°C. Typical materials include mica, glass fiber, asbestos, and other materials, not necessarily inorganic, with compatible bonding substances having suitable thermal stability.

Class F. Class F insulation is one in which tests have shown suitable thermal endurance exists when operated at a temperature of 155°C. Typical materials include mica, glass fiber, asbestos, and other materials, not necessarily inorganic, with compatible bonding substances having suitable thermal stability.

Class H. Class H insulation is one in which tests have shown suitable thermal endurance exists when operated at a temperature of 180°C. Typical materials used include mica, glass fiber, asbestos, silicone elastomer, and other materials, not necessarily inorganic, with compatible bonding substances, such as silicone resins, having suitable thermal stability.

Usual Service Conditions

When operated within the limits of the NEMA-specified "usual service conditions," standard motors will perform in accordance with their ratings.

For service conditions other than usual, the precautions listed below must be considered.

Ambient or room temperature not over 40°C. If the ambient temperature is over 40°C (104°F), the motor service factor must be reduced or a higher horsepower motor used. The larger motor will be loaded below full capacity so the temperature rise will be less and overheating reduced. (Note: *Service factor* refers to rated motor power and indicates permissible power loading that may carried by the motor. For example, a 1.15 service factor would allow 15% overload power to be drawn by the motor.)

Altitude does not exceed 3300 feet (1000 meters). Motors having class A or B insulation systems and temperature rises according to NEMA can operate satisfactorily at altitudes above 3300 feet. However, in locations above 3300 feet, a decrease in ambient temperature must compensate for the increase in temperature rise, as seen in Table 3-5.

Ambient temp. °C (°F)	Max. altitude (ft)
40 (104)	3300
30 (86)	6600
20 (68)	9900

Table 3-5. Temperature vs. altitude

Motors having a service factor of 1.15 or higher will operate satisfactorily at unity service factor and an ambient temperature of 40°C at altitudes above 3300 feet up to 9000 feet.

Voltage Variations. A voltage variation of not more than ±10% of nameplate voltage:

Operation outside these limits or unbalanced voltage conditions can result in overheating or loss of torque and may require using a larger-horsepower motor.

Frequency Variations. A frequency variation of not more than ±5% of nameplate frequency: Operation outside of these limits results in substantial speed variation and causes overheating and reduced torque.

A combination of 10% variation in voltage and frequency provided the frequency variation does not exceed 5%.

Mounting Surface and Location. The mounting surface must be rigid and in accordance with NEMA specifications. Location of supplementary enclosures must not seriously interfere with the ventilation of the motor.

AC Motor Types

Introduction

AC motors can be divided into two major categories—asynchronous and synchronous. The induction motor is probably the most common type of asynchronous motor (meaning speed is dependent on slip). When reviewing induction motors, there are two rating designations—NEMA and IEC.

Another type of asynchronous motor is the wound rotor motor. This type of motor has controllable speed and torque because of the addition of a secondary resistance in the rotor circuit. A third type of popular asynchronous motor is the single-phase motor. The single-phase AC motor will not be covered because of their limited use in industrial applications when connected with variable-frequency drives.

The synchronous motor is inherently a constant-speed motor, when operated directly across the line. This type of motor operates in synchronism with the line frequency. Two types of synchronous motors are non-excited and DC-excited.

The basic principles of AC induction motors have been previously covered. In this section, attention will be given to motor designations, ratings, and designs.

Standard AC Induction Motors (NEMA and IEC)

NEMA frame motors are in widespread use throughout U.S. industry. This motor design was developed before the 1950s and has well served many types of fixed-speed applications. In 1952 and 1964, NEMA evaluated standard frame sizes and re-rated the frame standards. The result was smaller diameter motor frames (e.g., original 326 frame prior to 1952, to a 284U frame in 1952, to a 256T frame in 1964). As the re-rating took place, the frame sizes (numbers) were reduced, as was the amount of iron in the stator. With less iron in the stator, less overload capability is realized compared with the "U" frame or the original frame size.

However, with smaller-diameter frames comes more efficiency and faster response to changes in magnetic flux. Figure 3-36 indicates the construction of a standard AC induction motor. All the major motor components are identified.

It should be noted that all standard motors include a small rectangular slot, cut lengthwise in the shaft, called a *keyway* or *keyseat*. This slot includes a tapered-cut rectangular piece of steel, call a *key*. The key is inserted into the keyway and pressure-fit snugly to mechanically connect the shaft and coupler or connection device, such as a pulley or gear.

As seen in Figure 3-36, the induction motor is a fairly simple device. However, precision engineering is required to create small tolerances and air gaps that will allow maximum efficiency and torque generation.

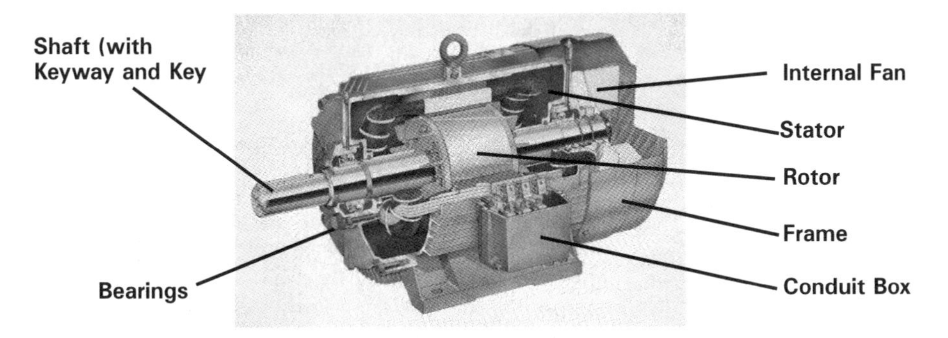

Figure 3-36. AC induction motor construction (Courtesy of ABB Motors)

The AC induction motor (polyphase induction motor) can be divided into five classifications, according to NEMA. The speed/torque characteristics for each classification have been presented in an earlier section. A brief description of each classification will be presented here, followed by a comparison to IEC frame motors.

- **NEMA Design A:** This type of motor has a high breakdown torque characteristic, compared with NEMA design B motors. These motors are normally designed for specific use, with a slip characteristic usually less than 5%.
- **NEMA design B:** This type of motor is designed for general-purpose use and accounts for the largest share of induction motors sold. The typical slip for a design B motor is 3–5% or less.
- **NEMA design C:** This type of motor has a high starting torque, with a relatively normal starting current and low slip. The type of load applied to a design C is one where breakaway loads are high upon start. The loads, however, would be normally run at the rated point, with very little demand for overload.
- **NEMA design D:** This type of motor has a high starting torque, high slip, but also low full load speed. Because of its high slip (5–13%), the speed can easily fluctuate because of changes in load.
- **NEMA design E:** This type of motor is known for high efficiency and is used mainly where the starting torque requirements are low. Fans and centrifugal pumps make up the bulk of applications using this type of motor.

Figure 3-37 indicates the NEMA designs and compares design with rated starting current and speed.

As shown in Figure 3-37, though design E may have the highest efficiency, it also has the highest starting current—about 800%. This fact must be reviewed when sizing the proper overload heater elements. Most standard induction motors have closer to a 600% starting current rating.

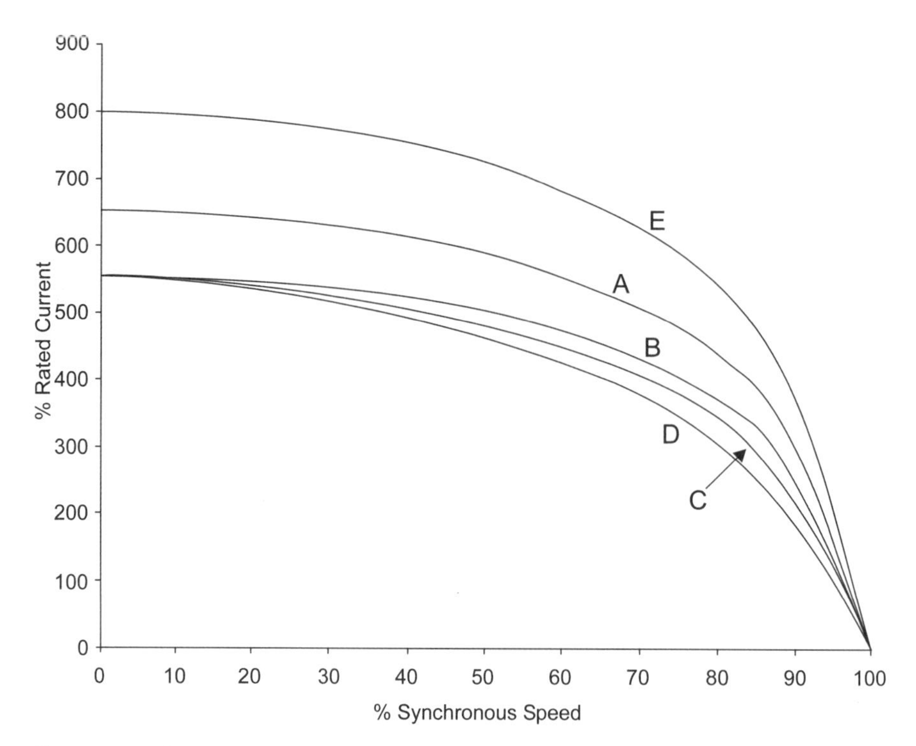

Figure 3-37. Current vs. speed for NEMA motor designs (Courtesy of ABB Inc.)

Though NEMA motors are rated in horsepower, there are times when a motor is specified on the basis of its frame size. NEMA supplies standard frame designations, up to the 445T frame. Above that rating, motor manufacturers can supply their own standards and designate the motor rating as exceeding the NEMA ratings.

There are standard frame sizes of motors and are based on a given horsepower or base speed. NEMA designates a *foot to centerline* dimension as an indication of the frame size. There is also a designator for frame diameter. Figure 3-38 indicates an AC induction motor, with an indication of frame size.

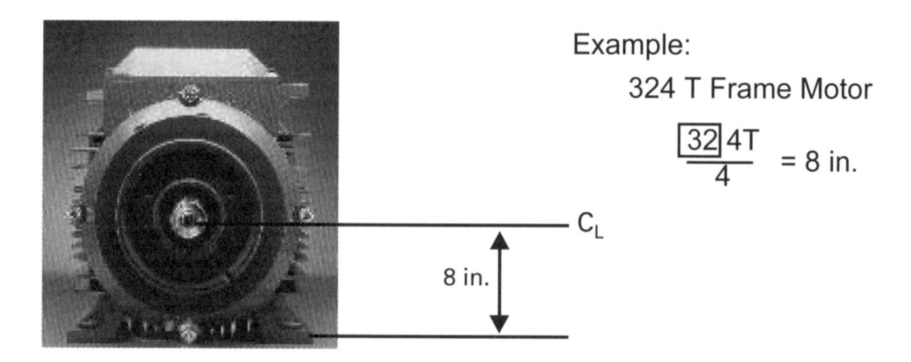

Figure 3-38. 324 frame motor designation (Courtesy of ABB Motors)

Using a 324 T frame motor as an example, the motor designer designates the shaft centerline distance to the foot at 8 inches. To figure any shaft centerline distance to foot, divide the first two digits of the frame number by 4 (32 ÷ 4 = 8 inches). With this information, an application engineer can design a machine with the motor dimensions in mind. This also assists in comparing one motor with one from another manufacturer. All motor dimensions are standard.

Since motor dimensions are standard, so too are motor nameplate ratings. As with DC motors, AC motor nameplates contain all the necessary information to effectively apply the motor. Figure 3-39 is an example of a typical AC motor nameplate.

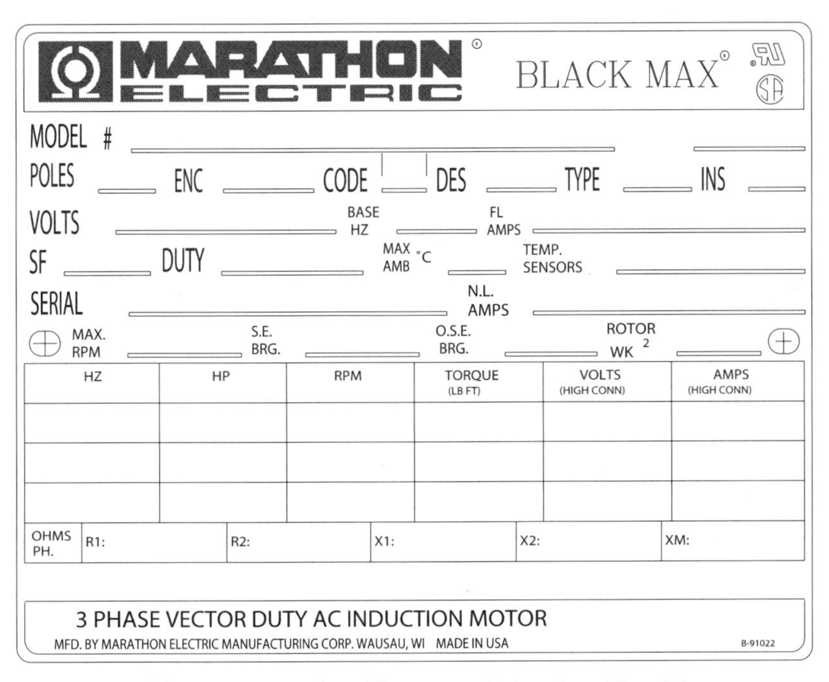

Figure 3-39. AC motor nameplate (Courtesy of Marathon Electric)

- **Frame:** Indicating the frame rating per specific horsepower, given the rated voltage and frequency (example: 256T frame).
- **HP:** Available horsepower at the designated voltage and frequency ratings.
- **Voltage, phase, and frequency:** Designations for the rated voltage, phase, and frequency in hertz. Many industrial motors contain a *dual-voltage* rating. This means that they can be connected to two different voltage lines. The operating voltage is designated by either jumper strips or wire configurations that are completed in the conduit box. Typically, NEMA frame motors are rated for 60-Hz operation.

- **FL Amps:** Current rating of the motor, listed in amperes. Some nameplates indicate current rating as FLA (full load amps). This would indicate that the motor would draw the stated amps under rated voltage, frequency, and load. If the motor is a dual-voltage motor, two values of amps would be listed. The first value would coincide with the first value of voltage stated. The second value would coincide with the second voltage value listed. (Example: A 230/460V motor may indicate nameplate amps of 68/34 amps. The motor would draw twice the amps on the 230-V connection, compared with the 460-V connection.)

- **rpm:** This is the motor speed in rpm at base speed. Base speed is indicated as rated voltage, frequency, and load. Due to less slip, an unloaded motor speed would rise from this speed to close to synchronous speed.

- **Design and insulation class:** The design class would indicate the NEMA designation for A, B, C, D, or E. Typically, the insulation class would indicate the temperature capability of the stator winding insulation. For example, a common designation of Class B insulation would allow for a maximum temperature rise of 130°C (266°F). A Class H insulation would allow for a maximum temperature rise of 180°C (356°F). *Temperature rise* means the amount of temperature increase, above the normal ambient rating of 40°C (104°F).

An additional classification is now being included with motors—that of the electrical strength of the stator winding insulation (referred to a *dielectric strength*). AC motors applied to variable-frequency drives run the risk of possible insulation damage from the power conversion technology in the drive. Voltage stress beyond the rating can cause microscopic pin holes in the insulation, which could result in an open phase and eventual motor failure. Motors designated as *inverter duty* have the electrical insulation strength to avoid failure due to drive technology issues.

NEMA MG-1, Part 31 standards indicate that motors operated on 600 V or less drives should be capable of withstanding peak voltage of 1600 V. Motor cable length and drive carrier (switch) frequency also play a part in the possible damage to a motor's insulation strength. Motors with a 1200-V or 1000-V insulation strength should not be applied to AC drives unless additional precautions are taken. Special drive output filters will reduce the effects of high-peak voltages and lower the risk of insulation failure.

The motor manufacturer should always be consulted when questions arise regarding the insulation strength of the windings. The manufacturer can make recommendations as to additional safeguards that may be needed to increase motor life when connected to a drive.

- **Duty and S.F. (Service Factor):** Most standard AC motors list duty as "continuous" or "intermittent." The service factor of the motor is the multiplier or additional safe power loading above the rating. Small fractional horsepower motors may carry a service factor of 1.4, while larger integral horsepower motors may list only 1.15 service factor. For example, a 1.15 S.F. would indicate a motor's capability of 15% additional horsepower output, above the rating. A 1.4 S.F. would indicate 40% additional horsepower output.

- **Efficiency and Ambient:** Many motors may list a designation of *premium* efficiency. In addition, an actual number may be referenced, such as 89.5. The efficiency is closely tied with the NEMA classification, such as design A, B, C, etc. The motor manufacturer will acquire the rating from an independent testing agency. The ambient temperature is the maximum normal operating temperature, below the amount indicated in the temperature insulation class.

Not all AC motors contain every piece of data listed above. But all motor nameplates would indicate the most important information, such as voltage, frequency, amps, and rpm. This information is required by an AC drive, in order for the drive to match internal diagnostics with the motor data.

Some motor nameplates indicate a wiring diagram for the dual voltage windings; others have a sticker or label inside the conduit box, stating the wiring connections. Some of the new motors manufactured today indicate the dielectric strength of the insulation or mounting design.

IEC Ratings

At this point, it would be helpful to briefly review IEC motor ratings and then compare IEC with NEMA. The motor market today has become more global, with IEC rated motors on equipment exported from Europe.

IEC is the acronym for the International Electrotechnical Commission. IEC, like NEMA, establishes and publishes mechanical and electrical standards for motors. Many IEC standards have been nationalized for a specific country, such as Germany, Great Britain, or France.

Though NEMA and IEC standards use different terms, they are essentially similar in ratings and in many cases are interchangeable. NEMA standards are probably more conservative, which allows for interpretations in design. IEC standards are more specific and categorized. They are typically more precise.

Both IEC and NEMA use letter codes to indicate mechanical dimensions. They also use code letters to indicate general frame size. The NEMA and IEC dimension codes are not interchangeable, nor are the frame sizes (exception being the 56 frame, which is the same in NEMA and IEC).

As expected, NEMA designations are listed in inches and horsepower, whereas IEC designations are listed in millimeters and kilowatts. NEMA lists a handful of enclosure designations and descriptions, whereas IEC uses numbers.

IEC lists two numbers: the first number indicates protection against solid objects; the second number indicates protection against water entry. The enclosure letters "IP" indicate *ingress protection*. (Example: IP55. The first "5" indicates complete protection, including dust-tight, and the second "5" indicates protection from water sprayed from a nozzle from any direction. This type of motor would be considered *wash-down duty*.)

NEMA would list the enclosure type to indicate the particular cooling method employed in the motor. IEC, however, would use a letter and number code to designate how a motor is cooled. (Example: IC40. The "4" indicates frame cooling, while the "0" indicates convection cooling with no fan.) The temperature insulation class ratings are identical, whether NEMA or IEC.

IEC motors are listed as "50 Hz" rather than the NEMA "60 Hz." A 50-Hz IEC motor will normally operate satisfactorily on 60 Hz, as long as the voltage is increased by the same ratio as the frequency. (Example: 50 Hz at 380 V to 60 Hz at 460 V) The motor speed would be 1/6 higher than at 50 Hz. However, operating a 50-Hz motor at the lower U.S. voltage of 230 V may not operate satisfactorily without derating (requiring the motor to deliver 15 or 20% less torque at nameplate rating, due to motor heating).

When applying an IEC motor instead of a NEMA motor, it is always sound practice to consult a motor rating table for comparisons. NEMA ratings include a factor for overload, whereas IEC strictly rates motors with little to no overload capability.

Wound Rotor

The speed and torque characteristics of an AC induction motor are essentially defined by the design, number of poles, and line power applied. In contrast, the wound rotor version of an induction motor does have controllable speed and torque characteristics. Different values of resistance are inserted into the rotor circuit to obtain various performance options.

Wound rotor motors are normally started with a secondary resistance connected to the rotor circuit. The resistance is reduced to allow the motor to increase in speed. This type of motor can develop substantial torque, and at the same time, limit the amount of locked rotor current. The secondary resistance can be designed for continuous operation at reduced speeds. Special consideration is required for heat dissipation at reduced speeds because of reduced cooling effects and high inertia loads. Figure 3-40 indicates a wiring diagram of a wound rotor motor.

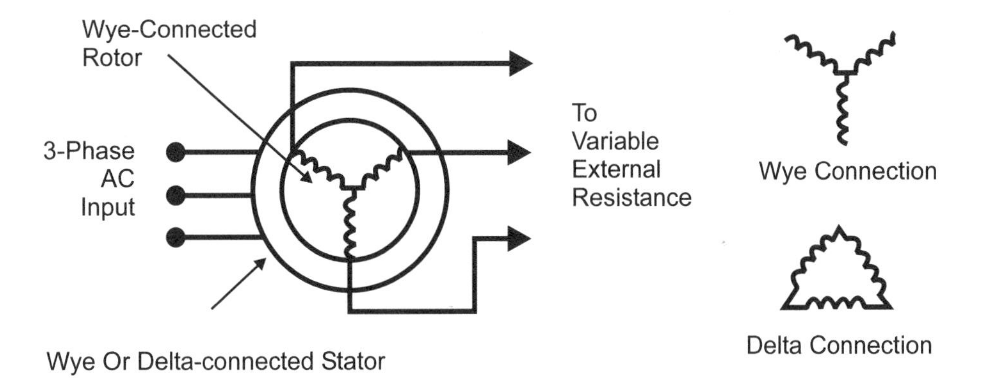

Figure 3-40. Wound rotor motor diagram

The advantages of this type of motor include a lower starting current (less than 600%) with a high starting torque. This motor type also provides for smooth acceleration and easy control capability.

A disadvantage of this type of motor is that efficiency is low. The external resistance causes a large drop in rpm, based on a small change in load. Speed can be reduced down to 50% of rated value. Another disadvantage is that the relative cost of this motor may be substantially higher than an equivalent three-phase induction motor.

Synchronous Motors

The three-phase AC synchronous motor is a unique and specialized type of motor. Without complex electronic control, this motor type is inherently a fixed-speed motor. This type of motor is used in applications where constant speed is critical. It is also in cases where power factor correction is desired, since it can operate at leading or unity power factor. The synchronous motor is a highly efficient means of converting AC electrical power to mechanical power.

The synchronous motor could be considered a three-phase alternator, operated backward. Direct current is applied directly to the rotor to produce a rotating electromagnetic field. The stator windings are connected in either a wye or delta configuration. Figure 3-41 indicates a diagram of the synchronous motor.

It should be noted that the synchronous motor has a "wound" rotor that is connected to a brush assembly system connected to DC power. In reality, synchronous motors have little to no starting torque. An external device must be used for the initial start of the motor.

Devices such as an auxiliary DC motor/generator or *damper windings* are typically used to initially start the synchronous motor. The motor is constructed such that it will rotate at the same speed as the rotating stator field. At synchronous speed, rotor and stator speed are equal, and therefore, the motor has no slip. With a load on the shaft, slip increases and the

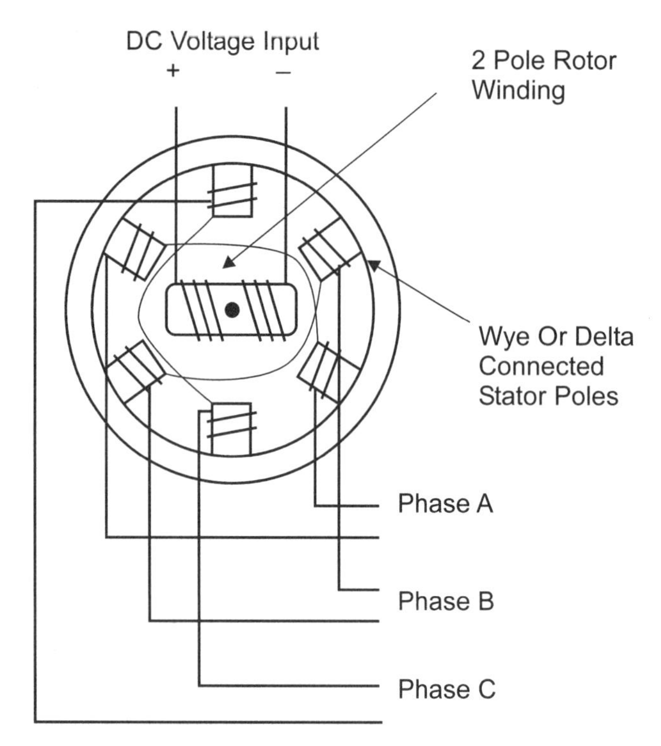

Figure 3-41. AC synchronous motor diagram

motor responds with more torque, which increases the speed back to "synchronism."

Synchronous motors in sub-fractional ratings are usually self-excited using damper windings. High-horsepower synchronous motors are usually DC excited using an external DC motor/generator.

Multiple Pole Motors

Multiple pole motors could be considered multiple-speed motors. As stated earlier, the speed is a direct result of the number of pole pairs. At 60 Hz, a four-pole motor would have a synchronous speed of 1800 rpm. At the same 60 Hz, a two-pole motor would have twice the synchronous speed—3600 rpm. Typically, an AC induction motor has only one set of pole pairs—2, 4, 6, or 8 poles, or more. However, specially designed multiple speed motors would be wound for two different pole pair connections.

Most of the multiple pole motors would be dual-speed or two-speed design motors. Essentially, the conduit box would contain two sets of wiring configurations: one for the low-speed and one for the high-speed windings. The windings would be engaged by a two-position switch or electrical contacts. The switch or contacts would connect either the low- or high-speed winding to the three-phase power source.

This type of motor configuration provides a certain amount of flexibility in manufacturing. Perhaps the low-speed winding would be used for a production process taking place on a feed conveyor. Once the process is complete and a limit switch is closed, that same conveyor would move the product at high speed to the packaging and labeling section. There are many other industrial, packaging, food processing, and HVAC applications where two-speed motors could be an advantage. The possible disadvantage of this type of motor is the additional cost of some type of external switch control.

Specialty Motors

General Principles of Operation—Stepper

A *step* or *stepper* motor is one in which electrical pulses are converted into mechanical movements. A standard DC motor, for example, rotates continuously; but a stepper motor rotates in fixed increments whenever it is *pulsed on*. A standard DC motor would be considered an analog device, while a stepper motor would be considered digital.

The size of the step, or the step angle, is determined by the motor construction or by the type of controller connected. (**Note:** The step angle is determined in fractions of 360°, which is one complete shaft rotation.) For example, the step resolution of 90° would be four steps per rev (revolution). A 15° resolution would indicate 12 steps per rev, and 1.8° would indicate 200 steps per rev. Microstep motors are capable of thousands of steps per rev.

Because of their exactness of rotation, stepper motors are used, "open-loop" in control systems where position is critical. In many high-accuracy applications, an encoder or position feedback device is used to confirm the actual position of the motor shaft.

Stepper motors require a drive package with an electronic controller, power supply, and feedback device, if needed. Figure 3-42 indicates the principle of stepper motor design.

The stepper motor is a two-phase type of motor. The indexer provides step and direction pulses to the drive controller (amplifier). The amount of current for each phase is determined by the controller, which is then used as an output to the stepper motor. The stepper motor is operated by pulses, which determine the "steps" of the motor shaft. The frequency of these steps determines the speed of the motor.

The most common types of stepper motors are probably the permanent magnet (PM) and the variable reluctance (VR). The diagram in Figure 3-42 is one type of a PM stepper motor. Is could be considered a design similar to the synchronous induction motor.

The rotor moves in step with the stator windings when the windings are energized. If the windings are continuously energized from the two-phase supply, then the motor would essentially act as a low-speed synchronous motor. As seen in Figure 3-42, the PM rotor is surrounded by the two-phase stator. The rotor sections are offset by 1/2 tooth pitch (180°) from

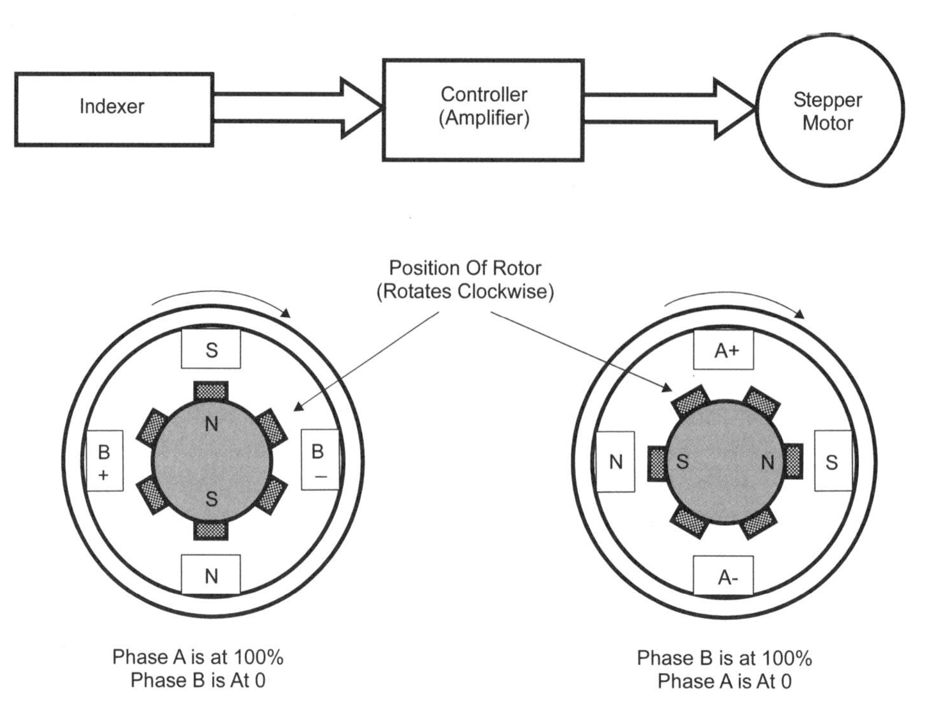

Figure 3-42. PM stepper motor diagram

each other. As the voltage rotates clockwise, from phase A to phase B, a set of rotor magnets will align themselves with the stator magnetic field. The rotor will therefore turn one step. If for some reason, both phases are energized simultaneously, the rotor will establish a location midway between the stator poles. If that were to happen, the motor would be considered *half stepping*.

The VR type stepper motor is basically constructed the same way as a PM motor. The difference is that the VR type does not have magnets in the rotor. It would contain, however, 2-, 3- or 4-phase stator windings. The motor would operate similar to an induction motor, with the rotor aligning itself with a stator pole that is energized.

The stepper motor is essentially a brushless motor. It can deliver high torque at zero speed, with no drifting of the shaft position. The direction of the motor can be reversed by reversing the direction of the pulses from the controller. The device has low inertia, similar to a servomotor, a result of the windings in the stator and a permanent magnet rotor.

There are several application considerations that come with stepper motors. Periodically, possibly at low speeds, this type of motor exhibits oscillations with every step. This is caused by poles in the rotor seeking the next available magnetic field. Many times, the magnetic fields of the rotor and stator do not match up, typically upon power-up. Also, the motor, controller, and load must be somewhat matched to minimize the oscillations. Stepper motors tend to run hotter than standard induction motors. This is due to the pulse waveform from the controller, especially at low speed, with high current levels present (a product of high torque response at low speed).

AC Vector Motors

This type of motor is a specific type that would be applied to an AC vector or flux vector drive. Principles of operation for this motor are basically identical to the standard AC induction motor. Because this motor is operated from a flux vector drive, special design characteristics are required.

Vector control basically means the requirement of full torque at zero speed. In applications such as elevators, hoists, and ski lifts, the motor usually is started while under rated load. If the device is an elevator car, the position of the device cannot change when the motor is started. If a standard induction motor were used, the motor would have to "slip back" for torque to be developed. During the process of developing "motor slip," the elevator car may have dropped several feet before the motor could develop enough torque to move it upward. The vector motor is specially designed to operate at extremely low slip and be able to handle the heat generated by providing full torque at zero speed.

The general principle of operation lies with analyzing the motor in terms of voltage and flux vectors. The rotor is divided into 360° of rotation, which is one complete rotation. A vector would be the direction and amount of a certain quantity in the motor circuit—in this case, rotor flux or stator flux. The relationship between rotor and stator flux is indicated in Figure 3-43.

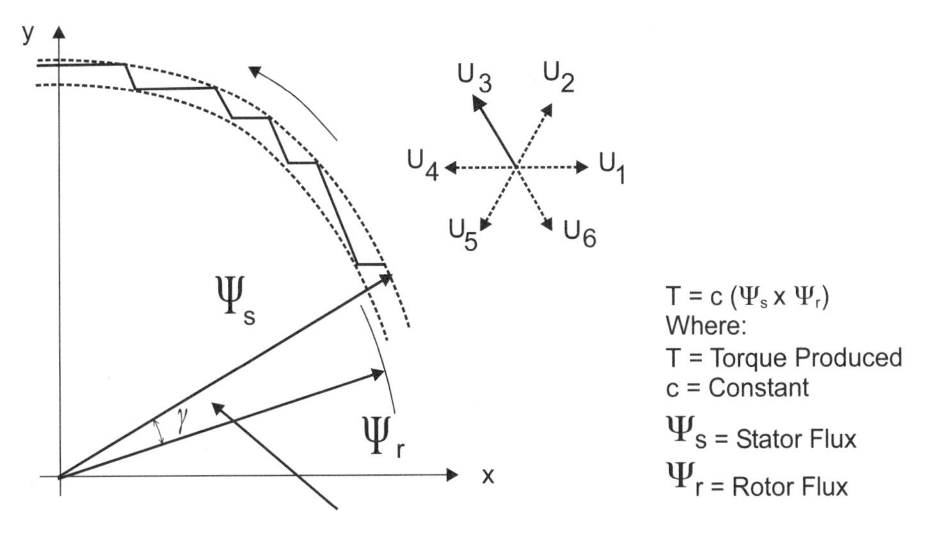

Figure 3-43. Vector motor relationships - stator and rotor flux (Courtesy of ABB Inc.)

The torque in an induction motor is developed by the relationship of rotor and stator flux. The physical torque developed is a byproduct of the magnitude of the stator and rotor flux vectors. Stator flux is a function of the input voltage to the motor. (The voltage vectors are indicated by U_1 to U_6 in the figure.) We could consider the dashed curve set the torque span developed in the motor. The device that would control the amount of stator and rotor flux generated would be considered a vector or flux vector AC drive.

The vector motor, in most cases, must have provisions for the mounting of a feedback device on the shaft end. The feedback device (encoder or resolver) sends information back to the drive control, indicating exactly where the rotor position is located. The drive control needs this information to calculate and generate V/Hz. The V/Hz waveform is then used by the motor to generate the flux vectors shown in the figure.

Vector control, drive control, and feedback devices will be discussed in Chapter 4 (AC Drives section) and Chapter 5 (Closed Loop Control section). This type of technology is definitely in high demand throughout industry today. The use of motor vector control (torque control) allows manufacturing systems to increase accuracy and productivity. The basic design of the AC induction motor has not changed much in the last few decades. Magnetism is magnetism. However, the ratings are now more precise than they were a few decades ago. The efficiencies are definitely higher than a few decades ago. There are AC drive manufacturers that require a flux vector drive and motor combination—a matched set. The direction of industry, however, is to be able to use a combination of vendor equipment to achieve the desired results.

Servomotors: General Principles of Operation

Introduction

The servomotors used in industry today are used in a closed-loop servo system. To understand how the servomotor is used in the system, it is first necessary to review the entire system. Figure 3-44 indicates a block diagram of a typical servo system.

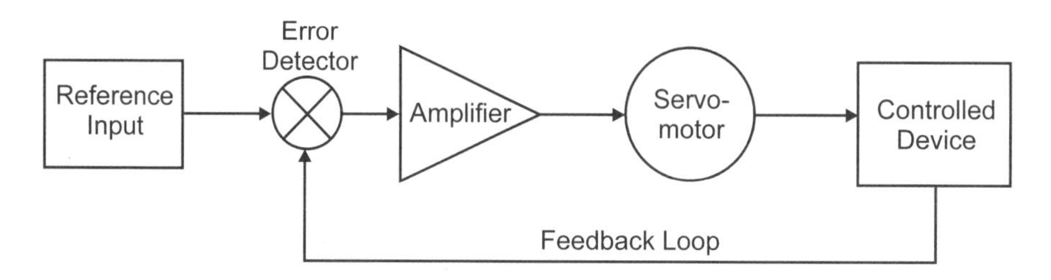

Figure 3-44. Typical servo system block diagram

A reference input (typically called a velocity input) is sent to the servo amplifier, which controls the speed of the servomotor. Directly mounted to the machine (or to the servomotor) is a feedback device (either an encoder or resolver). This device changes mechanical motion into electrical signals and is used as a *feedback loop*. This feedback loop is then sent to the *error detector,* which compares the actual operation with that of the reference input. If there is an error, that error is fed directly to the amplifier, which makes the necessary corrections.

In many servo systems, both velocity and position are monitored. (Note: In servo systems, the word "velocity" is often used to describe speed control. Velocity indicates a rate of change of position, with respect to time. It also indicates a rate of motion in a particular direction, with respect to time.) The velocity loop control may take its command from the velocity loop feedback device—a resolver or tachometer mounted directly to the motor. The position loop control may take its command from the position feedback device—an encoder. Depending on the system, both devices may be mounted to the actual machine or controlled device.

The stability of the entire system is dependent upon the tuning of the components in the system and how well those components are matched. Tuning the system involves working with a PID (proportional integral derivative) control. This type of closed loop control is standard on all high-accuracy systems. The main factors in this closed loop system are the gain, integration time, and derivative time of the loop.

The amplifier gain must be set satisfactorily. The gain sets how responsive the amplifier will be during changes in error signal. A high gain will cause the motor to overshoot the intended speed target. Too low of a gain may mean that the target is reached late in the cycle, or possibly not at all.

The integration time allows the amplifier to respond to changes in the error signal, mostly at zero speed. The zero speed error signal is multiplied by the gain setting, and results in increased motor responsiveness (stiffness) and accuracy.

The derivative function is the most difficult to accurately adjust. This controls the dampening or oscillations of the system. This function basically dictates the amount of correction given per unit of error. The error signal can be corrected immediately (in milliseconds), or throughout a longer period of time (seconds).

If there is a difficult part to the tuning task, it would be during the derivative setup. The gain and integration time is interactive. One setting affects the other. Proper setup of the derivative function involves multiplying the position error by the position error rate (how much correction should take place per unit of time). If the system components are not matched, oscillations, overshoot, or undershoot of velocity can result, which means unstable operation.

Servomotors are special electromechanical devices that operate in precise degrees of rotation. This type of motor quickly responds to positive or negative signals from a servo amplifier. Fast and accurate speed, torque, and direction control are the mark of a servomotor's characteristics. Very high starting torque must be obtained from the servomotor. The standard AC induction motor's torque is measured in pound-feet. By contrast, the servomotor's torque is measured in inch-pounds.

In today's servo systems, three basic types of servomotors are used: AC, DC, and AC brushless. As one might expect, the AC design is based on AC induction motor characteristics. The DC design is based on the design of a DC motor. The brushless DC design is based on that of a synchronous motor. The basic principles of the DC and brushless DC servomotor have already been reviewed. We will therefore review the general characteristics of the AC servomotor. Linear devices will also be reviewed, since most of the position systems operate on linear technology.

AC Servomotors

This type of motor is basically a two-phase induction motor, capable of reverse operation. To achieve the dynamic requirements of a servo system, the servomotor must have a small diameter, low inertia, and high-resistance rotors. The low inertia allows for fast starts, stops, and reverse of direction. The high-resistance rotor provides for almost linear speed/ torque characteristics and accurate control.

An AC servomotor is designed with two phases set at right angles to each other. A fixed or reference winding is excited by a fixed voltage source. The control winding is excited by a variable voltage source, usually the servo amplifier. Both sets of windings are usually designed with the same voltage per turns ratio (meaning that with equal voltage applied to each winding, the same magnetic flux will be produced). This allows for maximum control of speed, with very little speed drift. In many cases, the design of the AC servomotor offers only reasonable efficiency, at the sacrifice of high starting torque and smooth speed response. Figure 3-45 indicates a typical AC servomotor design.

Linear Stepper Motor Systems

Linear stepper motor systems are based on the principles of the stepper motors previously presented. The stepper drive system is basically a servo system, but often without the velocity feedback loop. Without the feedback loop, some sacrifice in accuracy is made. However, the cost of a stepper motor system is less than that of servomotor system.

Stepper motors, as you recall, are two-phase stator-type motors. The current is carried in the stator, which allows for maximum heat dissipation. Current that is switched on and off creates an electromagnetic field that produces rotation. The position of the motor shaft is determined by which phase is at maximum strength. The pole pair that is at maximum strength will interact with the permanent magnet rotor, and rotation will occur.

The linear stepper system could be of several different designs, but several common types for stepper and servo systems are the *rack and pinion* system and the *leadscrew* system. Figure 3-46 indicates these two types of systems.

Figure 3-45. AC servomotor design (Courtesy of Rockwell Automation, Inc.)

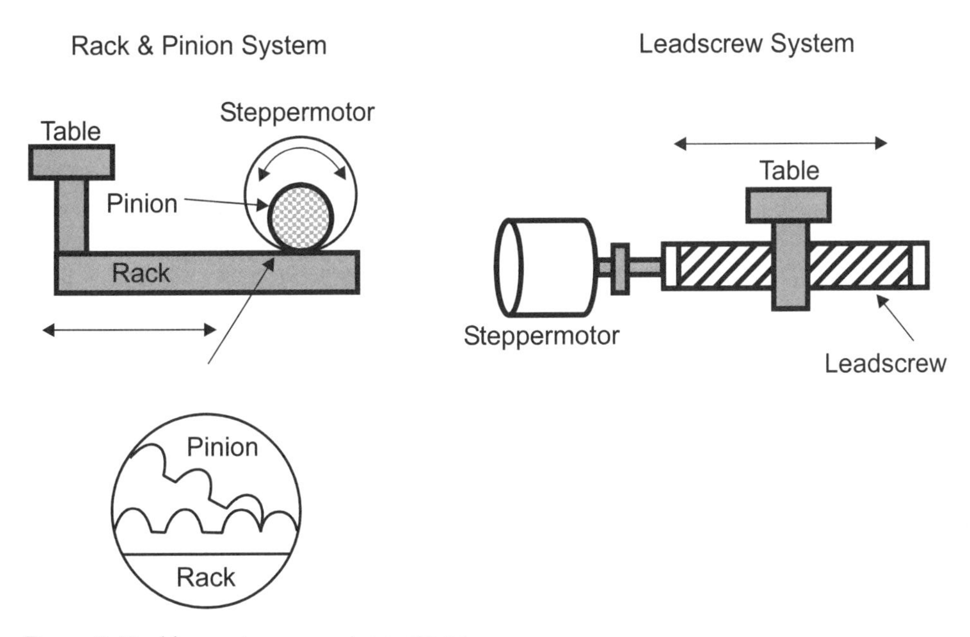

Figure 3-46. Linear stepper motor systems

In the rack and pinion design, the linear table is moved by the rotating motion of the stepper motor. The stepper motor shaft is fitted with a cylindrical gear that mates with linear table sprockets. When the stepper motor engages, the linear table moves in the forward or reverse direction, depending on the signal from the amplifier.

In the leadscrew design, the moveable table contains an integral nut that is threaded to the specifications of the long machine threaded screw. The stepper motor shaft is directly connected to the leadscrew by means of a coupling. When the motor engages, the leadscrew rotates in the direction dictated by the amplifier, thereby setting the table into motion.

A limiting factor to this system is the backlash that can occur, causing some sloppiness of motion. Backlash is the measured play or looseness between the gear and linear table sprocket (rack and pinion) or between leadscrew and moveable table (leadscrew). Since motion is transferred from the motor shaft to another device, this type of looseness is inevitable. Some backlash can be reduced by preloading the nut or linear device. This means that the linear device may be spring-loaded, keeping it in tight contact with the leadscrew nut, so there is no play in the system.

Linear Motors

Linear motor systems operate basically the same as rotating motors. The difference, of course, is that linear motion is produced, rather than clockwise or counterclockwise motion.

There are two main components of the linear stepper motor—the *platen* and the *slider* (sometimes referred to as the *forcer*). The platen could be considered the stator of the motor. The slider could be considered a linear rotor. Figure 3-47 indicates a linear stepper motor.

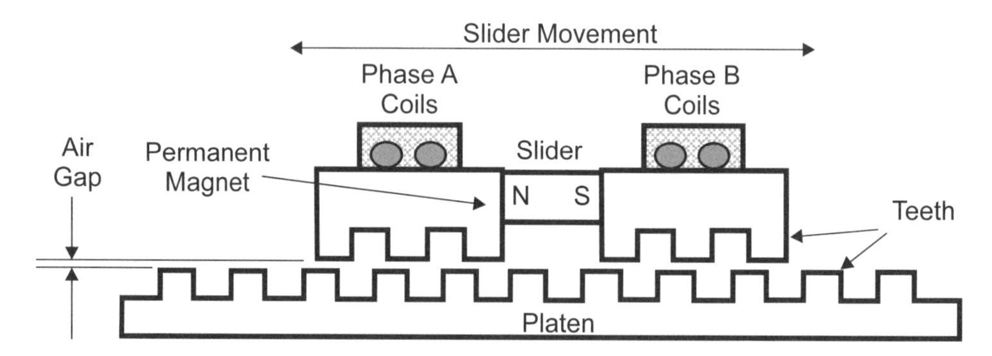

Figure 3-47. Linear stepper motor design

The electromagnetic "teeth" extend over the entire length of the platen. The slider also contains "teeth" and has both permanent magnets and coils that are electrically charged. It should be noted that the platen and slider have tooth structures that almost match. The slight offset is what causes the slider to be attracted to the next available magnetic field in the platen. The slider, in many cases, will contain air bearings that assist in developing a slight air gap. This air gap is where the magnetic flux is developed, and would be considered common to any standard AC induction motor.

When the slider coils are energized, the linear stepper motor moves in 1/4 tooth steps. Extremely fine resolution can be obtained from this type of motor, in some cases up to 25,000 steps per inch. This type of motor is well suited for applications where fast acceleration and high-speed movements are required, but where low mass or weight is needed.

Speeds of up to 100 ips (inches per second) are possible, with movements in increments down to 0.00005 inches. The linear stepper motor system has its advantages in precision open-loop control, mechanical simplicity, reliability, applications where space is limited, and the ability for multiple motion (more than one slider can be applied onto one platen). In addition, this type of system is an alternative in applications where leadscrews (with backlash issues), belts, pulleys, and gears are not practical.

Chapter Review

AC and DC motors are the two major types in use today that are related to the industrial and HVAC applications. These motors provide the speed, torque, and horsepower necessary to operate the application. The motor changes one form of energy (electrical) to rotational or linear motion (mechanical).

The two major components of a DC motor are the armature and field winding. The armature is the rotating part that is physically connected to the shaft and develops magnetic flux around its windings. The field winding is the part of the stationary frame and provides the flux necessary to interact with the armature flux to produce rotation. The commutator acts as an electrical switch and always ensures that a repelling force is present between the armature and field flux circuits. This repelling force against the field winding flux causes rotation of the armature. Brushes are the devices that physically connect the voltage supply to the armature circuit. Brushes are constructed of carbon material and require routine maintenance or replacement to reduce arching at the commutator segments.

Two separate voltage supplies are connected to the DC motor, one for the armature (variable DC voltage armature supply) and one for the field winding (fixed-voltage field exciter). Speed of the DC motor is directly controlled by the magnitude of the armature supply voltage. Speed is also inversely proportional to the magnitude of the field flux. If the field winding flux is reduced, the motor speeds up and could continue to infinite speed unless safety circuits are not implemented.

Torque is a direct result of the interaction of armature and field winding flux. If the armature windings are constantly energized, as well as the field windings, constant torque will result, as well as very high torque at zero speed.

Various types of enclosures are constructed to safeguard the DC motor against harm. For example, drip-proof motors provide a degree of protection against vertical falling materials and also allow for the ventilation of cool outside air. Totally enclosed motor frames provide a higher degree of protection, but are not practical for large frame motors because of the inability to remove heat.

Motors are listed with many types of ratings that indicate the torque generating ability, altitude, heat capability, vibration, and electrical specifications. DC motors are constructed in several different types, related to the field winding circuit: series wound, shunt (parallel wound), and compound wound. In addition, several armature styles are also available: standard armature windings and permanent magnet armatures. Specialty DC motors include the PM (permanent magnet) servomotor and the brushless DC servomotor.

AC motors are in widespread use today, both in the industrial and commercial HVAC markets, but also in the residential and consumer markets. AC motors are listed with one of two ratings: NEMA or IEC. NEMA ratings reflect the U.S. market demands, where IEC has its roots in the European marketplace, mostly in the union of European Common Market countries. All motors can be classified into single-phase or polyphase categories. Three-phase motors are the motor of choice in industry because of their relatively low cost, high efficiency, and ability for simple direction control.

The main components of the AC motor are the rotor and stator. The rotor is the rotating part and the stator is the stationary part connected to the frame. Only one power source is required to set the rotor into motion. The stator windings create magnetic flux that causes a magnetic field (flux) to be induced in the rotor. The attracting forces of the rotor and stator flux produce torque and rotation of the rotor.

Speed of an AC induction motor is related to the frequency applied and the number of pole pairs. The number of pole pairs causes an inverse relationship in speed, but the frequency applied has a direct relationship to speed. The AC motor will always operate at a slower speed than synchronous. This is due to the requirement of magnetic flux in the rotor to be attracted to the rotating magnetic flux in the stator. Various torque values are associated with an AC motor connected across the line. Locked rotor, peak, and rated torque are the three most common values needed to apply an AC induction motor.

AC motors typically draw 600% inrush current upon start-up. Once the speed has increased to near synchronous, the current draw drops closely in line with the torque being produced. All AC motors are designed with a specific torque producing characteristic in mind—V/Hz. If the volts per hertz relationship is kept constant, the motor will develop the rated torque it was designed to produce.

A common rating scale for AC induction motors is that of a NEMA design classification: A, B, C, D, and E. Each classification indicates a different motor torque-producing category. AC induction motor nameplates have similar designs to DC motors, only referring to AC input power. A major indication of motor durability is the temperature class of the stator windings. IEC ratings differ with NEMA in most categories. NEMA tends to include a certain amount of overload in its ratings, while IEC rates the motor exactly to its capability.

AC motor types range from the standard induction motor to wound rotor, synchronous, and multiple pole motors. Specialty motors include stepper, AC vector, servomotors, linear stepper, and linear motors.

Check Your Knowledge

1. What are the two main parts of a DC motor and what is the purpose of each?
2. What is the purpose of the brushes?
3. Why are the laminations in the armature skewed?
4. What is the purpose of the commutator?
5. What is the purpose of the commutation windings?
6. What is the purpose of compensation windings?
7. How is speed controlled in a DC motor?
8. How is torque controlled in a DC motor?
9. What is the difference between a DPFG and a TEFC motor?
10. Identify eight ratings listed on the DC motor nameplate and briefly indicate their meanings.
11. What is the difference between a series wound and shunt wound DC motor?
12. How is a permanent magnet DC motor different from the other standard DC motors?
13. How does a DC servomotor differ from a standard DC motor?
14. What are the main components of an AC induction motor, and what is the purpose of each?
15. How is speed determined in an AC induction motor?
16. What determines the horsepower of a motor?
17. What is the definition of base speed?
18. What is the V/Hz ratio?
19. What NEMA design class would provide the highest amount of starting torque, when connected across line power?
20. When considering inrush current draw, which NEMA motor type requires the highest amount of current upon start-up?
21. When reviewing NEMA frame sizes, how is the centerline shaft to foot distance determined?
22. What is the difference between IEC and NEMA ratings?

23. How does a synchronous motor differ from a standard AC induction motor?
24. What is the principle of operation behind an AC vector motor?
25. How do stepper motors differ from standard AC induction motors?

AC and DC Drives

Introduction

Probably the easiest of drive technologies to understand is the direct current (DC) drive. This type of drive converts fixed-voltage and frequency alternating current (AC) to an adjustable-voltage DC. A DC drive can operate a shunt wound DC motor or a permanent magnet motor. Shunt wound DC motors will be the target of this discussion on DC drives. Shunt wound motors are available in fractional to thousands of horsepower and are the most prevalent type of DC system in industry today. Permanent magnet motors are usually applied where horsepower requirements are 5 HP and below.

Before beginning this section, it is suggested that Chapter 1 (Electronic DC Drives) and Chapter 3 (DC Motor Types) be reviewed.

DC Drives

As discussed in Chapter 1, the DC drive contains the components listed in Figure 4-1. A closer look will now be taken into each circuit within the DC drive unit.

Presently, most DC drives use transistors to convert AC to DC. Historically, the most widely used method, however, is that of silicon controlled rectifiers (SCRs) in power conversion. Our focus will be on the SCR control, used in both analog and digital DC drive technology.

As recalled from Chapter 1, SCRs conduct current when a small voltage is applied to the gate circuit. Figure 4-2 illustrates this characteristic of SCRs. In Figure 4-2, the SCR is "gated on" early in the cycle, causing current flow for the remainder of the 1/2 cycle. Once the SCR goes through zero, it automatically shuts off (described as line commutation) until it is gated "on" again.

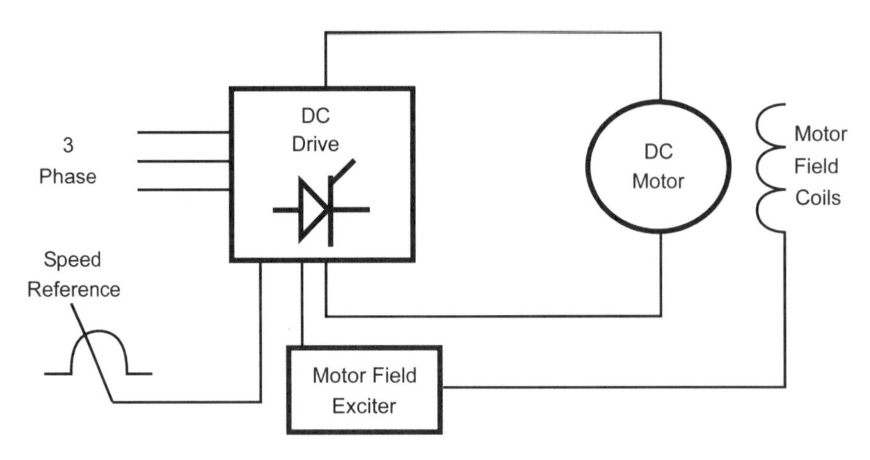

Figure 4-1. DC drive construction

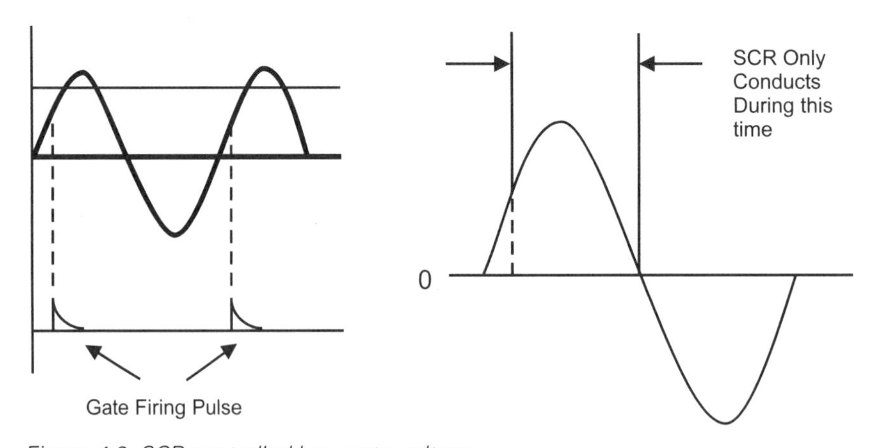

Figure 4-2. SCR controlled by a gate voltage

Some SCR DC drives operate on a single-phase power source and use four SCRs for full-wave rectification. The focus of this section will be on the three-phase DC drives, using six SCRs for a full-wave bridge rectification. Figure 4-3 shows a typical SCR, full-wave bridge circuit, operating from three-phase line power.

Though not widely used, some manufacturers replace the three SCRs on the bottom with diodes and then add a commutating diode across the DC output as a "shut off" circuit. The circuit in Figure 4-3 would be considered a standard analog DC drive.

When the speed-controller circuit calls for voltage to be produced, the M contactor (main contactor) is closed. In some cases the M contactor (sometimes considered a DC loop contactor) does not exist. Some manufacturers rely on a main incoming line contactor ahead of the drive. In that type of control scheme, the drive is completely off until the control calls for speed. In the method shown in Figure 4-3, the drive's power components are

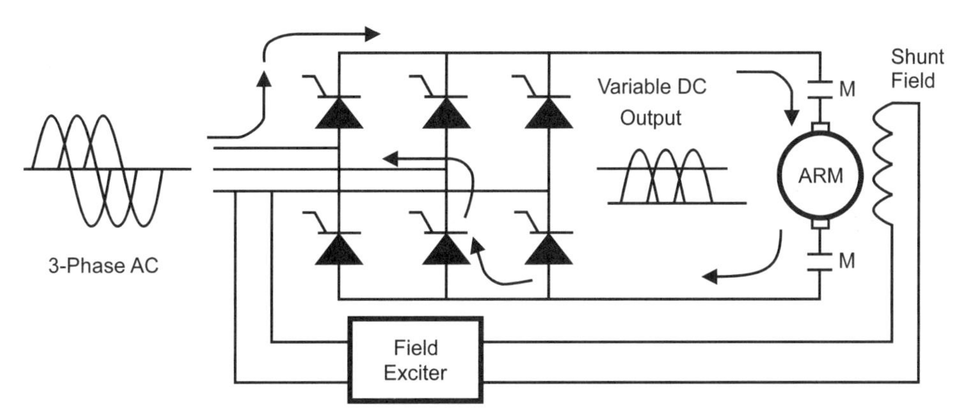

Figure 4-3. SCR full wave bridge rectification

always on and at zero, but not connected to the motor armature until actual speed is required.

When speed is required, the speed controller circuit calls for the SCRs to conduct. Instantly, voltage from the line enters the drive through one phase, is conducted through the SCR, and goes into the armature. Voltage flows through the armature, back into the SCR bridge, and returns through the power line through another phase. When this cycle is about complete, another phase conducts through another SCR, through the armature, and back into yet another phase. The cycle repeats 60 times per second because of the 60-Hz line input.

The amount of average DC voltage conducted depends on how early or late in the AC sine wave the SCRs are "pulsed" or "gated" on. Early gating means a higher amount of voltage output because the SCR conducts for a longer period of time. Late gating would achieve the opposite results.

It should be noted that gating on and off of SCRs occurs rapidly, in milliseconds. When one SCR is almost shut off, another is starting to conduct. For a brief instant, the bridge circuit actually has a "line-to-line" short. When this happens notching occurs, which is actually fed back into the line, supplying the voltage. This phenomenon is illustrated in Figure 4-4.

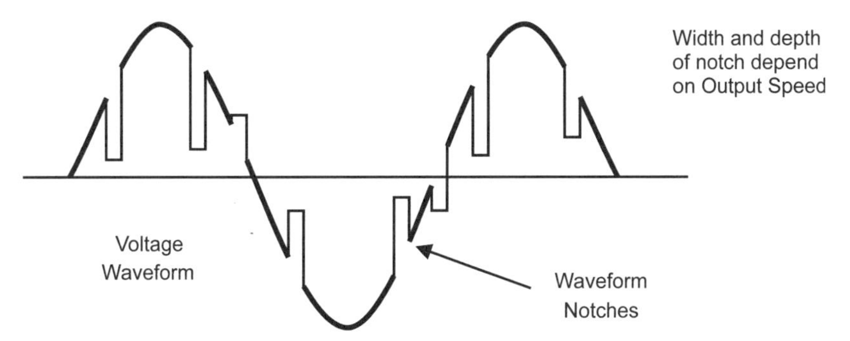

Figure 4-4. Line notching due to SCR rectification

To reduce the affect of notching back onto the power line, line reactors are typically specified by the DC drive manufacturer. A minimum of 1% impedance is required, but most manufacturers would recommend 3%. The line reactor reduces the effects of notching and cleans the power line that is used by other equipment in the building.

The shunt field winding power is supplied by a DC field exciter. In many cases, it is a two-phase unit, which is supplied by the three-phase input from the drive. It may only need to supply several amps, depending on the size of the motor field winding. Depending on manufacturer, the field exciter may be included in the armature supply unit or supplied separately as an additionally purchased item. The field exciter's mission is to supply a constant voltage to the field winding, creating a constant flux in the motor's shunt field. In cases where above base speed is required, many field exciters have the ability to reduce voltage supplied to the field. The drive control systematically reduces voltage to the field, which reduces flux and increases motor speed because there is less counter EMF to hold back the armature.

Drives (DC)– Digital

Digital control provides precise output of both motor speed and torque. Improvements in digital control have given this type of drive faster response times and greater flexibility compared with the older analog drives of the 50s and 60s. To fully appreciate the technology, a review of the controller circuitry is necessary. Figure 4-5 shows a simplified speed and current controller digital circuit and its major components.

The whole process starts at the *speed reference*. A reference signal is given to the drive's input, which is then fed to the *speed controller*. Given the amount of speed reference, the speed controller in the microprocessor determines what the output voltage should be to operate the motor at the desired speed. At the same time, the *current controller* in the microprocessor signals the SCRs in the *firing unit* to gate on. The SCRs in the *converter section* convert fixed three-phase voltage to a DC voltage and current output in relation to the desired speed. The *current measuring/scaling section* monitors the output current and makes current reference corrections on the basis of the torque requirements of the motor (e.g., additional load requiring more amps, more torque).

If precise speed is not an issue, the DC drive and motor could operate *open loop*. This means that there is no feedback correction signal fed back to the speed controller. Speed regulation of 5–8% can be achieved when operating open loop. (Note: Speed regulation is a measurement of motor speed accuracy when under load. A 2% speed regulation would indicate a 2% drop in speed, from no load to full load.) However, in most cases, the application requires a speed regulation lower than 5%.

When a speed regulation of less than 5% is the requirement, then the *speed measuring/scaling circuit* will be engaged by making the appropriate

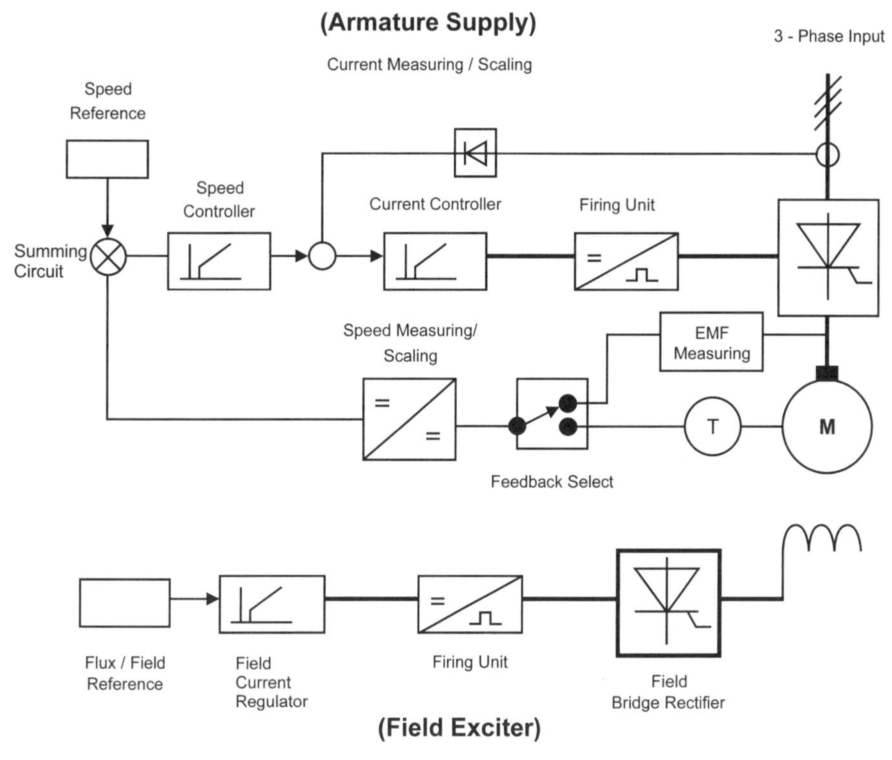

Figure 4-5. Digital speed and current controllers and field exciter

feedback selection. If the feedback is using the EMF measurement circuit, then the speed measuring/scaling circuit will monitor the armature voltage output. The measuring circuit will feed back a scaled voltage to the *summing circuit*. This scaled voltage is in proportion to the output voltage. The summing circuit will process the speed reference and feedback signal and create an error signal. This error signal is what is used by the speed controller as a new, or corrected, speed command.

Note: *Output voltage is a fairly good estimate of actual motor speed. This type of closed loop control is called EMF control, or armature voltage control, because of the corrections made to the armature voltage output. Speed regulation of 1 to 2% is possible with this type of feedback, depending on the motor characteristics.*

If tighter speed regulation is required, less than 1%, then *tachometer generator* feedback is required. Some manufacturers call this tach feedback, or simply tacho. A tachometer is a device that mounts to the end of the motor opposite the shaft. The output of a tach is very precise, in volts per 1000 rpm, for example. When this feedback is given to the summing circuit, very small corrections (error signals) are possible. The speed controller accepts these error signals and makes immediate corrections in the microprocessor.

It should be noted that typically the speed reference is sent to the summing circuit as a positive value (e.g., 0–10 VDC or 4–20 mA). The feedback signal is of opposite polarity. If the summing circuit generates a positive error, this would indicate a speed increase is required. If the summing circuit generates a negative error, this would indicate a speed decrease is required (the motor is operating faster than commanded speed). A closer look at feedback devices will be taken in Chapter 5.

To review regulation, any type of regulation circuit acts like a cruise control in an automobile. There is a speed reference in mph or kph (e.g., setting the desired speed on the steering wheel, using the speedometer as a guide). That reference is fed to the cruise control circuit and the engine responds accordingly with a fixed acceleration rate. During acceleration, a feedback circuit sends an opposite polarity signal to the summing circuit. The speed reference and the feedback signal create an error signal. That error signal is used to speed up or slow down the engine.

When going down a hill, the auto coasts and possibly goes over the speed setting. Because there is no real automatic braking method, the auto is at the mercy of inertia and gravity (the auto is in continuous negative error—meaning speed is not required). The only method of speed reduction or braking is a manual mechanical brake (the foot brake pedal). Unlike an auto cruise control system, there are several ways of bringing a DC motor to an automatic stop, quicker than just coasting. This will be the topic of our next section.

Field Exciter

The DC drive unit may also include a separate *field exciter* as shown in Figure 4-5. The sole purpose of this unit is to generate a fixed DC supply voltage to the motor field windings.

The *flux/field reference* signal is supplied to the *field current regulator.* Given the amount of flux reference, the field current regulator in the microprocessor determines what the output voltage should be to operate the motor field windings at the desired flux value. At the same time, the field current regulator signals the SCRs in the firing unit to gate on. The SCRs in the *field bridge rectifier section* convert fixed three-phase voltage to a DC voltage and current output in proportion to the field flux required.

In many cases, the field bridge rectifier section is powered by only a single phase or two phases, rather than three phases. The amount of current supplied by the field exciter is much lower than that supplied by the armature supply. In addition, the amount of voltage regulation (exactness) is not as critical in generating a field-winding current. The magnetic flux generated is a fraction of that generated by the armature supply.

If a drive is to be operated at extended speed (above base speed), then the field exciter must have the capability to reduce current to the field winding. This is known as *field control* or operating in the *field weakening* mode. As mentioned previously, an over-speed safety circuit is always employed. This circuit prevents a lightly loaded motor from rapidly accelerating in speed, possibly to the point of self-destruction. This is termed a *runaway* condition and is the result of reducing the field flux and the counter EMF, which allows the speed to increase.

When speaking of armature supplies and field exciters, the quality of the power output can be measured and given a rating. *Form factor* or *ripple factor* are the terms most commonly used. Basically, the form factor is a comparison of SCR output power with that produced by a DC generator. Generator power would be considered pure DC, where almost no ripple (distortion) is present. At a rating of 1.0 (generator power), there is a minimum of losses in the armature core and field windings. The form factor is used to match drive equipment to a potential motor. High ripple causes additional motor heating, reduced load rating, and less overall efficiency. Derating (reducing continuous rating) of the motor load could be anywhere from 5–15%, depending on the manufacturer's specifications.

Figure 4-6 shows several types of SCR power supplies with the corresponding form factor rating.

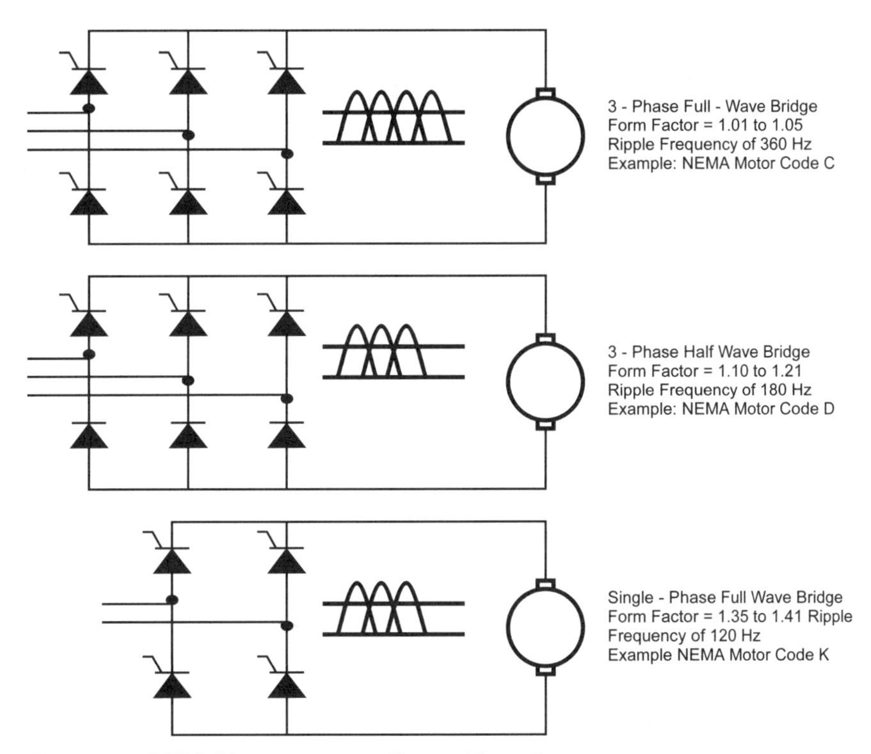

Figure 4-6. SCR bridge power supplies and form factors

As seen in Figure 4-6, the type of bridge rectifier will dictate the range of ripple produced and therefore be an indicator of additional motor heating. Since the SCR circuitry is more expensive (e.g., full wave bridge), the form factor is less. A power supply with a NEMA Motor Code of "K" would be suitable for motors of 5 HP or less. A power supply with a NEMA Motor Code of "E" would be suitable for motors up to 250 HP. A power supply with a NEMA Motor Code of "C" would be suitable for motors in the

1000-HP range. As a general rule, the DC motor manufacturer should always be consulted whenever questions of armature/field exciter suitability arise.

Now that the armature supply and field exciter circuits have been explored, it is appropriate to review the possible operating conditions of a DC motor. By learning the operational characteristics of a DC motor, DC drive systems can effectively be applied.

Single-, Two-, and Four-Quadrant Operation

There are actually four possible modes of motor operation, determined by the relationship of speed, torque, and direction. A brief description of the modes of operation will be helpful at this time. Describing the modes of operation is easiest done by indicating the forward and reverse operation of a DC motor in quadrants. Figure 4-7 indicates the quadrant relationships.

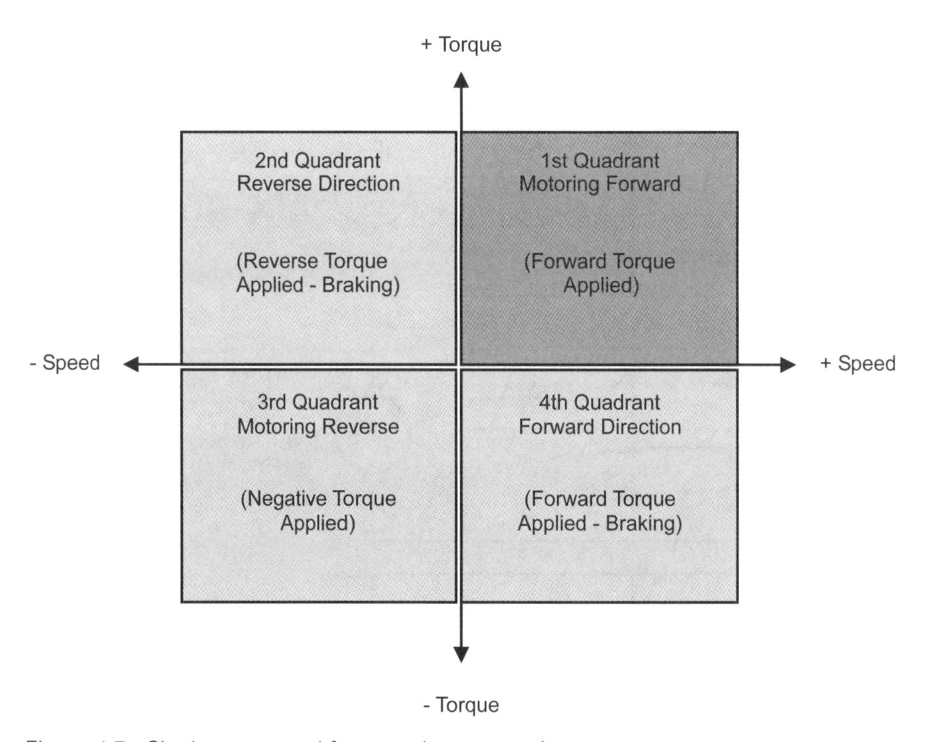

Figure 4-7. Single-, two-, and four-quadrant operation

As seen in Figure 4-7, operating a DC motor in the first quadrant means that the motor is actually driving the load, with torque and speed in the positive direction. This method of operation is usually accomplished with a single controller (one armature SCR bridge rectifier and a field winding supply). To stop the motor, some method of braking is needed. In many cases, the natural inertia of the system will bring the motor to a stop in an acceptable time. This is called *coast-to-stop* and is a condition of single-quadrant operation.

If coasting to a stop is not acceptable, then a reverse-polarity voltage is applied to the armature, reversing the magnetic field and bringing the motor to a quick stop. This is usually done by a reverse contactor connected to the armature. This method has sometimes been referred to as *plug* stopping, plugging the motor armature into a reverse polarity.

A drawback to this method is that if the deceleration rate is quick, high levels of current are drawn during the plugging cycle. This places the motor windings under additional stress. If the deceleration time is within the current settings of the drive, a smooth, controllable stop can be accomplished. (Additional methods of stopping will be discussed in the next section.) Using reverse torque to stop a motor is called two-quadrant operation.

If true control throughout the positive and negative speed and torque range is desired, then a 12-SCR bridge controller is required (two armature SCR bridge rectifiers—one in the forward and one in the reverse direction). A field winding supply is also required. The motor can be brought to a very fast stop by engaging the reverse armature supply bridge and *regenerating* the motor's energy back into the power line. This procedure is called *regenerative braking.*

If *motoring* the load in the reverse speed and torque direction is required, the *four-quadrant supply* is the device needed to accomplish the procedure. The reverse SCR bridge is now used as the driving supply and the forward SCR bridge acts as the braking device to bring the motor quickly back to zero speed. This mode is called *four-quadrant operation.*

It should also be noted that another method of regeneration exists. That method is to use a single controller bridge and a four-quadrant field exciter. In this way, control of speed and torque in both the positive and negative direction can be accomplished. However, because of the longer time constant of magnetic field reversal, this method is used when quick reversal of torque and speed is not required.

DC Drives—Braking Methods

The easiest way of bringing a motor to a stop is the simple method of allowing it to coast to zero speed. This method is called coast-to-stop and is used in many applications where the element of stopping time is not a factor.

In fan applications, for example, it may require 60 s for a 75-HP drive to bring the fan up to full speed and keep the drive's current draw below the maximum limit. Once the fan is at process speed, it may operate there until the end of the work day. Then the fan may be preset to a lower speed for nighttime operation. It is not urgent for the motor to immediately drop in output speed. If it takes the motor 3 to 5 minutes to reduce speed, that is acceptable—especially since no additional power is required.

Note: *DC drives are typically not used in fan applications, though they do provide the adjustable speed needed. Fan applications are more easily done with AC drives, for reasons explored in the AC drive section.*

There are occasions where motor speed must drop in a specified amount of time. Those methods of reducing speed are explored in the following paragraphs.

Figure 4-8 indicates the relationship of various braking methods employed in DC drives. It should be noted that these methods are also available in AC drives, with several other options available.

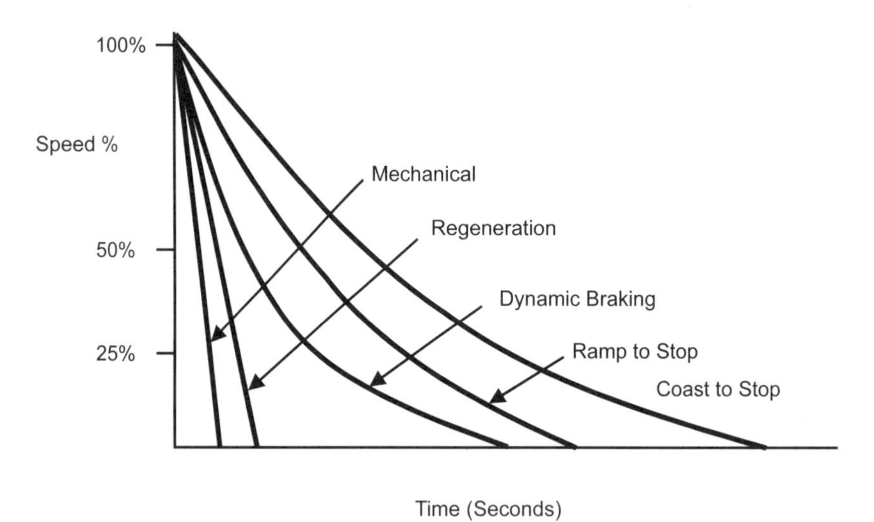

Figure 4-8. Braking methods for DC drives

Coast-to-Stop and Ramp-to-Stop

As seen in Figure 4-8, the coast-to-stop method takes the most time. Basically, during this method the motor is completely disconnected from the drive. Through friction and the dissipation of inertia energy, the free-wheeling motor eventually comes to a stop. It should be noted that there is no control over the motor during this time. The motor is at the mercy of inertia and friction forces.

The next fastest method of stopping is called the ramp-to-stop mode. During this mode, the drive has complete control over the motor. The drive's deceleration setting forces the motor down in speed, within acceptable voltage limits. (**Note:** During the deceleration process, the motor operates faster than commanded speed. The drive's deceleration ramp in seconds dictates how fast the motor should decelerate. If the drive's deceleration rate is faster than the motor speed is dropping, the motor acts as a generator. The motor, now acting like a generator, sends energy back into the drive.) Depending on the drive horsepower, deceleration circuitry, and motor inertia, possible deceleration time could be half of the coast-to-stop time.

Dynamic Braking

As shown in Figure 4-8, the next fastest stopping time would be achieved by dynamic braking. This form of stopping uses a fixed, high wattage resistor (or bank of resistors) to transform the rotating energy into heat. Figure 4-9 indicates a typical DC drive dynamic braking circuit.

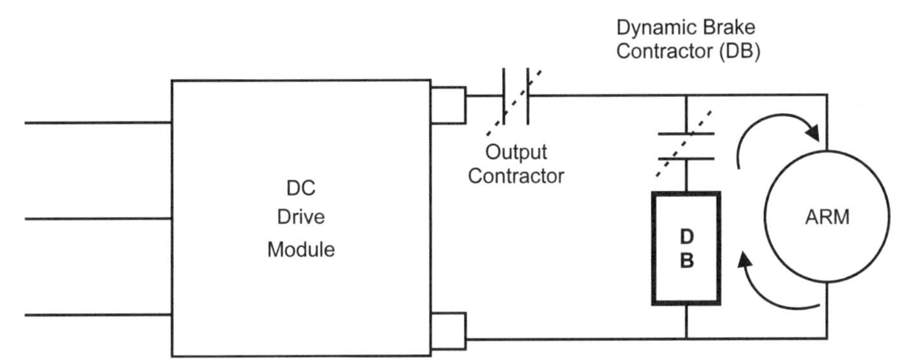

Figure 4-9. DC drive dynamic brake circuit

Under normal operation, the *output contactor* is closed, the dynamic braking contactor is open, and current is flowing through the armature. When a fast stop is commanded, the output contactor opens and the *dynamic braking* contactor closes. This allows all of the motor's rotating energy to be fed into the *dynamic braking resistor bank* (DB). The resistor bank transforms mechanical energy into heat. By allowing all of the motor's energy to be drained into a resistor, the speed of the motor quickly drops.

It should be noted that the main stopping power of a DB system occurs when the resistor is cold and during the first few seconds of the process. Once the resistor heats up, the amount of braking torque diminishes. This is shown by a flattened out curve close to the zero speed line. The number of times per minute DB is engaged will also determine the effectiveness of braking torque. *Duty cycle* is the number of times per minute the DB resistor is used. Many DB circuits require a maximum of 10% duty cycle (6 s on, 54 s off time to cool).

Regeneration

The fastest electronic stopping method is that of *regeneration*. With regenerative braking, all of the motor's energy is fed directly back into the AC power line. To accomplish this, a second set of *reverse-connected SCRs* is required. This allows the drive to conduct current in the opposite direction (taking the motor's energy and generating it back to the line). Figure 4-10 indicates two sets of six SCR bridge rectifier circuits.

This type of drive is known as a *four-quadrant drive*. It allows driving the motor in the forward and reverse directions, as well as regeneration in both the forward and reverse directions. The control board usually contains the microprocessor that controls the status of the reverse SCR bridge.

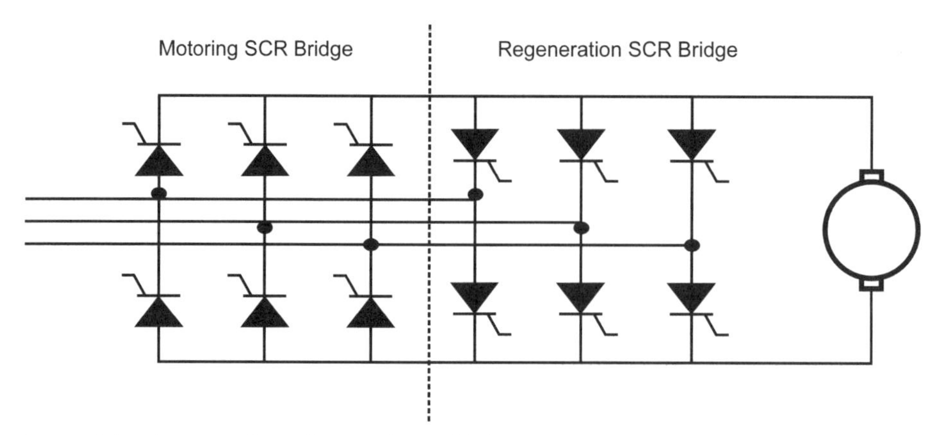

Figure 4-10. Regenerative DC drive (two SCR bridges)

When the speed of the motor is faster than commanded, the motor's energy is fed back into the drive. The regeneration circuit senses the increase in reverse voltage and turns on the reverse SCR bridge circuit.

The key to this type of circuitry is to synchronize the voltage fed back to the line with the voltage being generated by the utility. As expected, this type of circuitry requires advanced processing to sense line phase and create SCR timing signals in phase with the existing line.

It should be noted here that this is a very cost-effective means of stopping a motor quickly. It should also be noted that this braking method would be useless if power were to be removed from the drive (e.g., during a power outage). The reverse SCRs could not conduct, and the microprocessor would not operate, if power were not present. Therefore, this method, though quite fast, would not be used for emergency stop situations (at least not without having another method available such as mechanical braking).

Regenerative braking is used in many applications where the possibility of the motor going faster than commanded speed is quite high. Applications such as cranes, elevators, hoists, and ski lifts are just a few examples. Machine tool applications also require regeneration for high speed, high performance, and fast reverse of direction. Figure 4-11 shows another application for regeneration—conveyors.

The out-feed conveyor in Figure 4-11 would be a prime candidate for a regenerative DC drive. The feed conveyor sends the finished product up a slight incline to the next stage (the feed conveyor would be operating in Quadrant 1—motoring). Once the product reaches the process conveyor, the product is moved into the labeling and inspection machine (still operating in Quadrant 1—motoring). When the product has completed its production cycle, it is fed to the out-feed conveyor to be packed at the warehouse.

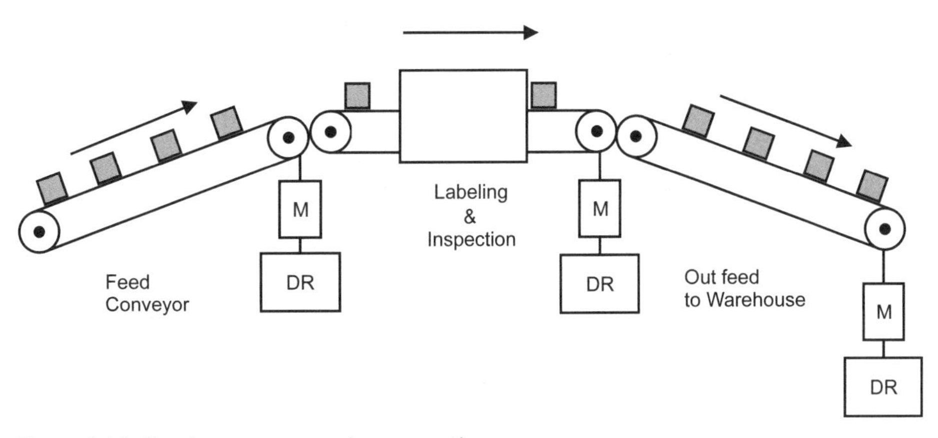

Figure 4-11. Feed conveyors and regeneration

Because the out-feed conveyor is at a slight downward decline, the packages will tend to drive the conveyor motor to a faster speed. Once this happens, the motor turns into a generator and sends excess voltage back to the drive. The drive senses the over-voltage condition and engages the reverse SCRs to accomplish regeneration (operating in Quadrant 4—regeneration). The drive actually uses regeneration for hold-back torque to keep the conveyor from operating at too high of a speed.

Dynamic braking could be used just as well in this application. Excess energy from the motor could be sent to a DB resistor. However, the energy consumed by the resistor would be given out as heat, which is energy wasted. Sending the energy back to the power line is the most effective means of braking and conserving energy.

Mechanical Braking

The fastest means of stopping a motor would be through mechanical braking. In this method, the motor is disconnected from the drive and a brake circuit is activated in the drive. The motor is then subjected to a brake unit clamping onto the shaft, much like an auto brake system (locking the brakes in an emergency stop). The motor quickly comes to a forced mechanical stop.

In industrial applications, this method is often used in conjunction with dynamic braking during emergency stop situations. The energy is fed to the DB resistor, and the mechanical brake effectively locks onto the motor shaft.

Mechanical brakes are typically used in many applications, such as printing presses. Part of the press commissioning deals with emergency stops (e-stops). When the e-stop button is pressed, the entire press must come to a complete stop within 8 s, for example. Massive amounts of inertia must be brought to zero speed. Mechanical braking, as well as DB, is most often used for e-stop in DC drive systems. Mechanical braking is also the most controlled, positive method of bringing a motor down to zero speed. If power is lost to the drive, the drive's brake circuit is immediately activated and the brake engages.

Drives (DC)—Technical Concerns

With the advent of SCR control in the 1960s, DC drives and motors enjoyed an increased amount of use in industry. In many DC applications, the existing motor continued to work as specified. The regular motor maintenance (brush replacement, commutator repair, etc.) was a common way of life in these types of industrial environments. With SCR and digital microprocessor control, the DC drive was not just a simple power converter. The DC drive's ability to provide 200% of full load current for short periods of time makes it a solid choice in applications were overloads are common. The drive has also gained acceptance in communication systems and automated manufacturing schemes.

There are, however, some technical issues with any type of drive (AC or DC) that must be addressed. Those issues will be reviewed here and additional comments made regarding DC drive installation.

Harmonics and Line Notching

Harmonics will be considered in greater detail later in this chapter. For now, it is sufficient to say that both DC and AC drives create harmonic distortion. Harmonic voltage distortion will be fed back onto the AC line, which may affect other equipment connected to the same power system. This harmonic voltage distortion is a result of the commutation (switching on/off) of the SCRs. This distortion takes the form of line notching, which was previously discussed.

The need for harmonic limitation is related to the entire system, of which the DC drive is a part. The size (capacity) of the distribution system, the kVA of connected drives, and the total system impedance all play a part in harmonic mitigation requirements.

When viewing *electrical-noise* output generated by the drive, DC drives of today create far less distortion than drives used before SCR technology. Figure 4-12 indicates DC drive input voltage and output current to the motor.

The ability of the DC drive's filter circuitry will dictate how smooth of a DC output waveform the motor will see. Any distortion in the output will result in motor heating, which contributes to overall reduced efficiency.

To reduce the effects of harmonic distortion, it is accepted practice to install some type of inductor ahead of the drive. The inductor slows down the rate of rise of notches. The notches fed back to the power line are shallower and narrower compared with no line reactor being connected. Figure 4-13 compares line disturbances with, and without, the use of a line reactor.

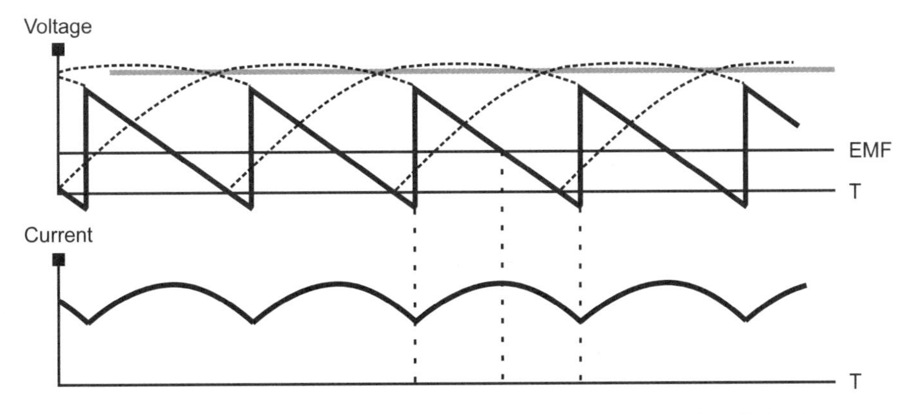

Figure 4-12. DC drive voltage and current waveforms (Courtesy of ABB Inc.)

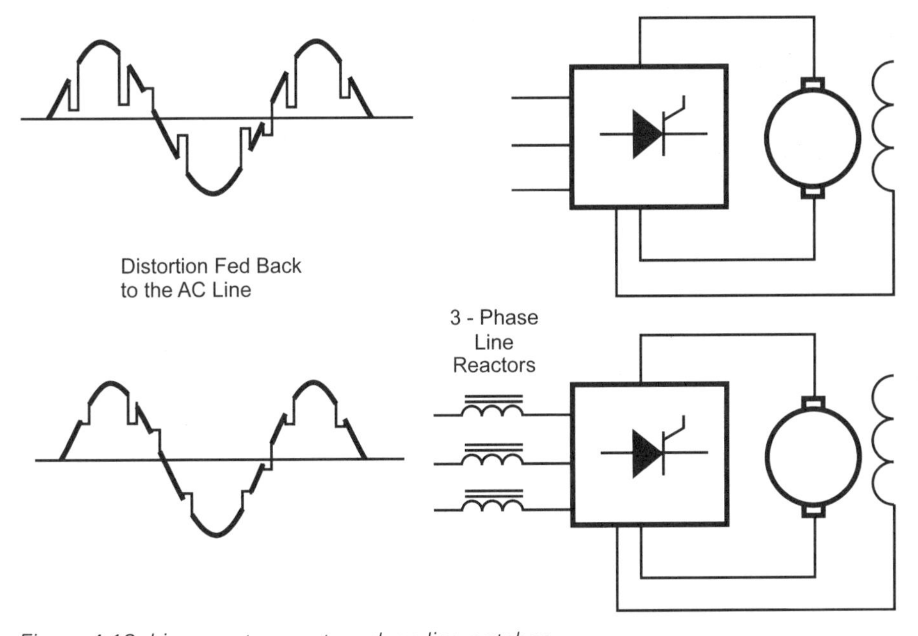

Figure 4-13. Line reactor use to reduce line notches

The minimum impedance for a line reactor would be as little as 1%. Many manufacturers recommend reactors of 3% as a minimum. If an input *isolation transformer* is used, a line reactor would not be required. From a line-disturbance standpoint, a transformer would have the same equivalent effect as that of a line reactor. Figure 4-14 indicates a typical DC drive installation, with line reactors, contactors, and associated control circuitry.

Displacement Power Factor

When discussing electronic power conversion equipment, there are two ways to identify power factor (PF): displacement and total power factor. Displacement PF is the power factor of the fundamental components of the input-line voltage and current. On the other hand, total PF indicates the effects of harmonic distortion. No matter how the PF is viewed, the

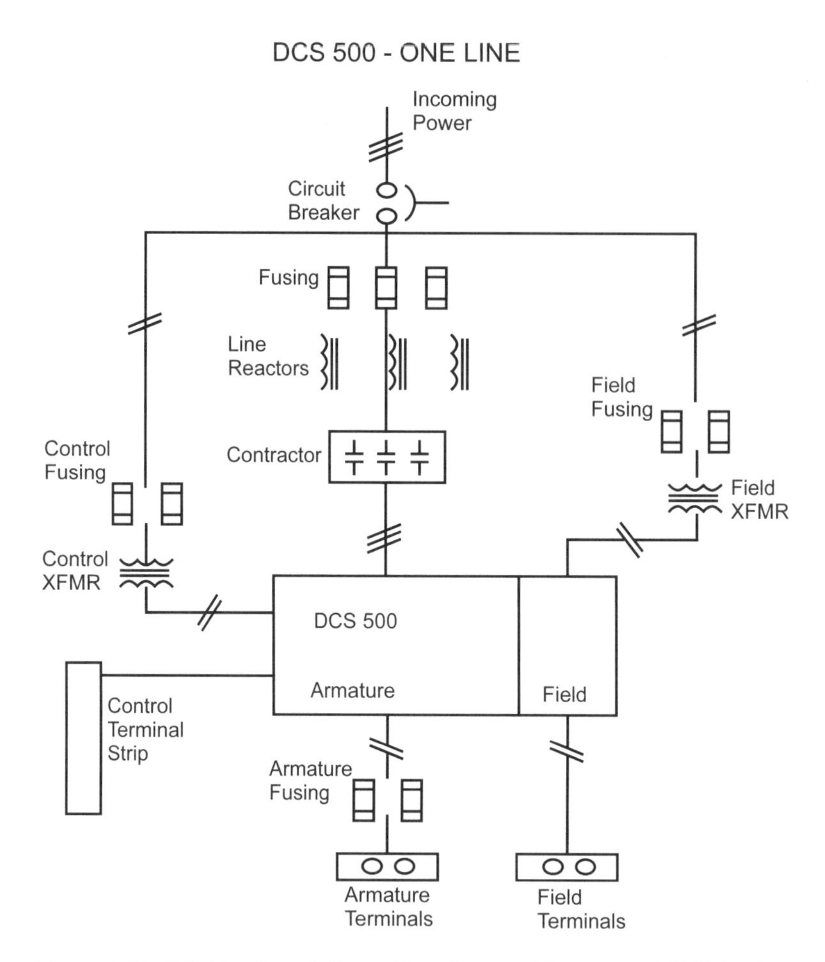

Figure 4-14. DC drive installation wiring diagram (Courtesy of ABB Inc.)

power utility may impose penalties for customers that use equipment with a poor PF.

The displacement PF for a DC drive is roughly 0.8 when at full load and speed. This number drops off to zero when the speed is reduced to zero. The harmonic current distortion is determined by the total values of inductance, capacitance, and resistance, from power source to the load. The power distribution system has impedance, which also enters into the calculations for total PF. Figure 4-15 gives a general indication of displacement and total PF for both DC and AC drives.

The curves shown in Figure 4-15 are for drives at full load and constant torque operation. The shaded area indicates a variation of total PF for typical drive installations.

Shielding and Grounding

In a certain sense, all electrical and electronic devices are radiation generators. Devices that fall into the radiation generator category include electrical contacts and semiconductors, microprocessors, radio transmitters, and cell phones. These human-made devices can cause interference with other

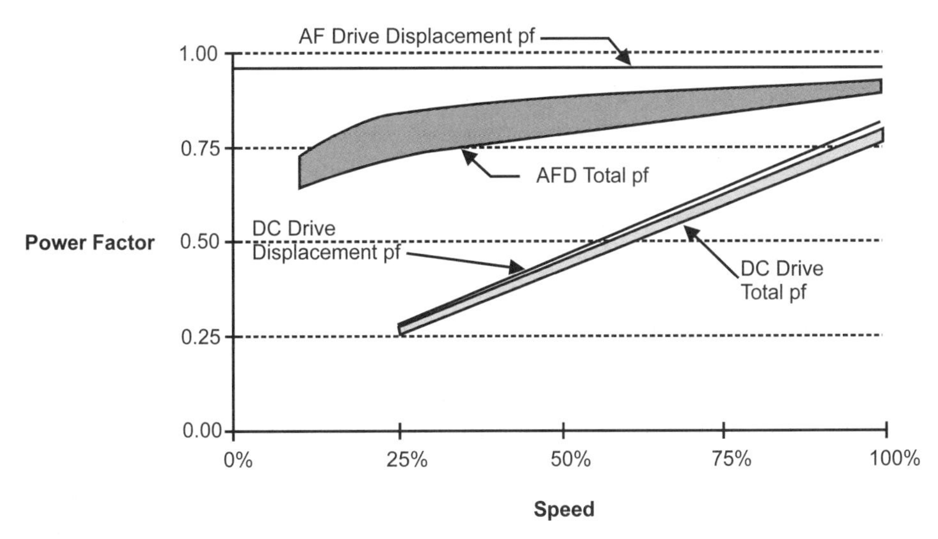

Figure 4-15. Total and displacement PF (DC and AC drives)

electrical equipment. Devices such as cell phones contain transmission circuitry that behaves like a radio station and creates radio frequency interference (RFI).

Electronic drives also fall into the interference category, since they contain semiconductors, contacts, and a small oscillator for timing that would be considered a transmitter. Devices that are considered *switch mode power supplies* also create interference. These power supplies convert one form of electrical energy into another. In doing so, they alter the original form of energy and create a phenomenon known as electromagnetic interference (EMI). In drives, the rapid switching of the microprocessor and power semiconductors cause high-frequency interference.

Conducted energy generated by drives can be very disturbing to other electronic equipment operated on the same power feed. In addition, SCRs and control circuits in DC drives can be adversely affected by other radiation generators listed above. DC drive-control circuitry could misfire or cause several SCRs to conduct simultaneously, causing short circuits in the power semiconductor circuits.

The most important precaution used in control of EMI is the grounding and shielding of DC drive equipment. This is a must when the drive is installed in environments where it could be affected by other equipment or vice versa. Figure 4-16 shows a DC drive installation from the standpoint of shielding and grounding of components.

As shown in Figure 4-16, there are several grounding points in the installation, but they are all tied to one common grounding point. Multiple *common grounds* create *ground loops* or circulating currents. If a conductor in a closed circuit is near another conductor that is energized, the closed circuit conductor will contain an induced voltage. This voltage can contradict or

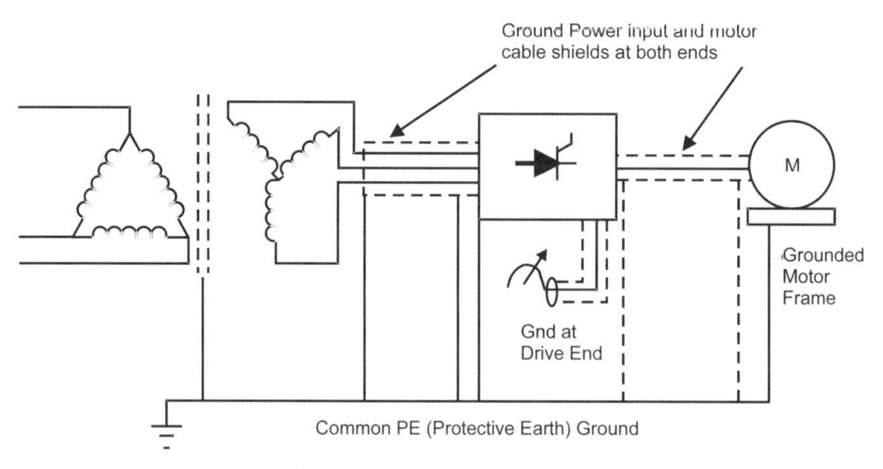

Figure 4-16. DC drive installation—shielding and grounding

detract from voltage already flowing and can cause unstable operation of the entire system. Several other items should be noted here.

Tachometers and process sensors would be shielded and grounded the same point as the speed reference pot indicated in the figure. Therefore, the shield from the tachometer cable would be grounded only at one end—typically at the drive chassis (follow manufacturer's recommendations). Motor shunt field cables are also considered power conductors and an EMI source, therefore both ends of the cable shielding should be grounded.

When installing DC drives, it is accepted practice to keep the following wiring *practices* procedures in mind:

Never place motor power cables and low voltage/current control cables in the same cable tray or conduit.

Use shielded cable for control signals (low-voltage or current analog signals) operating at 24 V and below.

If control signal wiring is not in a separate steel conduit, keep them at least 12 inches away from power wiring. (Note: Cross the control and power wiring at 90° if they must be close to one another or intersect.)

Use EMC (electromagnetic compatibility) rated shielded cable where required by the drive manufacturer or by code.

It would be impossible to predict all EMI- and RFI-interference possibilities. Each installation is somewhat different in how the control-, power-, and interface-equipment cabling lies near each other. However, if the above steps are taken, the likelihood of any interference issues will be greatly reduced or eliminated.

Drives (DC)—Innovations and Technology Improvements

DC drives have come along way—from vacuum tube power structures of the 1940s to the SCR semiconductor technology of today. Design improvements have taken the drive from a simple analog "motor turner" to a sophisticated microprocessor design, which includes a minicomputer. The DC drive was once thought to be the "brawn" that was located in harsh industrial environments and caused an application to operate at a specific speed. Now the DC drive, with its microprocessor and PLC-type control, is looked upon as the "brains" and an important piece of automation equipment.

To make intelligent applications choices, it is necessary to review the improvements made in DC drive technology. DC drives have lost their foothold in the industrial world to the more popular AC drives and motors. In a certain sense, the control technology of the DC world revolves around the performance of the DC motor, which requires routine maintenance procedures.

Though more applications are leaning toward AC, the DC drive and motor system has, and will continue to have, its place in certain industrial applications. The DC drive is simple to maintain. When armed with the proper information, anyone who applies the DC drive can realize a cost-effective means of variable-speed control.

The following sections will outline, in general and specific terms, improvements in DC drive design and control. It is meant to generate ideas as to where DC drives and motors can be applied, with little additional equipment required.

All-in-One Package Design

The DC drive systems of today include all of the needed components to operate, troubleshoot, and maintain the system. Typically, the drive unit includes line circuit breaker (or fuse), main contactor, line inductor, SCR converter module, field exciter, line, control and field exciter fuses, auxiliary transformer, heat sink fans, motor blower, motor starter and circuit breaker, communications connector, and control (i/o) wiring terminal block. The entire unit can be operational with three wires in (power input) and four wires out (two armature and two field wires). An additional set of wires would also be needed if an optional tach feedback unit is included in the motor assembly.

The "all-in-one" design is in contrast to the systems of the 1950s and 60s, where separate field exciters, converters, interconnections, and safety devices were found in various areas of the control cabinet. This type of installation required more space and more time to troubleshoot because of the nature of wiring, cable harnesses, and documentation. Designs of today are more compact and require little documentation to troubleshoot (many diagnostic features are visible through the software) and have less parts that require replacement. In short, DC drives of today are more reliable. Figure 4-17 illustrates this type of package design.

Figure 4-17. Package DC drive design (Courtesy of ABB Inc.)

Digital I/O (Inputs/Outputs)

Digital drives are programmable, which allows for a high degree of application flexibility. The idea is to connect all control and power wiring and set up the drive for the application through software programming. If the application is altered, the drive functions can quickly be reprogrammed through the software instead of rewiring the drive. The programming is typically done with a removable keypad or remote operator panel.

With older analog drives, the drive had to be shut down, and the control terminal block rewired for the new application. Downtime is costly. The less time a system is shut down; the more productivity is obtained.

Typically, the control wiring section of a DC drive will contain analog inputs (AI's for speed reference), digital inputs (DI's for controls like start/stop, reverse, etc.), analog outputs (connection for an auxiliary meter), digital outputs (DO's for devices such as fault relays, at-speed relays, etc.), and provisions for tach feedback wiring (A+ and A-, B+ and B-, etc.). The digital inputs and outputs would typically operate on ±10 VDC or ±24 VDC logic. A software function would operate if the assigned terminal voltage is high (meaning 8 V or higher on a 10-VDC control). Any voltage less than that would indicate a digital logic low and the function would not operate.

In addition to the standard start and stop speed-reference inputs, the drive would also include I/O for diagnostics such as blower motor acknowledgement, main contactor closed, field exciter operational, and emergency-stop energized—just to name a few. Figure 4-18 shows a typical I/O diagram for a package DC drive.

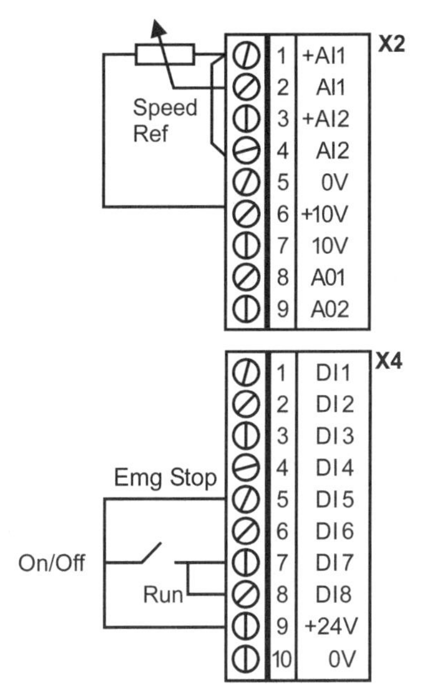

Figure 4-18. Packaged DC drive with standard I/O (Courtesy of ABB Inc.)

IGBT Technology

IGBT technology has been successfully applied to AC drives since the late 1980s. It has not been until recently that DC drives have included these devices in the power structure. SCRs are the standard conversion device for armature circuits because of the current capability and easy control scheme. However, IGBTs are now emerging as field exciter power stage semiconductors. IGBTs can be "turned on" and "turned off" with a small milliamp signal. Smaller control "driver" circuits are required because of the smaller control signals needed, compared with SCRs. Smaller control circuitry also means a smaller-sized field exciter, which translates to less cost. In addition, IGBT technology is ideal for operating a DC motor in the field weakening range and does not require a voltage-matching transformer (typically required to match SCRs to higher input voltage lines).

Multi-Language Programming Panel

Many of the programming panels (touch keypads) are removable and may or may not include a panel extension cord. Up until the last decade and a half, programming panels required continuous attachment to the drive control board. Storage of parameter values was a function of the control board and associated memory circuits.

With the latest advancements in *E^2PROM™s* and *flash PROMs*, the programming panel can be removed from power. Values can now be stored for an extremely long period of time, with no batteries required for backup. This type of capability allows for a "backup" plan in case any or all parameter values are lost because of a drive malfunction or electrical damage due to lightning.

Drive panels are, in many cases, "back-lit," meaning that the LCD digits have an illuminated background that can be increased or decreased in intensity. This is helpful when the drive is installed in a brightly or dimly lit room. Many programming panels allow for individual display of several different languages. This is very helpful when the drive is mounted on a machine and shipped to another country. The programming setup can be accomplished in English, for example, and then the language changed to Spanish before shipment to Mexico. Figure 4-19 shows a typical programming keypad.

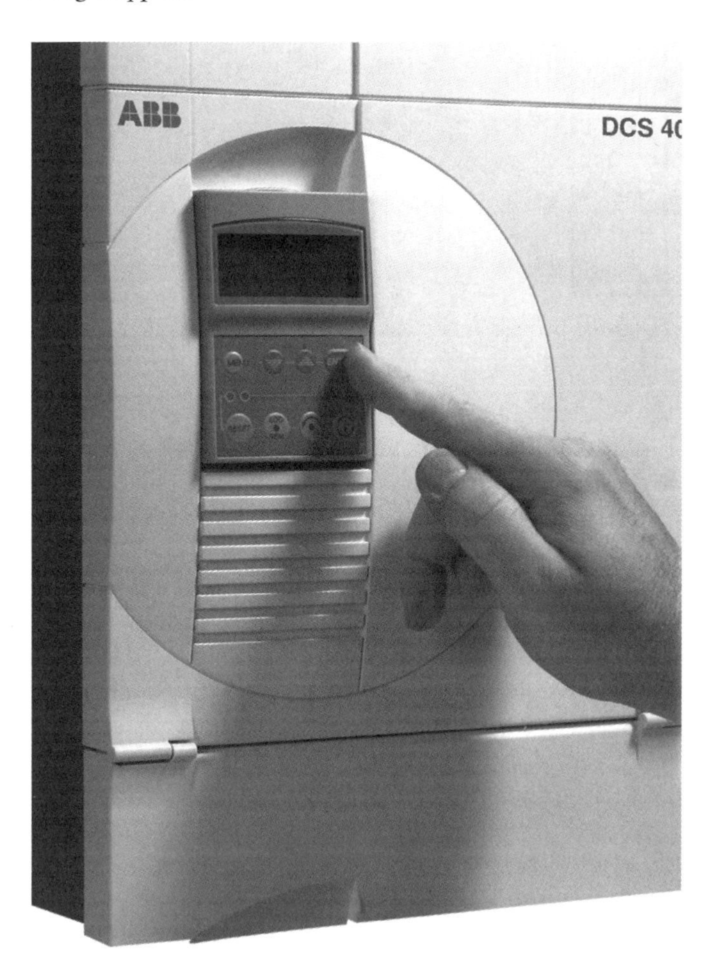

Figure 4-19. Removable, programmable drive panel (keypad) (Courtesy of ABB Inc.)

Programming Macros and Software Function Blocks

Because of the digital design, many DC drives require a multitude of parameters for setup of the system. Armature and field supply parameters are required, along with start/stop, speed reference, current, voltage and feedback controls, and diagnostic parameters for troubleshooting. All totaled, many DC drives contain well over 150 parameters, which all need some type of value attached.

At first glance, it would be a daunting task to individually set each of the parameters. Fortunately, many manufacturers preassign "default" values to each of the parameters. The values would not exactly match the motor and application, but would allow the drive to operate a motor. In addition to defaults, several manufacturers include preprogrammed "sets" of values, known as *macros*. Individual macros would allow the operator to match the drive parameters and diagnostics to the motor and application that it is connected to. In many cases, all of the parameters can be set in a matter of seconds, rather than individually setting parameters, which could take more than an hour. Macros such as hand–auto, three-wire control, torque control, and jog are available for easy configuration and setup of the drive.

Drive manufacturers try to make required parameter setup easy (i.e., armature and field voltage and current, field weakening point, etc.). One manufacturer includes a "commissioning template" or "wizard" that is much like a template wizard seen in office software programs. The template states the required parameter on the display and waits for the operator's input before advancing to the next screen display. In a matter of 8 to 10 keypad inputs, the operator can quickly set up the drive for initial operation.

There may be cases where the standard parameter set will not effectively meet the application requirements. In those cases, several manufacturers allow the operator to reconfigure the internal drive software (typically called *firmware*). The firmware (parameter names and values) can be adjusted through *function blocks*. These blocks are actually the building blocks of software that, when connected inside the drive, allows for a specific outcome (e.g., three-wire control with a jog and two constant speeds). If a macro does not exist, the operator can create a macro to match a particular application. As expected, this type of programming would be reserved for the more advanced operator or engineer, schooled in drive technology. Serious safety concerns could result when software function blocks are connected and results not completely verified. Figure 4-20 shows a function block screen found in one manufacturer's firmware.

Self-Tuning Armature, Field, and Current Loops

The DC drive system normally requires "tuning," once the standard software parameters are set in the drive. The fine adjustments allow the drive to match the feedback loop with the speed reference circuit. Current loops

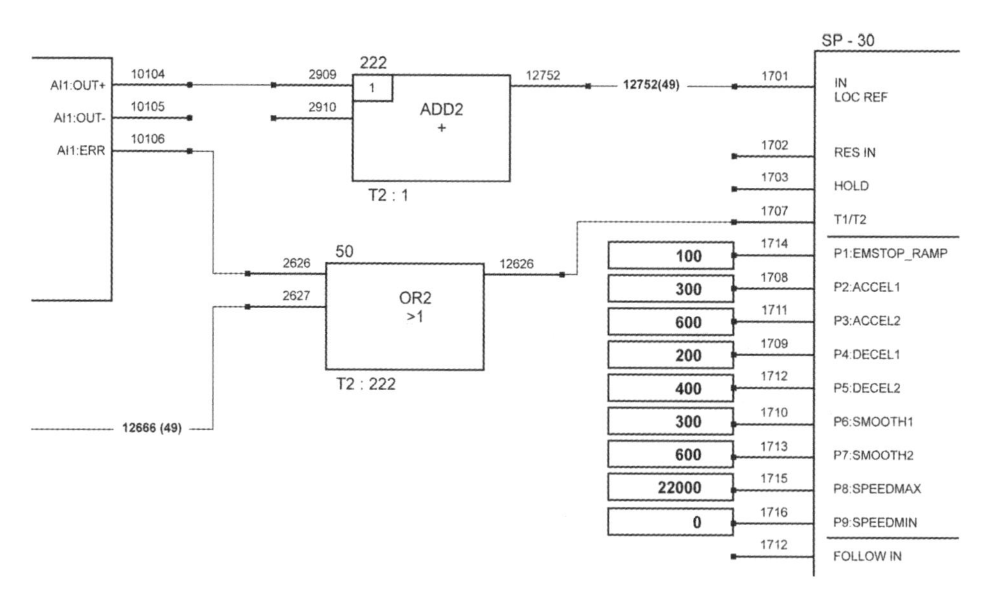

Figure 4-20. Software function block programming (firmware) (Courtesy of ABB Inc.)

also require adjustment if the operator is to obtain the response times when accelerating and changing directions.

In some older DC drives, this tuning procedure is a manual process. The operator must accelerate then decelerate the load, observe the behavior of the system, and make manual adjustments. In some drives, however, this tuning process is done automatically by the drive-control circuitry. The response gains and recovery times are preloaded at the factory. When the drive sees dynamic adjustments occurring during commissioning, it adjusts the tuning parameters to match the outcome of a pre-assigned value set. Drive response times as low as 500 to 800 ms are possible with some systems.

Serial and Fiber-Optic Communications

With today's digital drives comes access to digital communications. Drives prior to the digital age required hardwiring to the control terminal block. This allowed remote operation only from a distance where control voltage or current loss could be kept to a minimum (maybe 25 feet or less). With today's serial and parallel mode of information transfer, the DC drive can accept control and speed commands from process equipment several thousand feet away. This allows the DC drive to be integrated into the factory automation environment, where process control equipment is located in a clean, dry control room.

Serial links (3 wires plus a shield conductor) are more normal today, compared with a decade ago. Control and diagnostic data can be transferred to the upper-level control system at a rate of 100 ms. With only three wires for control connections, the drive "health" and operating statistics can be available at the touch of a computer button. The communication speed of a serial link makes it ideal for simple process lines and general coordination of conveyors, where high-speed accuracy is not required.

Fiber-optic communication uses long plastic or glass fiber and an intense light source to transmit data. With optical fiber, thousands of bits of information can be transmitted at a rate of 4 mega baud (4 million bits per second). An entire factory can be wired with high-speed fiber optics, with very little, if any, electrical interference. This is due to the high frequency of light waves, as opposed to the lower frequency of a wire conductor serial link. With fiber-optic communications, steel processing, coating lines, and high-speed "cut-to-length" applications are possible. With small error signals fed back to the speed controller, the drive can immediately respond with a correction. This keeps the quality of the product very high and the deviation very low in size.

Several drive manufacturers offer serial and fiber-optic software that installs directly to a laptop or desktop computer. With this software installed, all drive parameters are accessible from the stand-alone computer. This makes parameter changes simple and fast. Parameters can be changed in the computer, downloaded to the drive for verification, and saved in the computer as a file or macro. The file can then be easily transferred to other computers or networks, or e-mailed to another factory within the same company. Hundreds, even thousands, of macros and file sets can be saved. The ultimate result is the ability to quickly respond to required changes in drive and application setup.

Serial and fiber-optic communications will be discussed in more detail in Chapter 6. Figure 4-21 shows a possible fiber-optic connection scheme.

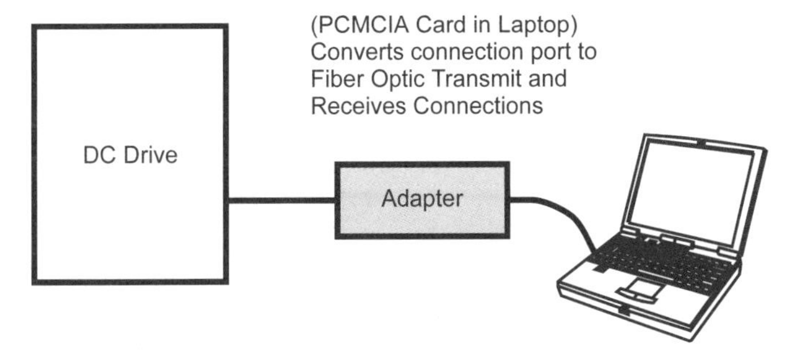

Figure 4-21. Fiber-optic communications

Field Bus Communications (PLCs)

When factory automation systems are engineered, some type of communication system is always specified. Data links to PLCs (programmable logic controllers) are common in many high-speed systems that process control and feedback information. PLCs provide the mathematical calculations, timing circuits, and software "and/or" logic signals required to process drive, sensor, and switch status.

Several manufacturers of PLCs offer a direct connection to many drive products. Because each PLC uses a specific programming language (usually ladder-logic programming), drive manufacturers are required to build an adapter box. This adapter (sometimes called a *field bus module*) is used to translate one language to another (called a protocol). The drive manufacturer installs one internal protocol and the PLC installs another. Field bus modules allow for a smooth transfer of data to the PLC, and vice versa, with little loss of communication speed. Field bus communications will also be address in Chapter 6.

AC Drives

Introduction

The term *AC drives* covers a wide range of drive types. When talking mostly industrial terms, an AC drive could also be considered a variable frequency drive (VFD), adjustable-speed drive (ASD), variable-speed drive (VSD), and "inverter." If a technician was discussing ASDs and the factory contained mostly DC equipment, then ASD or VSD would refer to a DC drive. The term *inverter* is actually the final or power section of the drive—and is considered an acceptable term for the entire unit.

There are actually many different types of AC drives, but all of them have one concept in common—they convert fixed voltage and frequency into a variable voltage and frequency output.

Though they do not meet the strict definition of an AC drive, reduced voltage starters (e.g., soft starts) and wound rotor slip recovery units fall into the variable-speed category. Soft starts immediately deliver line frequency to the motor but at a reduced voltage value for a specified period of time. The result is reduced motor torque, as the motor is accelerating.

Load commutated inverters (LCIs) and *cycloconverters* are also part of the variable-frequency drive category. Cycloconverters actually use SCRs in very large horsepower amounts that require regeneration. Though the output of a cycloconverter may not be considered variable, the unit does alter the frequency output, thereby reducing the speed. This unit would actually step down the frequency to 1/2 or 1/3 of the line frequency. This frequency would then be applied to motors of 30- or 20-Hz design. The cycloconverter got its start in the 1930s but is not much in demand today because of its complexity and cost of circuitry.

The primary focus of this section will be on three common types of VFDs: the *variable voltage input* or *inverter* (VVI, sometimes referred to as the *six-step drive*), the *current source inverter* (CSI), and the *pulse width modulated* (PWM). The VVI and PWM would be considered a *voltage source inverter,* while the CSI would be considered a *current source inverter.*

Several other types of drives fall under the category of voltage source inverters. Vector (or flux vector) drives and sensorless vector drives will be considered later in this chapter.

If not already done, it would be helpful to review the section on AC induction motors in Chapter 3. That section will provide a foundation upon which to build the basic concepts of variable-frequency drives.

Basic Theory of Major Drive Types

The easiest way to understand drives is to take a brief look at what a drive application looks like. Figure 4-22 shows a simple application with a fixed-speed fan using a motor starter. The three-phase motor starter can be replaced by a VFD, allowing the fan to be operated at variable speed.

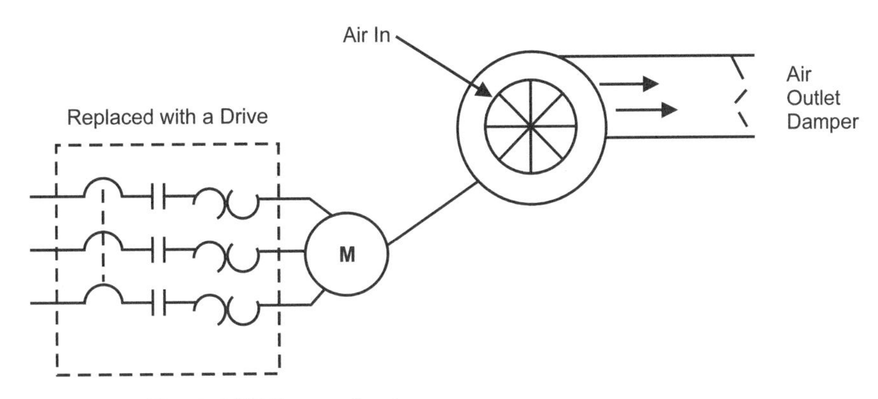

Figure 4-22. Simple VFD/fan application

If the fan can operate at virtually any speed required (below maximum motor speed), the air outlet damper can be "fixed" open. Using the fixed-speed motor starter method, the only means of varying the air out was by adjusting the air outlet damper.

Now the question is: How does this induction motor work with a drive? As mentioned earlier, a standard three-phase induction motor can be controlled by a VFD. There are two main elements that are controlled by the drive, speed, and torque. To understand how a drive controls these two elements, we will take a short review of AC induction motor characteristics.

Figure 4-23 shows the formula for determining the shaft speed of an induction motor.

As you can see, this formula includes a characteristic called *slip*. The slip speed in a motor is actually termed *base speed*. As indicated earlier, a VFD controls two main elements of a motor—speed and torque.

The speed of a motor is conveniently adjusted by changing the frequency applied to the motor. The VFD adjusts the output frequency, thereby adjusting the speed of the motor. The torque of a motor is controlled by a

Motor Slip:

$$\text{Shaft Speed} = \frac{120 \times F}{P} - \text{slip}$$

Slip for NEMA B Motor = 3 to 5 % of Base Speed which is 1800 RPM at Full Load

F = Frequency applied to the motor
P = Number of motor poles

Example:

$$\text{Shaft Speed} = \frac{120 \times 60\ \text{Hz}}{4} - 50 = 1750\ \text{RPM}$$

Figure 4-23. Motor speed formula (including slip)

basic characteristic of every motor—the volts per hertz ratio (V/Hz). A review of this ratio is shown in Figure 4-24.

$$\frac{460\ \text{V}}{60\ \text{Hz}} = 7.67\ \frac{\text{V}}{\text{Hz}}$$

If 230 VAC Power Line:

$$\frac{230\ \text{V}}{60\ \text{Hz}} = 3.83\ \frac{\text{V}}{\text{Hz}}$$

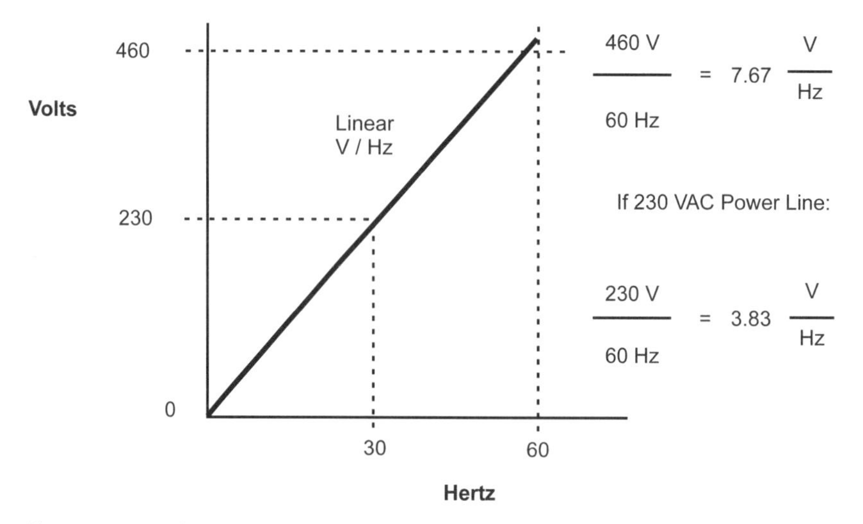

Figure 4-24. AC motor linear volts per hertz ratio

If an induction motor is connected to a 460-V power source at 60 Hz, the ratio is 7.67 V/Hz. As long as this ratio is kept in proportion, the motor will develop rated torque.

Figure 4-25 indicates a typical speed/torque curve for a motor. This curve represents a motor operated at a fixed voltage and frequency source.

A VFD provides many different frequency outputs, as shown in Figure 4-26. At any given frequency output of the drive, another torque curve is established. A typical operating point is where the curve intersects the 100% level, indicating rated torque.

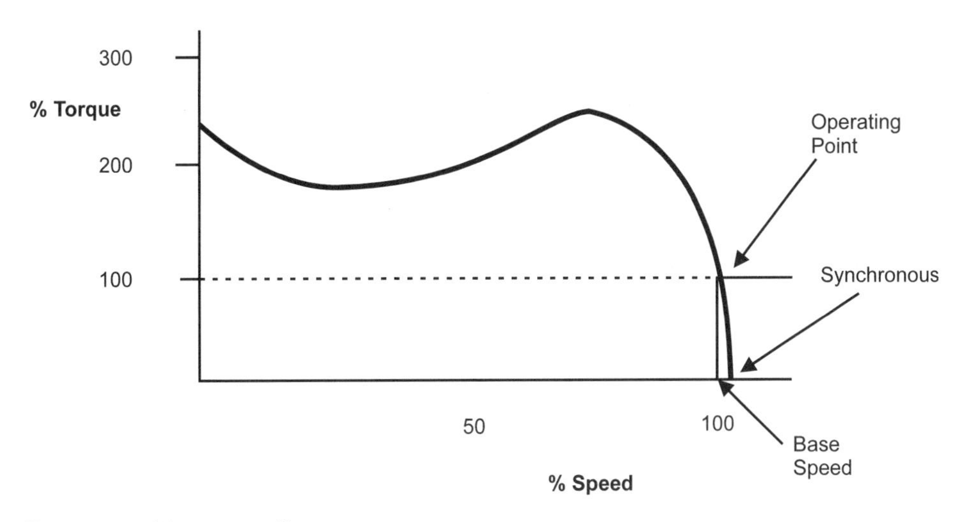

Figure 4-25. Motor speed/torque curve

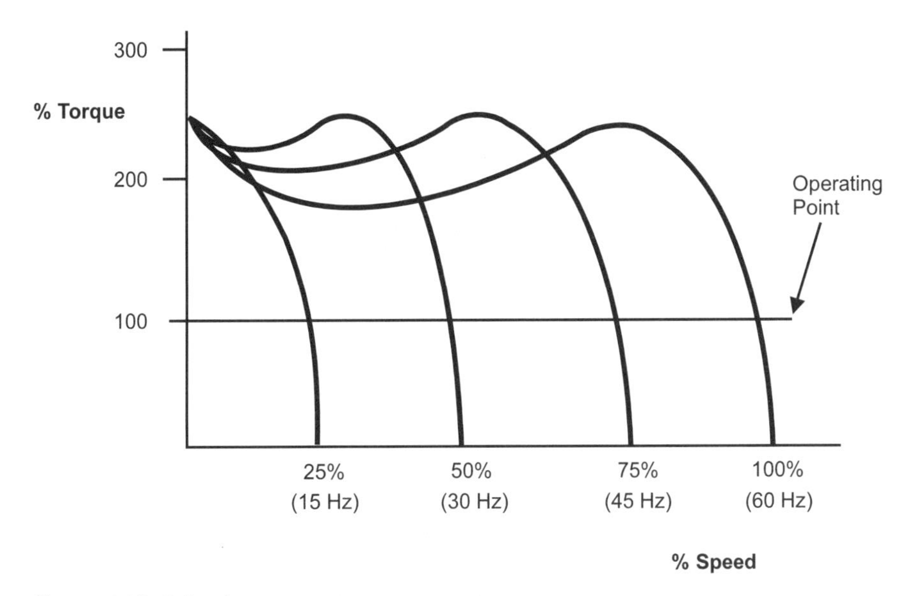

Figure 4-26. Drive frequency output vs. motor torque

The VFD provides the frequency and voltage output necessary to change the speed of a motor. A block diagram of a basic PWM drive (pulse-width modulated) is shown in Figure 4-27. All PWM drives contain these main parts, with subtle differences in hardware and software components. A PWM drive will be used as an example here, then the characteristics of a VVI and CSI drive will be compared with the PWM.

Although some drives accept single-phase input power, a three-phase unit will be considered for illustration purposes. (To simplify illustrations, the waveforms in the following drive figures only show one phase of input and output.)

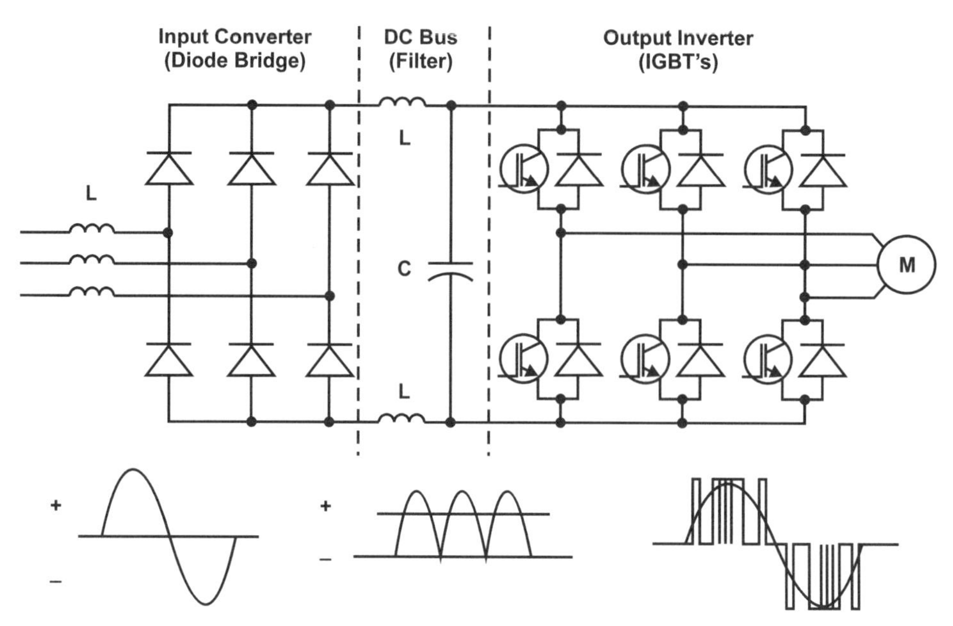

Figure 4-27. PWM drive (VFD) block diagram (Courtesy of ABB Inc.)

Three-phase power is applied to the input section of the drive, called the *converter.* This section contains six diodes, arranged in an electrical bridge. These diodes convert AC power to DC power. Because diodes are used in the converting process, the next section sees a fixed DC voltage.

The DC bus section accepts the now converted, AC-to-DC voltage. The role of this section is to filter and smooth out the waveform. The "L" and "C" indicate inductors and capacitors. (**Note:** Many drive manufacturers install only one DC bus inductor, along with the filter capacitor(s). Some manufacturers install line reactors, "L" ahead of the drive converter. Later in this chapter, innovations and technology improvements will be reviewed in detail.)

As shown, the diodes actually reconstruct the negative halves of the waveform onto the positive half. An average DC voltage of ~650–680 V is seen, if the drive is a 460-VAC unit. (Line voltage × 1.414 = DC bus voltage.) The inductor and the capacitor(s) work together to filter out any AC component on the DC waveform. The smoother the DC waveform, the cleaner the output waveform from the drive.

Once filtered, the DC bus voltage is delivered to the final section of the drive, called the *inverter* section. As the name implies, this section actually inverts the DC voltage back to AC—but in a variable voltage and frequency output. Devices called *insulated gate bipolar transistors* (IGBTs) act as power switches to turn on and off the DC bus voltage at specific intervals. In doing so, the inverter actually creates a variable AC voltage and frequency output. Control circuits, called gate drivers, cause the control part of the IGBT (gate) to turn "on" and "off" as needed.

As seen in Figure 4-28, the output of the drive does not provide an exact replica of the AC input sine waveform. It actually provides voltage pulses that are at a constant magnitude in height. The IGBTs switch the DC bus voltage on and off at designated intervals.

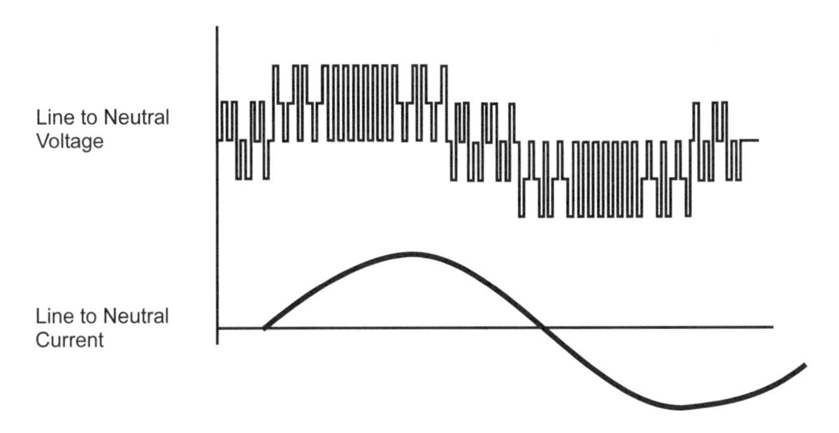

Figure 4-28. PWM output waveform (voltage and current)

The control board in the drive signals the gate driver circuits to turn on the waveform positive half or negative half IGBT. This alternating of positive and negative switches recreates the three-phase output.

The longer the IGBT remains on, the higher the output voltage; the less time the IGBT is on, the lower the output voltage (shown in Figure 4-29). Conversely, the longer the IGBT is off, the lower the output frequency.

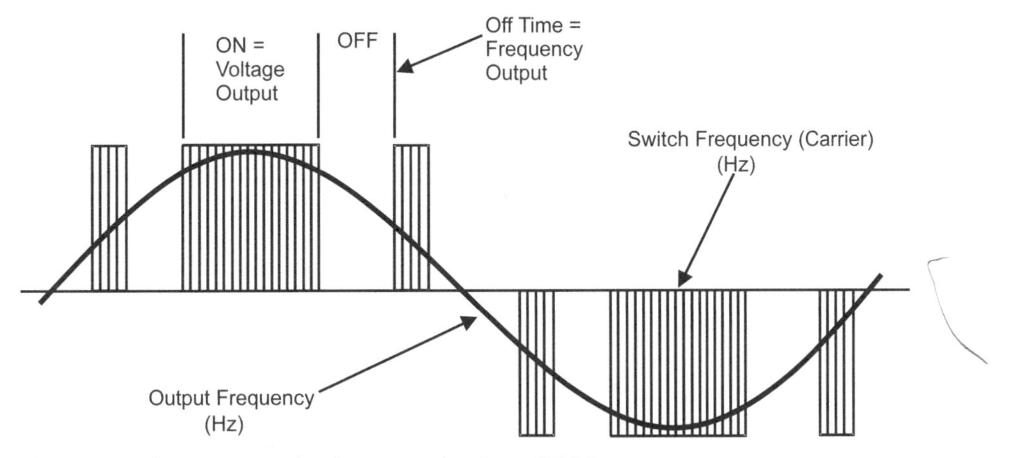

Figure 4-29. Frequency and voltage creation from PWM

The speed at which IGBTs are switched on and off is called the *carrier frequency* or *switch frequency*. The higher the switch frequency, the more resolution each PWM pulse contains. Typical switch frequencies are 3000 × 4000 times per second (3–4 kHz), but some manufacturers use a carrier as high as 16 Hz.

As you can imagine, the higher the switch frequency, thc smoother the output waveform (the higher the resolution). However, there is a disadvantage. Higher switch frequencies cause decreased efficiency of the drive. The faster the switching rate, the faster the IGBTs turn on and off. This causes increased heat in the IGBTs.

Now that the standard PWM VFD has been reviewed, the next step will be to review the characteristics of VVI and CSI VFDs. This will be followed by an analysis of how PWM compares with VVI and CSI drives.

VVI (Variable Voltage Inverter)—Input

This design takes the supply voltage (e.g., 230 or 460 V), rectifies it, and sends the variable voltage to the DC bus and then to the inverter section. The inverter section then inverts (changes DC to AC) the variable voltage DC to a variable-voltage and variable-frequency AC. The inverter section contains power semiconductors such as transistors or thyristors (SCRs).

To deliver variable voltage to the inverter, the input rectifier section or front-end consists of a controllable rectifier—SCRs. The control logic fires the SCRs at the appropriate time during the sine wave, thereby providing the variable voltage to the DC bus. Figure 4-30 shows a block diagram of a VVI drive.

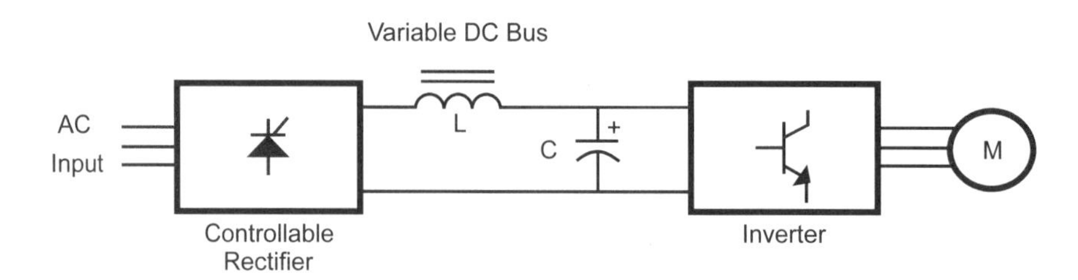

Figure 4-30. VVI drive block diagram

Some of the advantages of a VVI drive include good speed range, ability to connect multiple motors to the drive (within drive current limitations), and a fairly simple control regulator. However, there are some limitations.

One of the major disadvantages, in terms of AC drives, is the input power factor. It decreases as the speed of the drive/motor decreases. This is due to the "controllable" rectifier front end being constructed of SCRs. This issue is identical to that of DC drives.

Another disadvantage is the inability of the drive to "ride through" a low-input voltage situation. The term *power loss ride-through* is defined as the ability of a drive to ride through a low- or zero-voltage input and still remain in operation. This may be 2 to 3 cycles of the AC Sine wave, or more. (**Note:** Each AC cycle lasts about 16 ms). At low operating speeds (low hertz output), the SCR rectifier is not constantly keeping the DC bus charged at full potential. This means that the motor has voltage to draw from, in the event of a low line input.

Other disadvantages include the requirement of an input isolation transformer or line reactor. This is needed because of the SCR control technology (line spike generation). In addition, the generation of additional output harmonics is a possible result of the technology being applied to the AC motor.

The VVI drive has one additional disadvantage—the characteristic of low-speed motor cogging (shaft pulsations/jerky motion). Though not an issue at mid to high speeds, cogging at low speeds can cause equipment problems. This limitation is best illustrated in Figure 4-31.

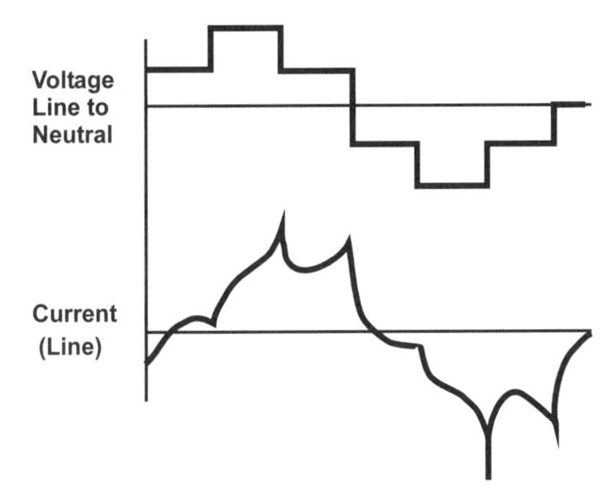

Figure 4-31. VVI voltage and current waveforms

As seen in Figure 4-31, the voltage waveform approximates a series of steps. Because of this characteristic, this drive is sometimes called a *six-step* drive. During low-speed operation (>15-20 Hz), the rotor actually searches for the next available magnetic field in the stator. The result is a jerky rotation of the motor shaft. Because of this, gears or gear reducers connected to the motor shaft will suffer additional friction and wear. At high speeds, the inertia of the motor will provide continuous movement of the motor shaft. Therefore, cogging is not a problem.

As shown in the current waveform, there are several spikes that occur at regular intervals. These spikes, or transients, are caused by the SCRs gating on, or triggering. The DC bus filter circuit (shown by an L and C) does reduce the effects of these spikes, but they are not eliminated. These spikes translate into additional motor heating and inefficiency.

The VVI drive was one of the first AC drives to gain acceptance into the industrial drives market. It may be considered one of the most economical drives in the 25- to 150-HP range if a 6:1 speed range is acceptable (operation from 10–60 Hz). This type of drive is also widely used in high-speed drive applications—400 to 3000 Hz.

CSI (Current Source Inverter)

This type of AC drive (sometimes referred to as *current source input*) has basically the same components as a VVI drive. The major difference is that it is more of a current-sensitive drive as opposed to a VVI, which is more of a voltage-sensitive drive.

This design also takes the supply voltage (e.g., 230 or 460 V), rectifies it, and sends the variable voltage to the DC bus and then to the inverter section. As with the VVI, the CSI drive inverter section inverts (changes DC to AC) the variable-voltage DC to a variable-voltage and variable-frequency AC. The inverter section is made up of power semiconductors such as transistors or thyristors (SCRs).

To deliver variable voltage to the inverter, the input-rectifier section also consists of a controllable rectifier—SCRs. The control logic fires the SCRs at the appropriate time during the sine wave, thereby providing the variable voltage to the DC bus. Figure 4-32 shows a block diagram of a CSI drive.

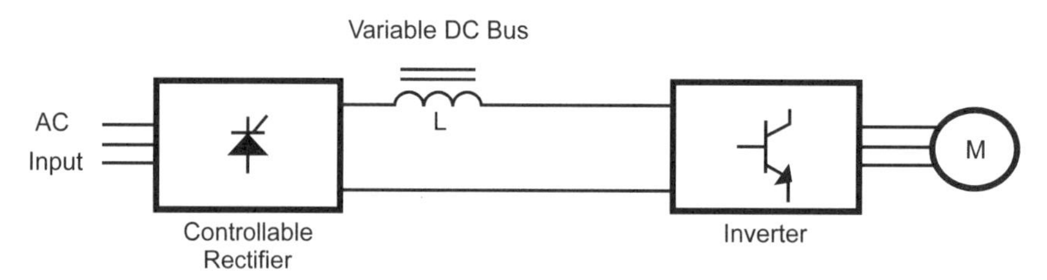

Figure 4-32. CSI block diagram

Some of the advantages of a CSI drive include high efficiency, inherent short-circuit protection (due to the current regulator within the drive), inherent regenerative capability back to the AC line during overhauling load situations, and the capability of synchronous transfer (bringing other motors on-line during full-voltage output).

However, there are also some limitations. As with a VVI drive, the input power factor decreases as the speed of the drive/motor decreases. Also, this drive has a limited speed range due to low-speed motor cogging (shaft pulsations/jerky motion). This drive is also unable to "ride through" a low-input voltage situation. This drive also has the requirement of an input isolation transformer, due to the SCR control technology (line spike generation).

Unlike the VVI drive, the CSI drive cannot operate more than one motor at a time. The motor is an integral part of the drive system and its characteristics must be matched to the drive. (Usually the motor and drive are sold as a complete package.) Multiple motors would cause malfunctions in the drive-control system. In addition, the motor normally requires a feedback device (e.g., tachometer) to provide information to the drive current regulator.

Also related to motors is the requirement for the motor to always be connected to the drive. This means that the drive cannot be tested without the motor connected. In some cases, one additional disadvantage is the drive size. Typically, it is physically larger than other drive types because of internal power components.

As mentioned earlier, the VVI and CSI drives produce low-speed cogging. This is illustrated in Figure 4-33.

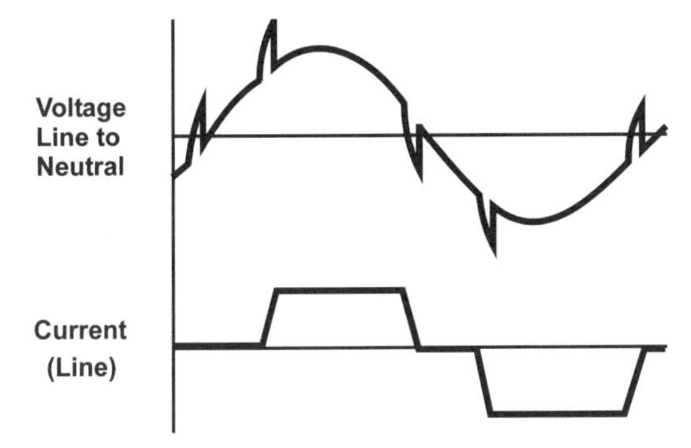

Figure 4-33. CSI voltage and current waveforms

As seen in Figure 4-33, line notching or spikes developed from the gating of SCRs in the drive front end. Compared with a VVI drive, the voltage waveform is somewhat closer to the sine wave voltage required by the motor. The current waveform appears to simulate a trapezoid. In addition, there are times when no current flows. These gaps in current cause the rotor to search for the next available magnetic field in the stator. This characteristic, like that of the VVI, results in jerky rotation of the motor shaft at low speeds (<15–20 Hz).

As with the VVI drive, the DC bus filter circuit (shown by an L) does reduce the effects of these spikes, but they are not eliminated. Here again, these spikes translate into additional motor heating and inefficiency.

CSI drives are the latest addition to the line-up of AC variable-frequency drives. They are usually used in applications requiring 50 HP or larger. These VFDs are well suited for powering pumps and fans because of the inherent synchronous transfer capability. The cost of a CSI drive may be less than either a VVI or PWM in powering pumps, fans, or similar applications. However, the efficiency of the CSI drive matches that of the DC drive and may not provide a total energy-saving package compared with the PWM drive.

PWM (Pulse-Width Modulated)

As seen earlier, the power conversion principle of this drive is different from that of VVI and CSI. One of the major differences is that of a fixed diode front end, not a controllable SCR front end. This fixed diode bridge provides a constant DC bus voltage. The DC bus voltage is then filtered and sent to the inverter section. Another difference between PWM and the other types is the operation of the inverter section. The inverter in the PWM drive has a dual purpose—it changes fixed-voltage DC to variable-voltage AC and changes fixed frequency to variable frequency. In the other types, the inverter's primary purpose is to change the fixed-frequency to a variable-frequency output.

PWM drives use several types of power transistors; IGBTs, and GTOs (gate turn-off—SCRs) are examples. These semiconductors offer the advantages of PWM technology without the expense of commutation circuits. (Commutation circuits are required to turn off the SCRs once they start conducting. They are found in early VVI or CSI units.)

Another major difference is the actual voltage output of the inverter itself. The DC bus voltage is fixed and approximately equal to the RMS value of the drive input voltage (e.g., 460 V × 1.414 = 650 V). By chopping or modulating the DC bus voltage, the average voltage (output voltage) is increased or decreased. The output voltage value is controlled by the length of time the power semiconductors actually conduct. As seen earlier, the longer the on time for the semiconductors, the higher the output voltage. The longer the off times occur in the process, the lower the frequency output. Thus the inverter accomplishes both variable voltage and frequency. Figure 4-34 shows a block diagram of a PWM drive.

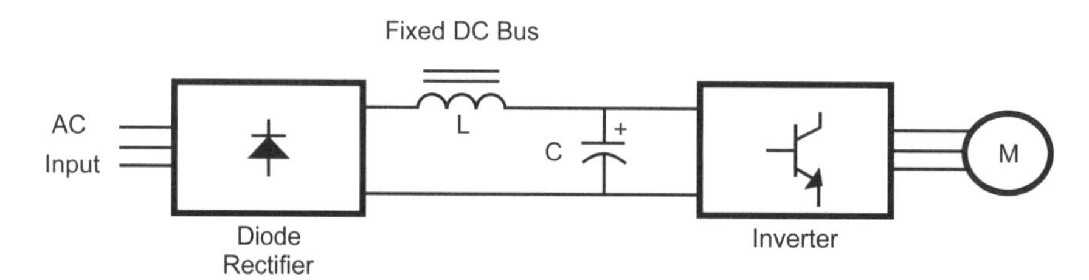

Figure 4-34. PWM block diagram

Some of the advantages of a PWM drive include high efficiency, the capability of optional common bus regeneration (operating several inverter sections off of one DC bus), and a wide controllable speed range (in some cases up to 200:1, with no low speed cogging under 20 Hz operation).

The PWM drive offers other advantages, such as power loss ride-through capability, open circuit protection, and constant input power factor. This is due to the fixed diode front end and DC bus inductor. Constant power factor is not seen by CSI, VVI, or DC drives.

Like the VVI drive, the PWM also allows multi-motor operation (within the current capability of the drive). However, there are a few limitations.

Extra hardware is required for line regenerative capability (discussed later in this chapter). Also, the regulator is more complex than a VVI. However, microprocessor control has nearly eliminated significant economic differences between the two drives.

As mentioned, low-speed cogging is not an issue with PWM drives. This is illustrated in Figure 4-35.

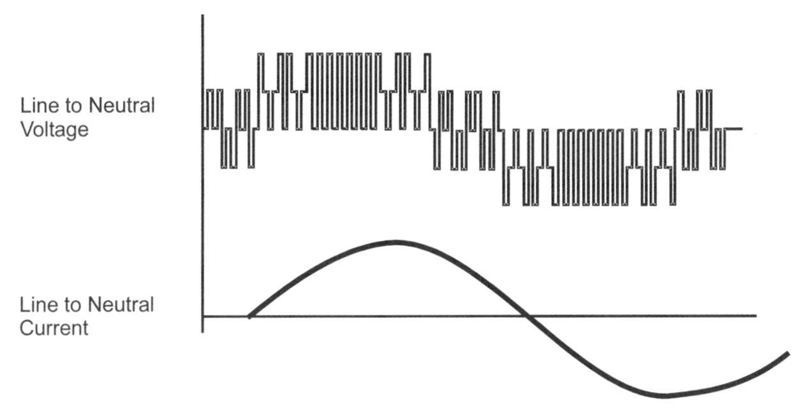

Figure 4-35. PWM voltage and current waveforms

Figure 4-35 has been seen before. Of particular interest is the fact that there is no line notching or spikes developed, thanks to the diode front end. The voltage waveform, which could be superimposed on the modulations, very closely approximates the sine wave voltage required by the motor. If the carrier frequency is high (8–16 kHz), the quality of low-speed operation is improved. The higher the carrier frequency, the smoother the motor operation. (Remember—carrier frequency is the speed at which the power semiconductors are switched on and off.)

Another benefit of high carrier frequencies is that of reduced audible noise. The higher the frequency, the less motor noise is generated. Audible motor noise can be an issue with low switching rates (e.g., 1–3 kHz). The current waveform, though it contains some ripple, is the smoothest of the three types of drives. It closely approximates the AC sine wave. The efficiency is therefore very high with little motor heating.

Continued improvements in drive technology have enabled PWM drives to deliver a response almost equal to that of DC servos. High response applications such as machine tools and robots require very precise control of motor speed and torque. PWM flux vector drives provide this type of capability and are covered later in this chapter.

AC Drives—Braking Methods

Braking methods of DC motors has already been reviewed earlier in this chapter. In this section, attention will be given to AC drive braking methods, which, for the most part, are similar to DC drive braking methods, with a few exceptions. Figure 4-36 is a review of the stopping methods of an AC motor, with a minor variation.

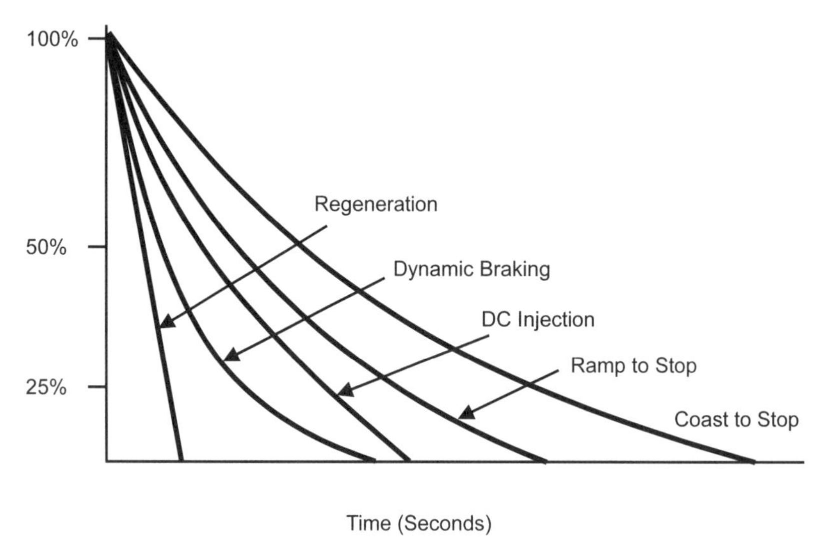

Figure 4-36. Braking methods for AC drives

As indicated, the easiest way of bringing an AC motor to a stop is the simple method of coast-to-stop. This is followed by the next fastest means, called *ramp-to-stop*.

During this method, the drive actually forces the motor down to a stop by systematically reducing the frequency and voltage. This is done in a deceleration ramp format, which is set through a parameter in the drive. It should be noted that the motor will contain energy or inertia that must be dissipated—in this case voltage. The DC bus circuit will have to absorb the back fed voltage. When this happens, the DC bus voltage rises—possibly to a point of a voltage trip (called *over-voltage fault* or *DC bus fault*). A typical drive will automatically protect itself by shutting down at ~135% of nominal DC bus value. (For example, a 460-VAC drive will carry ~650 VDC on the bus. The trip point would be ~878 VDC.)

The DC bus of a typical AC drive will take on as much voltage as possible without tripping. If an over-voltage trip occurs, the operator has three choices—increase the deceleration time, add DC injection braking, or add an external dynamic braking package. If the deceleration time is extended, the DC bus has more time to dissipate the energy and stay below the trip point. This may be a trial-and-error approach (keep setting the deceleration time until the drive does not trip). A few of the recent drives offered on the market automatically extend the deceleration time, without an operator having to do so. If 30 s is a deceleration time and the drive stops the motor in 45 s, the motor cannot be stopped in 30 s without DC injection braking or external hardware (e.g., dynamic braking). If a 30-second stop is required by the application, DC injection braking is a possibility.

DC Injection Braking

As the name implies, during this braking process, DC voltage is "injected" into the stator windings for a preset period of time. In doing so, a definite north and south pole is set up in the stator, causing the same type of magnetic field in the rotor. Braking torque (counter torque) is the action that results, bringing the motor to a quicker stop, compared with ramp. The rotor and stator dissipate the energy within itself through heat. This method of braking is usually used in lightly loaded applications, where braking is not often used. Repetitive operation of injection braking can cause excessive heat buildup, especially in high-inertia applications, such as flywheels or centrifuges. Excessive heat can cause permanent damage to the stator windings and rotor core.

Dynamic Braking

If DC injection braking cannot bring the motor to a stop in the required time, then dynamic braking will need to be added. Figure 4-37 indicates a typical dynamic braking system for an AC drive.

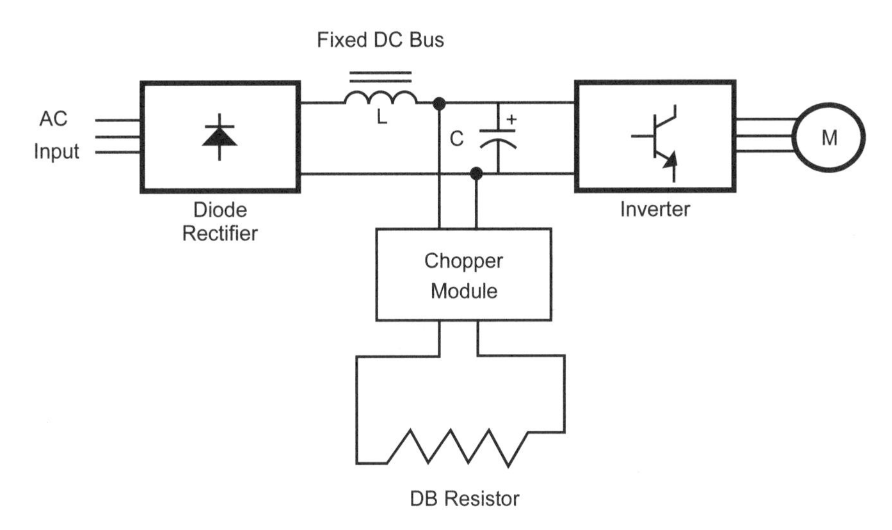

Figure 4-37. AC drive dynamic braking

This form of stopping uses a fixed, high-wattage resistor (or bank of resistors) to transform the rotating energy into heat. When the motor is going faster than commanded speed, the energy is fed back to the DC bus. Once the bus level increases to a predetermined point, the chopper module activates and the excess voltage is transferred to the DB resistor. The chopper is basically a sensor and is constructed of a transistor or IGBT switch device. The DB resistor is not mounted within the drive box or inside a drive cabinet. It is always mounted in an area where the heat developed cannot interfere with the heat dissipation requirements of the drive.

As previous indicated, the main stopping power of a DB system occurs when the resistor is cold, during the first few seconds of the process. Once the resistor heats up, the amount of braking torque diminishes. The number of times per minute DB is engaged will also determine the effectiveness of braking torque. *Duty cycle*, as it is called, is the number of times per minute the DB resistor is used. Many DB circuits consider a maximum of 10% duty cycle (6 s on, 54 s off-time to cool).

Regenerative Braking (Four Quadrant)

The process of regenerative braking has already been discussed. However, this type of braking uses different components in the AC drive, compared with DC. The end result is still the same—generation of voltage back to the AC line in synchronization with utility power.

To accomplish this, a second set of reverse-connected power semiconductors is required. Some AC drives use two sets of fully controlled SCRs in the input converter section. The latest AC regenerative drives use two sets of IGBTs in the converter section (some manufacturers term this an active front end).

The reverse set of power components allows the drive to conduct current in the opposite direction (taking the motor's energy, and generating it back to the line). Figure 4-38 indicates a block diagram of a regenerative braking (four quadrant) system.

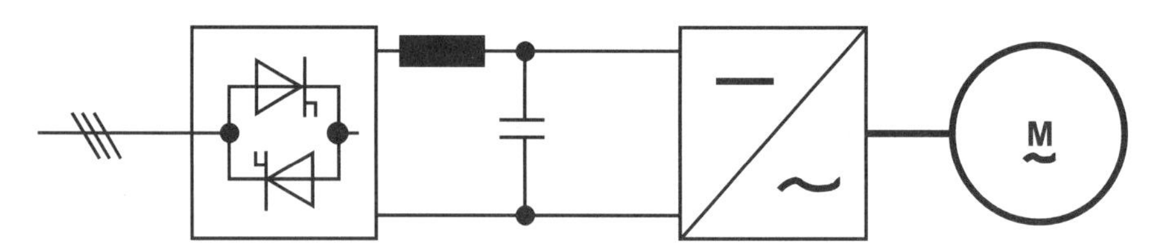

Figure 4-38. Regenerative AC drive (two IGBT bridges)

As expected with a four-quadrant system, this unit allows driving the motor in the forward and reverse directions, as well as regeneration in both the forward and reverse directions. The control board contains the microprocessor that controls the status of the forward and reverse IGBT bridges. When the speed of the motor is faster than commanded, the motor's energy is fed back into the DC bus. The regeneration circuit senses the increase in reverse voltage and turns on the reverse IGBT bridge circuit.

In this method, the reverse IGBTs need to be able to conduct in the reverse direction. Therefore, if power is removed from the drive, the microprocessor and the reverse IGBTs would not operate. Therefore, this method would not be used for emergency stop situations. However, one method of working around this issue is to include brake resistor and chopper across the DC bus. This provides the best of both worlds, regeneration and e-stop capability.

Drives (AC)—Torque Control

Up until now, standard PWM voltage-controlled drives have been discussed. In this type of drive, the voltage and frequency applied are the controlling variable, when talking about motor torque produced. Torque produced is actually a product of the amount of slip in the motor. The motor has to have a certain amount of slip present to produce torque. As the motor load increases, slip increases and so does torque. This type of AC drive is termed a *volts per hertz drive,* primarily because of the two controlling elements—volts and hertz. It is also given the label of a *scalar drive.*

The drive technology of today has moved beyond a "motor turner" philosophy. Drive systems of today need to accurately control the torque of an AC induction motor. Controlled torque is required by automation systems such as wind–unwind stands, process-control equipment, coating lines, printing, packaging lines, hoists and elevators, extruders, and any place where standard motor slip cannot be tolerated (typically 3–5%). Enter the realm of *controlled-slip* drives—called *flux vector* or simply, *vector* drives.

Flux Vector Drives

One of the basic principles of a flux vector drive is to simulate the torque produced by a DC motor. As indicated in the DC drive section, one of the major advantages of DC Drives, and now Flux Vector Drives – is full torque at zero speed. Up until the advent of flux vector drives, slip had to occur for motor torque to be developed. Depending on motor design, 30–50 rpm of slip might be needed for torque to be developed. An output frequency of 3–7 Hz may be needed from the drive before the motor actually starts turning. With flux vector control, the drive forces the motor to generate torque at zero speed.

A flux vector drive features field-oriented control—similar to that of a DC drive where the shunt field windings continuously have flux, even at zero speed. The motor's electrical characteristics are simulated in the drive controller circuitry called a *motor model.* The motor model takes a mental impression of the motor's flux, voltage, and current requirements for every degree of shaft rotation. Due to the way the drive gathers information for the motor model, it would be termed a closed loop drive. Torque is indirectly controlled by the creation of frequency and voltage on the basis of values determined by a feedback device. Figure 4-39 indicates a block diagram of a closed loop, flux vector-controlled AC drive.

To emulate the magnetic operating conditions of a DC motor, that is, to perform the field orientation process, the flux vector drive needs to know the spatial angular position of the rotor flux inside the AC induction motor. With flux vector PWM drives, field orientation is achieved by electronic means rather than the mechanical commutator and brush assembly of the DC motor.

During field orientation, information about the rotor status is obtained by feeding back rotor speed and angular position. This feedback is relative to

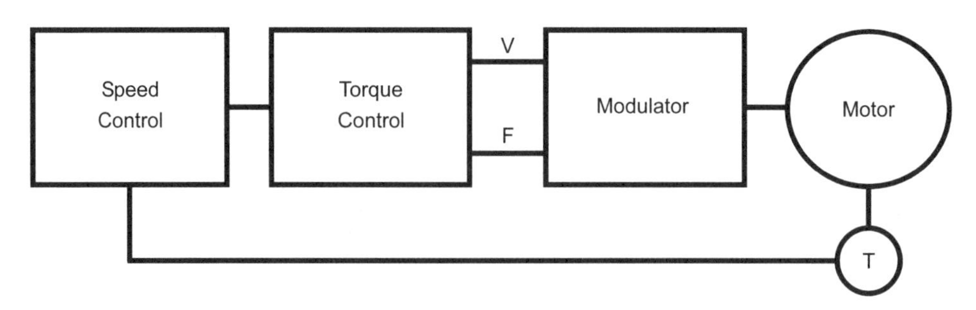

Figure 4-39. Closed loop flux vector AC drive (block diagram)

the stator field and accomplished by means of a *pulse encoder.* A drive that uses speed encoders is referred to as a *closed-loop drive.* In addition, the motor's electrical characteristics are mathematically modeled with microprocessors, processing the data. The electronic controller of a flux vector drive creates electrical quantities such as voltage, current, and frequency. These quantities are the controlling variables, which are fed through the modulator and then to the AC induction motor. Torque, therefore, is controlled indirectly.

The advantages of this type of drive include good torque response (<10 ms). Some manufacturers consider this response as the limiting response of standard AC induction motors because of the inherent inertia of the machine. Other advantages include full torque at zero speed (at ~0.5 Hz output).

Note: *Special caution must be taken when an "off-the-shelf" motor is used to provide full torque at zero speed. A specialized cooling system may be needed, in addition to the internally mounted fan. This is due to drastically reduced airflow. The motor is developing full torque and increased heat buildup.*

Accurate speed control is possible because of the pulse tachometer feedback. This speed control approaches the performance of a DC drive. Accurate speed control would be stated as ±5% of rated torque.

Depending on point of view, there may be several drawbacks to this type of control. They may be considered drawbacks when compared with the next version of vector control discussed—sensorless flux vector control).

Sensorless Vector Drives

To achieve a high level of torque response and speed accuracy, a feedback device is normally required. This can be costly and adds complexity to the traditionally simple AC induction motor. Also, a modulator is used, which is a device that simulates the AC sine wave for output to the motor. A modulator, slows down communication between the incoming voltage and frequency signals and the ability of the drive to quickly respond to signal changes.. Although the motor is mechanically simple, the drive is electrically complex. Figure 4-40 indicates a simple sensorless flux vector control scheme, which is achieving increased recognition in recent years.

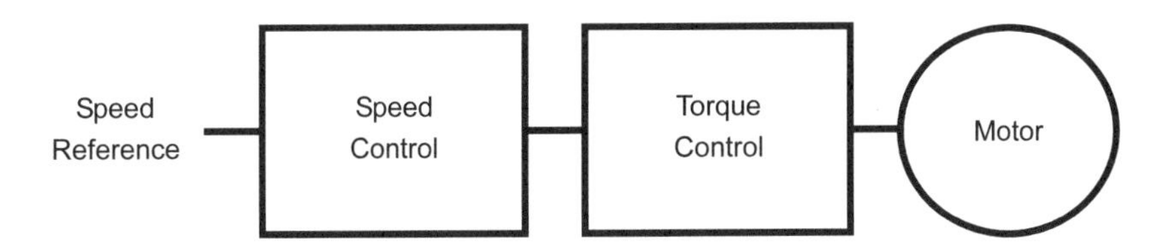

Figure 4-40. Sensorless flux vector control block diagram (Courtesy of ABB Inc.)

Sensorless flux vector control is similar to a DC drive's EMF control. In a DC drive, the armature voltage is sensed, and the field voltage is kept at constant strength. With sensorless flux vector control, a modulator is used to vary the strength of the field, which is in reality, the stator.

The role of sensorless flux vector fits generally in between the standard PWM open loop control method and a full flux vector, closed loop control method. As previously indicated, the role of sensorless flux vector control is to achieve "DC-like" performance, without the use of a shaft position feedback device. This method provides higher starting and running torque, as well as smoother shaft rotation at low speed, compared with standard V/Hz PWM drives. Additional DC-like performance comes from benefits such as a wide operating speed range and better motor-speed control during load variations.

As indicated, there are many advantages of sensorless flux vector over standard PWM control, a main advantage being higher starting torque on demand. However, standard sensorless flux vector drives may not accomplish torque regulation or full continuous torque at zero speed, without more complex circuitry. Several drive manufacturers use a software design that estimates rotor and stator flux. The result of the flux calculations (estimations) is current that produces a type of regulated motor torque.

If more accurate torque control is required by the application, even more sophisticated control technology is needed. Though more complex in design, high-speed digital signal processors and advanced micro circuits make the electronics design easier to manage. These newer designs also do not require a feedback device and provide the smooth control of torque, as well as full torque at zero speed.

The Direct Torque Control Method

The idea of vector control without feedback (i.e., open loop control) has been researched for many years. A German doctor, Blaschke, and his colleague Depenbrock published documents in 1971 and 1985 on the theory of field-oriented control in induction machines. The publications also dealt with the theory of *direct self control*. One manufacturer in particular, ABB Inc., has taken the theory and converted it into a refined hardware and software platform for drive control. The result is similar to an AC sensorless vector drive, which uses a *direct torque control* scheme. The theory was documented and tested in lab experiments for more than 30 years. However, a practical drive ready for manufacture was not possible until the development of application-specific circuitry.

Specific circuits such as the DSP (digital signal processor) and ASIC (application specific integrated circuit) are imbedded in IC (integrated circuit) chips. These chips perform a certain function in the overall production of direct torque control. The controlling variables are *motor magnetizing flux* and *motor torque*.

With this type of technology, field orientation is achieved without feedback using advanced motor theory to calculate the motor torque directly and without using modulation.

There is no modulator used in direct torque control and no need for a tachometer or position encoder for speed or position feedback of the motor shaft. Direct torque control uses the fastest digital signal processing hardware available and a more advanced mathematical understanding of how a motor works.

The result is a drive with a torque response that is as much as 10 times faster than any AC or DC drive. The dynamic speed accuracy of these drives are many times better than any open-loop AC drive. It is also comparable with a DC drive that uses feedback. One drives manufacturer indicates this drive is the first universal drive with the capability of performance like either an AC or DC drive. It is basically the first technology to control the induction motor variables of torque and flux.

Figure 4-41 shows a block diagram of direct torque control. It includes the basic building blocks upon which the drive does its calculations, based on a motor model.

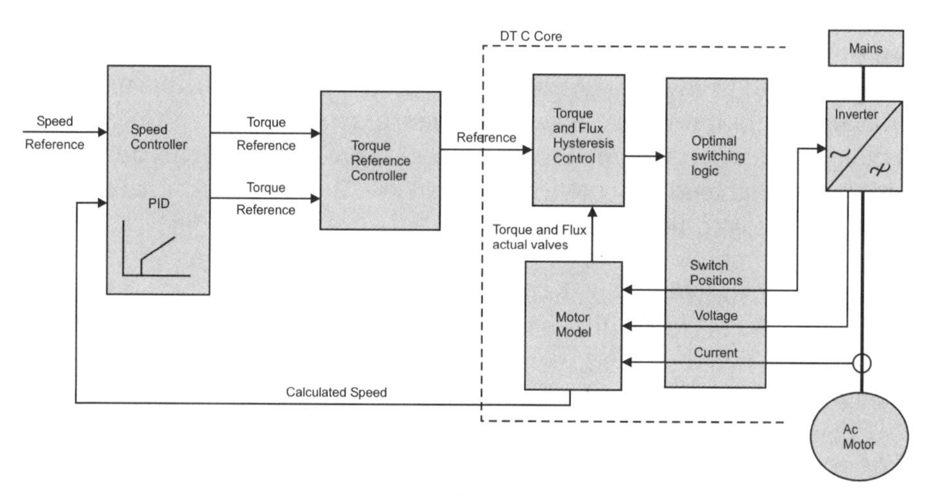

Figure 4-41. The direct torque control (DTC™) method (Courtesy of ABB Inc.)

The two fundamental sections of direct torque control are the *torque control loop* and the *speed control loop*. During drive operation, two output-phase current values and the DC bus voltage value are monitored, along with the IGBT switch positions. This information is fed to the *adaptive motor model.* The motor model calculates the motor data on the basis of information it receives during a self-tuning process (motor identification).

During this automatic tuning process, the drive's motor model gathers information such as stator resistance, mutual inductance, and saturation coefficients, as well as the motor inertia. In many cases, the motor is operated by the drive automatically for a short period of time, to gather the information required.

The output of this motor model is the representation of actual motor torque and stator flux for every calculation of shaft speed. The values of actual torque and actual flux are fed to their respective *comparators,* where comparisons are performed every 25 μs.

The *optimum pulse selector* is a fast digital signal processor (DSP) that operates at a 40-MHz speed. Every 25 μs, the inverter IGBTs are sent information for an optimum pulse for obtaining accurate motor torque. The correct IGBT switch combination is determined during every control cycle. Unlike standard PWM control, in this control scheme there is no "predetermined" IGBT switching pattern. The main motor control parameters are updated as much as 40,000 times per second. This high-speed processing brings with it static speed control accuracy of ±0.5% without an encoder. It also means that the drive will respond to changes in motor torque requirements every 2 ms.

The speed controller block consists of a PID controller and a circuit that deals with dynamics of acceleration. The external speed reference signal is compared with the actual speed signal given by the motor model. The resulting error signal is fed to the PID section of the speed controller. The *flux reference controller* contains circuitry that allows the drive to produce several dynamic motor features. *Flux optimization* is performing *just-in-time IGBT switching*. This IGBT switching method is controlled by a *hysteresis block,* which controls the switching action—when to switch, for how long to switch, and which IGBT switches are to be used. This reduces the resulting audible noise emitted from the motor and reduces energy consumption. In addition, *flux braking* is also possible, which is a more efficient form of injection braking.

Field-oriented control is a term commonly used by one manufacturer when describing continuous torque control. Similar to the direct torque control method, an advanced motor reference model acquires motor parameters during actual operation. An auto-tuning procedure determines the motor values to be used in the motor reference model. These voltage values are fed back to an adaptive software control block, which controls output current, thereby controlling torque. The proper amount of slip is provided, thereby maintaining field orientation (precise stator flux control).

Drives (AC)—Technical Concerns

SCR and GTO control of AC drive power structures have been around since the 1960s. Forced commutated SCR PWM drives gained increased acceptance in the mid-1970s. This was followed by GTO and bipolar transistor-based PWM drives in the mid-1980s. In the late-1980s, IGBT PWM drives were emerging as the drive to take the variable-speed industry into the 21st century. By the early 1990s, several manufacturers were promoting a full-line of IGBT based AC drives for the industrial, as well as HVAC, marketplace. With these AC drive offerings came several advantages and some challenges. Figure 4-42 illustrates to one of the advantages and challenges.

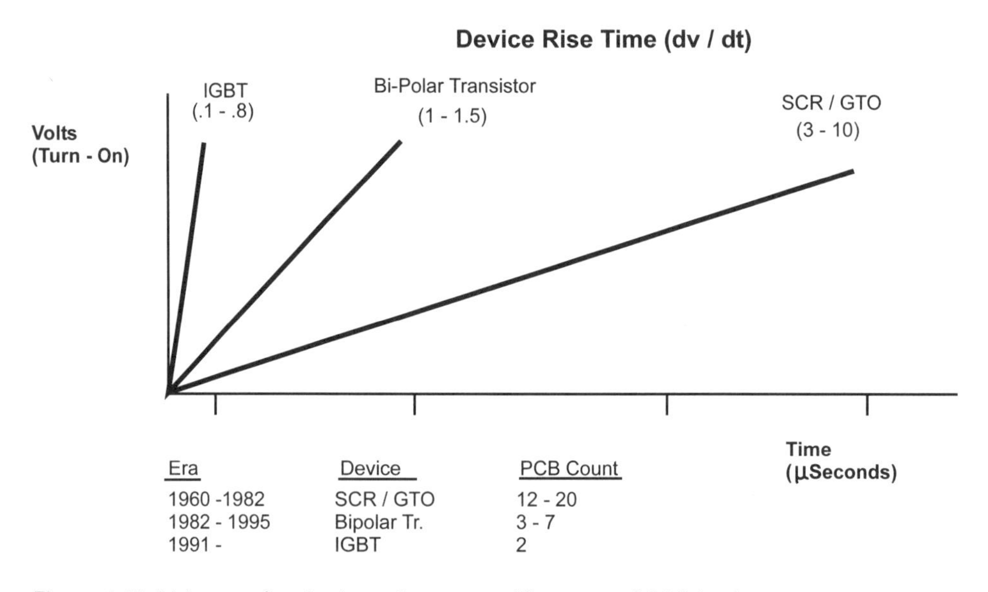

Figure 4-42. Voltage reflection/standing waves (Courtesy of ABB Inc.)

As seen in Figure 4-42, as the technology era of power semiconductor devices changed, so did the number of circuit boards needed to support that technology. In the 1960s and 1970s, SCRs and GTOs needed more than a dozen circuit boards to support the gating of the power device. Given the fact that each board had a retail value of $500–$1000, it is easy to understand the high cost of AC drives in that era. Separate gate driver boards were needed for each SCR or GTO device to turn off the device and control timing circuitry. In relative terms, the device turn-on time was rather slow, compared with the other emerging technologies. With slower turn-on or switch times, the drives caused audible noise in the motor of 500–1000 Hz, quite a noticeable level. The laminations in the stator winding vibrated at the switch frequency, producing the noise much like an audio speaker.

With the advent of bipolar transistors came the requirement for fewer boards. Less sophisticated control circuitry was required since there was no need for separate gate driver boards. Fewer circuit boards meant less overall cost for the drive. In addition, the relative size of the drive was reduced, compared with SCR-based products. On the positive side, the bipolar transistor switched 3–6 times faster than SCRs or GTOs (in the 1- to 3-kHz range). This meant that the audible noise was also reduced to a more tolerable level.

When IGBT technology emerged in the early 1990s, it was considered the power technology of the future. The device switched over 10 times faster than bipolar transistors (3–12 kHz), which meant a drastic reduction in audible noise. The circuit board count was reduced to two. The control board contained all the circuits for timing and signal processing. The motor control board contained all the circuits to turn on and off the device. With only two circuit boards needed, the drives industry realized the lowest cost drive possible. There was also a reduction in size to about 1/3 that of bipolar transistor drives. With this technology advancement came an acute challenge for the device connected to the drive—the motor.

With the extremely fast switching times, came the rise of a phenomenon called *voltage reflection*. Voltage reflection is caused by the fast-rising voltage waveform versus unit of time. In essence, the IGBT turns on immediately compared with 30 times longer with other devices. When a drive switches at this high rate, a reflected wave back from the motor adds to the voltage leaving the output of the drive. The result is a voltage at the motor terminals greater than the original voltage output from the drive. This is illustrated in Figure 4-43.

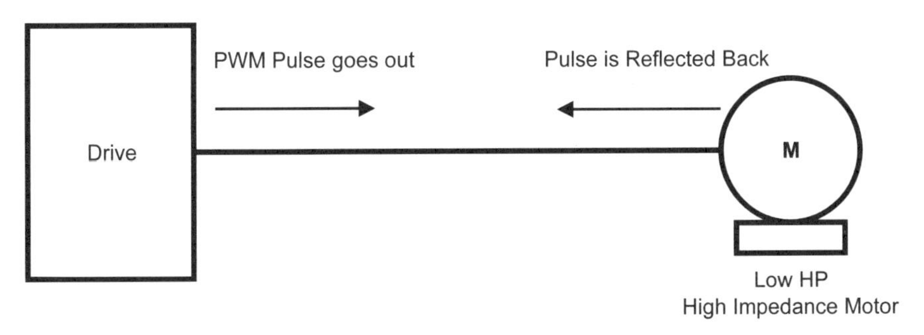

Figure 4-43. Voltage reflection characteristics

As seen in Figure 4-43, this situation is more of an issue when an impedance mismatch exists between the drive output/motor cables and the motor terminals. The phenomena is similar to the *standing wave ratio* (SWR) that exists in citizens band (CB) radio antenna setups. The coil of the CB antenna must be installed and tuned correctly, so that there are no waves reflected back to the transmitter, which could cause damage. If tuned properly, the antenna absorbs all the energy the transmitter can deliver.

The amount of increased voltage at the motor terminals is a function of the drive output voltage, length of motor cable, and the amount of mismatch. This situation is a possibility more often in smaller motors, which have a higher impedance compared with motors in the 150-HP range or more. In some cases, it is not uncommon to see more than twice the drive output voltage at the motor terminals. Many 460-V motor insulation systems are not designed to handle that type of spike voltage. The motor voltage spike issue can be seen in Figure 4-44.

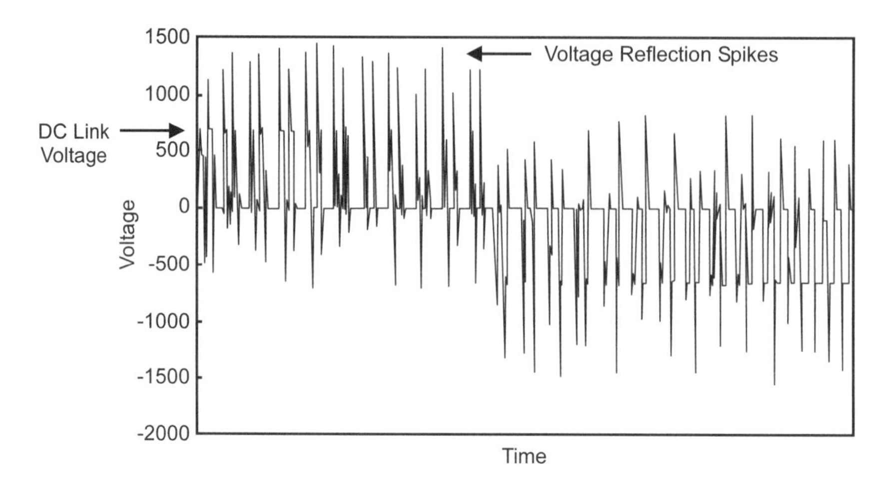

Figure 4-44. Motor terminal voltage (Courtesy of Trans-Coil, Inc.)

The spike voltages created in this particular case are close to 1500 V (460 V drive). Because AC, IGBT drives are installed at significant distances away from the motor, the impedance mismatch can be present for various types and brand names of motors. For example, it has been determined that a typical IGBT drive would cause twice the output voltage at the motor terminals. This would be true if the motor is installed greater than 75 feet away from the drive.

There are several possibilities in protecting motors against damage or coping with the issue. On new drive installations, verify that motors installed a significant distance away from the drive meet NEMA MG1, part 31.4.4.2 standards. These motors are designed with insulation systems that are able to handle the over-voltage stress. Figure 4-45 indicates the construction of a *random wound* versus a *form wound* motor. The *concentric wound* or *form wound* motor is designed to handle spike voltages generated.

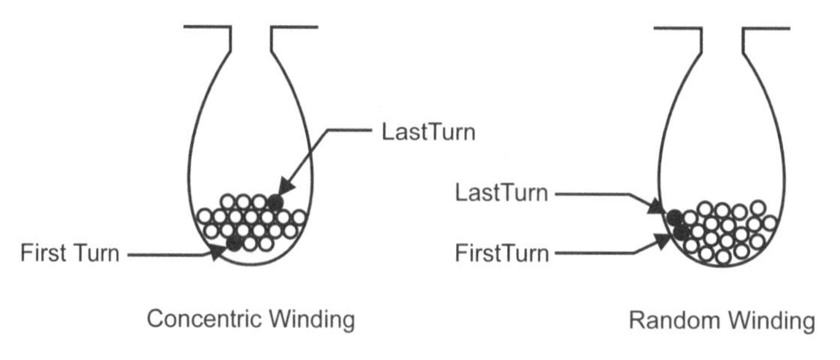

Figure 4-45. Random wound vs. concentric wound motors

Motors that meet the MG1 standard are *concentric wound* and are termed *inverter duty* motors. These motors contain stator windings that are carefully formed around the stator slots, so that the first winding turn is not next to the last winding turn. Voltage spikes poke minute holes in the insulation. When that occurs in a *random wound* motor, the likelihood is that the first and last turn are next to each other. A voltage spike hole would therefore short out the winding and make the motor useless until rewound. Inverter duty motors also have extra slot paper insulation separating the windings of different phases. In addition, these motors are typically dipped in lacquer insulation after the windings are complete to add to the insulation strength and cover insulation holes that may have occurred. Some inverter duty motors are actually dipped a second time to improve the dielectric (insulation) strength.

Another means of protecting the motor against possible damage is to install output reactors, (similar to line reactors) at the output of the drive. The drive manufacturer can make recommendations. Usually 1.5–3% impedance will protect existing motors to about 500 feet. If distances greater than 500 feet are encountered, dv/dt filters can be installed at the output of the drive. These filters are usually effective up to distances of about 2000 feet. (**Note:** dv/dt means change of voltage vs. change in time.) This is a special resistor–inductor–capacitor filter designed to drastically reduce the over-voltage spikes at the drive output.

Additional precautions include installing a *sine filter* at the output of the drive, which is not limited to motor distance. In addition, a *snubber circuit* installed at the motor will have over-voltage reduction similar to dv/dt filters. Snubber circuits do not usually have any distance limitation. Figure 4-46 shows a reduction in spike voltage generation with the installation of an output dv/dt filter.

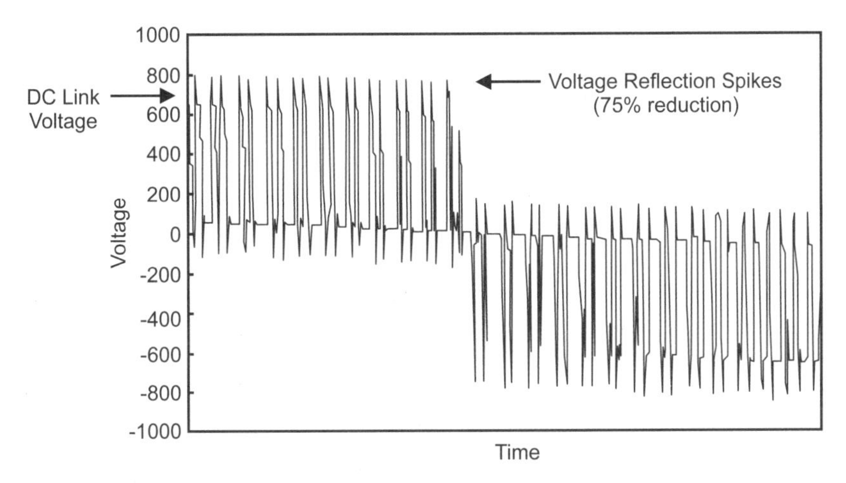

Figure 4-46. Effects of a dv/dt filter on voltage reflection (Courtesy of Trans-Coil, Inc)

Harmonics Generation

Harmonics are basically a distortion of the original waveform. In the case of AC drives, harmonics are a distortion of the three-phase waveform, with the harmonic components fed back onto the AC power line. Harmonics are caused by the fact that AC drives draw current from the supply line in "bursts" rather than in a "linear" fashion. Because of this characteristic, AC drives are considered *nonlinear loads*. As a matter of fact, any electronic device that draws nonlinear currents causes a certain amount of harmonics.

VCRs, big screen TVs, stereos, and laptop and desktop computers all fall into the nonlinear load category. They include a *switch mode* power supply that changes AC to DC—a rectifier. Because rectifiers draw current in bursts, they create harmonic currents, which are fed back to the power source.

A six diode bridge AC drive (called a *6 pulse drive*) produces the 5th, 7th, 11th, and 13th harmonic. The values of these harmonics is enough to distort the AC supply waveform. An example of distortion created by the 5th and 7th harmonic is illustrated in Figure 4-47.

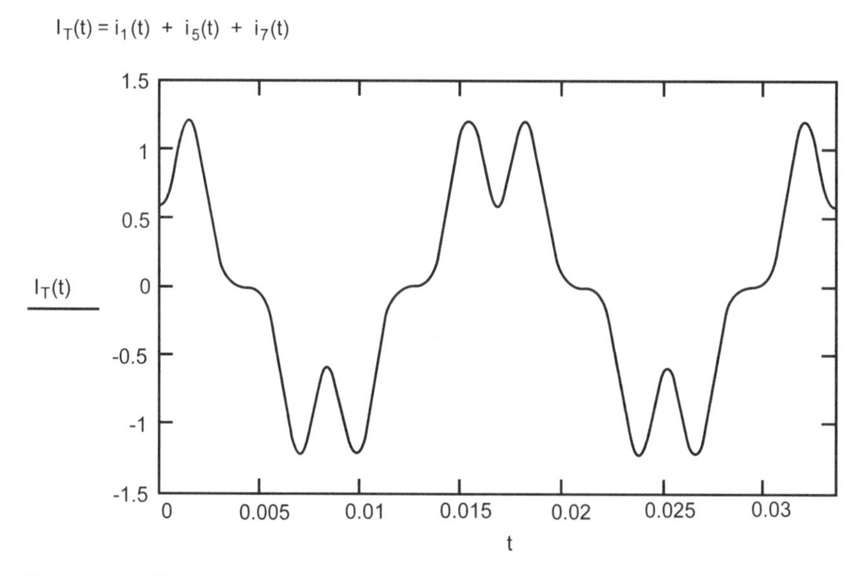

Figure 4-47. Distortion caused by the 5th and 7th harmonic (Courtesy of Trans-Coil, Inc.)

Note: *The fundamental frequency is 60 Hz. Harmonic frequencies are multiples of the 60-Hz waveform (e.g., 5th = 300 Hz, 7th = 420 Hz, and so on).*

Users of AC drives need to be concerned about harmonics, which are generated back to the line supply. Harmonic currents do not provide any useful work. Harmonic current distortion generates additional heating in transformers and cables, reducing the available capacity of the equipment. Current distortion can also create resonance conditions between the line supply reactance and power factor correction capacitors (if used). In addition, the high frequencies of harmonics can cause electronic interference with telephone and telecommunications equipment.

Harmonic voltage distortion causes increased heating in motors. Voltage distortion can also cause malfunctions in sensitive communications and computer equipment. In many areas, local electrical codes or drive-installation specifications require compliance with IEEE 519–1992. The locations where voltage and current harmonics can be an issue are termed the *point of common coupling* or simply, PCC.

The local power utility deals with the PCC, where the customer's building connects directly with utility power. This is the *current harmonic distortion* concern and is termed the *total demand distortion* or simply, TDD. The utility customer is faced with the *voltage harmonic distortion* concern, where non-linear loads meet other loads, such as linear loads (inductors, line operated motors). Figure 4-48 indicates the locations of concern for both harmonic current and voltage distortion.

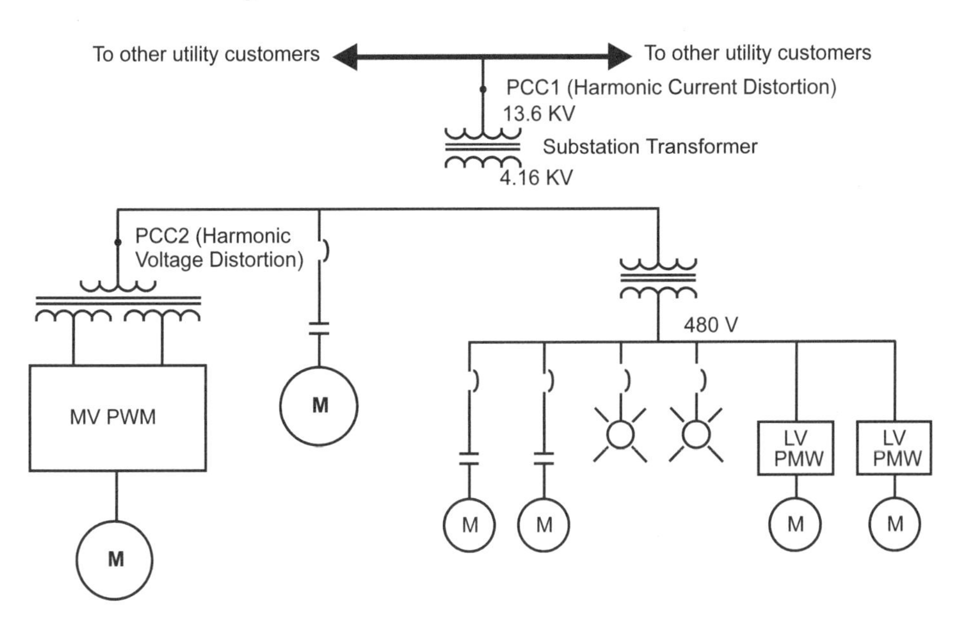

Figure 4-48. PCC and harmonic distortion (Courtesy of ABB Inc.)

Overall, harmonics are a system issue. Harmonics that are produced by an individual drive are only important when they represent a significant portion of the total system. For example, if the drive load on a transformer represents over 1/4th of the kVA load, then harmonics could be an issue and requires further investigation. If the total drive load is 5 HP on a 1000-kVA transformer, harmonics would not be an issue. It is worth noting that the addition of linear loads, such as line-operated motors, tend to reduce the overall system harmonic levels.

IEEE 519–1992 indicates limits of THD (voltage distortion) as 5% for general systems (e.g., factories and general office buildings, not including hospitals, airports, and power systems dedicated to drive loads). Current distortion limits (TDD) are based on a ratio. The ratio is the short-circuit current available at the PCC divided by the maximum fundamental load current. Therefore the limits will vary on the basis of the amount of the *electrical current tank* available. If the current capacity ratio is high, the allowable TDD will be high, compared with a low ratio. (Example: If a 10-lb rock is dropped in a bathtub full of water, the waves created represent the current harmonics generated—quite a significant amount. If that same rock is dropped off the Golden Gate bridge in San Francisco, the amount of waves hitting the shoreline would be almost non-existent—no significant current harmonics generated.)

It is important to note that an 80% THD nonlinear load will result in only a 8% TDD if the non-linear load is 10% of the total system load. With that in mind, there are several ways of reducing (mitigating) harmonics.

Using the above 80% THD example, the following comparisons could be drawn. Line reactors could be added to the input of the drive. A 5% line reactor (or equivalent DC bus inductor) could drop the THD from 80% down to 28%. Adding a 5th harmonic trap filter to the line reactor could drop the THD down to 13%. The cost of a line reactor may be 15–25% the cost of the drive (depending on drive horsepower). A harmonic trap filter could add 25–50% the cost of the drive (depending on drive horsepower).

Beyond these techniques, more serious mitigation could be realized, including higher associated costs. A 12-pulse drive input rectifier could be installed, along with a 5% impedance transformer. (**Note:** A 12-pulse drive is two six-diode bridge rectifiers, with a special delta-delta-wye input transformer, which could be 1/2 the cost of the drive unit itself. A 12-pulse drive effectively reduces the 5th and 7th harmonic. The total cost of the drive and transformer could be about double that of a six-pulse drive, depending on horsepower.) With this configuration, the THD could be reduced to 8%. With a 12-pulse drive, a 5% impedance transformer and an 11th harmonic trap filter, a reduction of THD down to 4% could be realized. Installing an *active harmonic filter* would reduce the THD down to 3%.

An active harmonic filter is essentially a regenerative drive. As stated above, this type of drive would yield the highest amount of harmonic mitigation of all the techniques. It could also be over twice the cost of a standard 6-pulse drive.

When dealing with harmonics, it is helpful to work with the drive's manufacturer or a company specializing in harmonic mitigation techniques. Some drive manufacturers offer a "no-cost" analysis service—submitting a harmonics report on the basis of the installation of their drive in a specific system. Harmonics will be even more of an issue in the future, with VFD's being applied in applications traditionally deemed fixed speed. The positive side to harmonics is that cost-effective techniques are available for a wide variety of installations.

Power Factor

When discussing electronic power conversion equipment, there are two ways to identify power factor: displacement and total or true power factor. Displacement PF is the power factor of the fundamental components of the input line voltage and current. Total PF indicates the effects of harmonic distortion in the current waveform. No matter how PF is viewed, the power utility imposes penalties for customers that use equipment with a poor PF.

Displacement PF for an AC drive is relatively constant. It is approximately 0.96–0.97. This value is primarily independent of the speed of the motor and its output power. The harmonic current distortion is determined by the total values of inductance, capacitance, and resistance, from power source to the load. The power distribution system has impedance, which also enters into the calculations for total PF. Figure 4-49 gives a general indication of displacement and total PF for AC as well as DC drives.

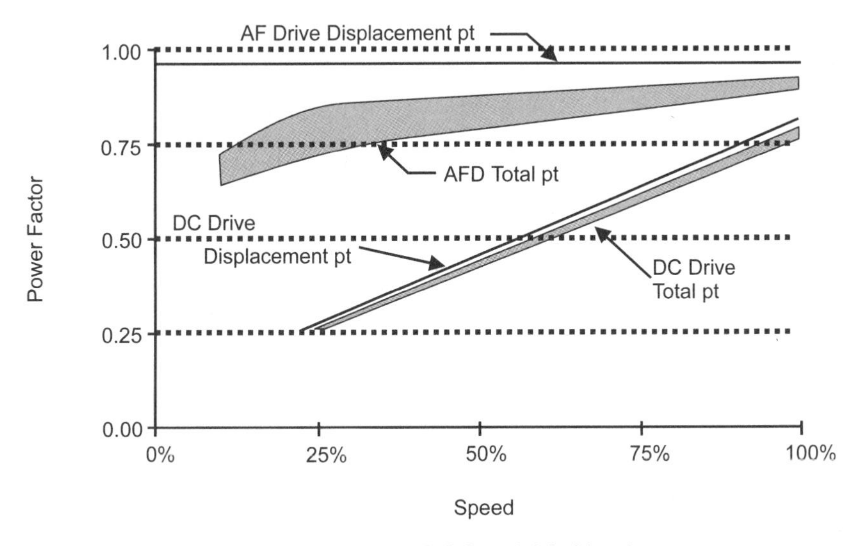

Figure 4-49. Total and displacement PF (DC and AC drives)

The curves shown in Figure 4-49 are for drives at full load and constant torque operation. The shaded area indicates a variation of total PF for typical drive installations. For an AC drive, the total (true) PF varies from roughly 0.94 at rated load, down to below 0.75 when under a light load.

As you may recall, a lagging PF is seen for an AC induction motor used in a power system. The AC drive does an effective job in isolating the input power source from the lagging PF at which the motor operates. In a certain sense, AC drives could be considered PF correctors by means of its isolation from the AC line. Because of this fact, PF correction is not normally applied to AC, PWM drives. If existing PF capacitors are connected of the motor, they must be removed when an AC drive is installed in place of a full-voltage starter. PF capacitors between the drive output and the motor can cause physical damage to the drive output IGBTs.

Shielding and Grounding

Nearly all of the procedures related to DC drives shielding and grounding apply to AC drives. However, there are some additional guidelines that must be followed regarding AC installations.

AC, PWM drives tend to expose AC induction motors to high levels of common mode voltages. Common mode voltages are created at the neutral zero point of the output of a three-phase AC drive. This is due to the creation of three-phase AC, generated from a DC bus. Also at issue is the fact that a high level of dv/dt is also possible because of the IGBT power structure. (**Note:** dv/dt is defined as delta voltage per delta time, that is, change of voltage per change of time.) Common mode voltages can become apparent in several ways.

Damaging high-frequency-bearing currents can occur, causing damage inside the bearing inner race. The phenomena of bearing currents have been around for years. The incidence of motor damage, however, has increased during recent years, after the introduction of IGBTs. This is due to the rising voltage pulses and high switching frequencies that are created by the IGBT power structure. These voltage pulses and frequencies can cause repeated discharging through the bearings and result in a gradual erosion of the bearing inner race. Figure 4-50 indicates this discharge path through the bearings.

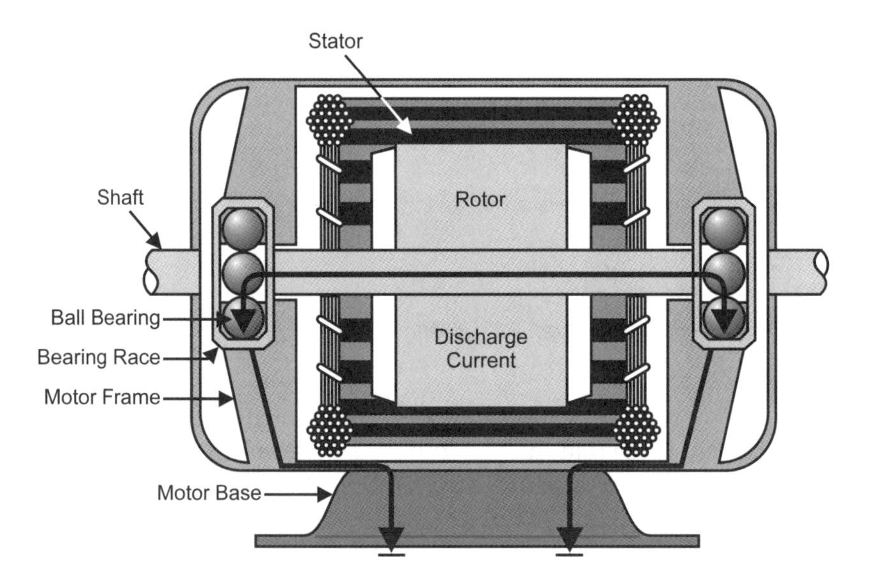

Figure 4-50. Bearing currents discharge path

High-frequency current pulses are generated through the motor bearings. If the energy of the pulses is high enough, metal transfers from the ball bearing and the races to the lubricant. This process is known as *electrical discharge machining* (EDM). Because of the high-frequency pulses, thousands of these *machining pits* are created, which translate to metal erosion that can accumulate quickly. Figure 4-51 indicates the inner race damage caused by bearing currents.

Figure 4-51. Bearing "fluting" caused by bearing currents (Courtesy of ABB Inc.)

In addition to bearing erosion, high-frequency ground currents can lead to malfunctions in sensitive sensor and instrumentation equipment.

To avoid these damaging bearing currents, a high-frequency, low-impedance path to ground must be provided between the drive and the motor. This is accomplished by installing continuous corrugated aluminum armored cable, shielded power cable, and a properly installed conduit system. Figure 4-52 indicates cabling, shielding, and grounding that provides low impedance paths to avoid high frequency and bearing current damage.

Recommended motor cable construction is described in Figure 4-53. It consists of aluminum armor that provides a low-impedance, high-frequency return path to ground.

Once the motor cable is installed in the proper location, the termination of the cable is vitally important. Figure 4-54 indicates the recommended termination method for AC drives.

The proper termination method includes 360° contact with the corrugated armor and grounding bushings for the connection of safety grounds. Metal-to-metal contact with the mounting surface is extremely important in the installation.

Following these guidelines will reduce the effects of *frequency generation* in typical AC drive installations.

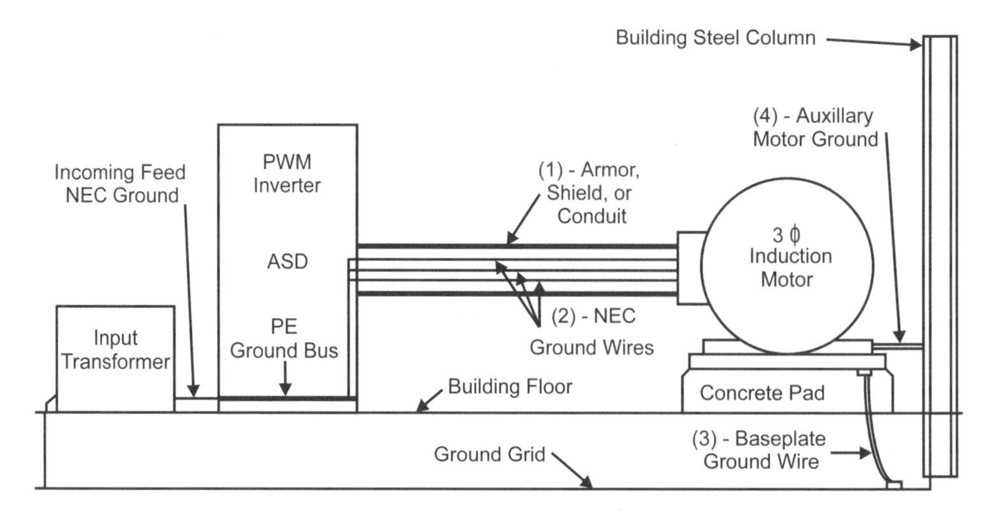

Figure 4-52. Motor cabling, shielding, and grounding (Courtesy of ABB Inc.)

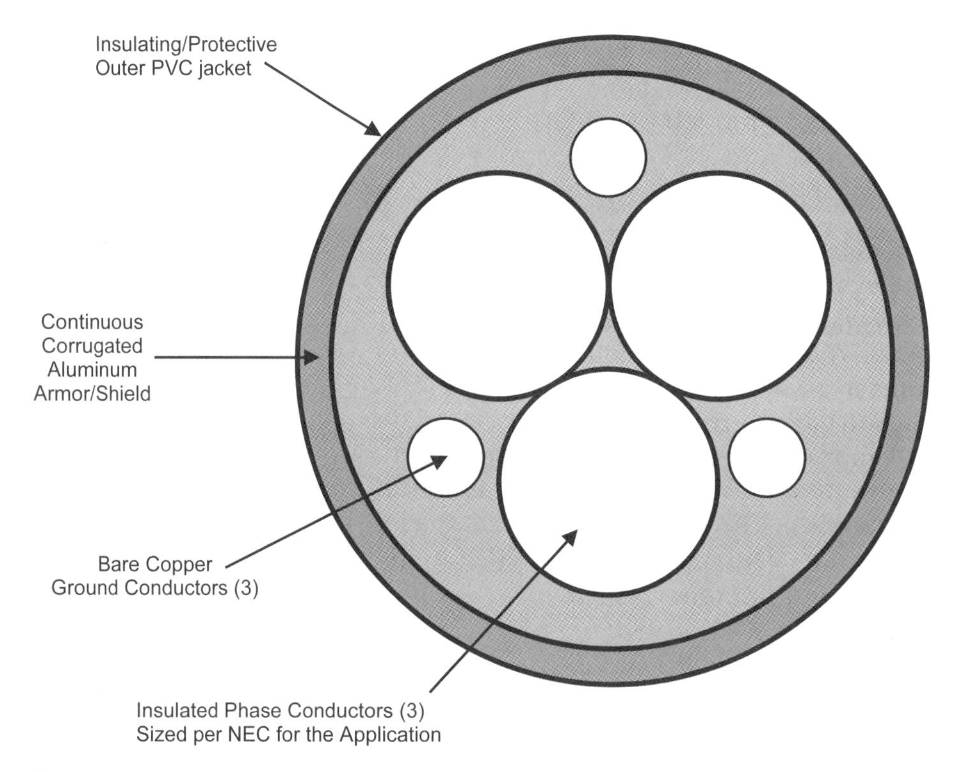

Figure 4-53. Recommended motor cable construction (Courtesy of ABB Inc.)

EMI and RFI

AC variable frequency drives generate a certain amount of electromagnetic interference (EMI). The same installation procedures for DC drives apply to AC, with a few additional guidelines. The following would be considered general wiring practices related to AC drives. Many of these items have been presented before, but deserve a review.

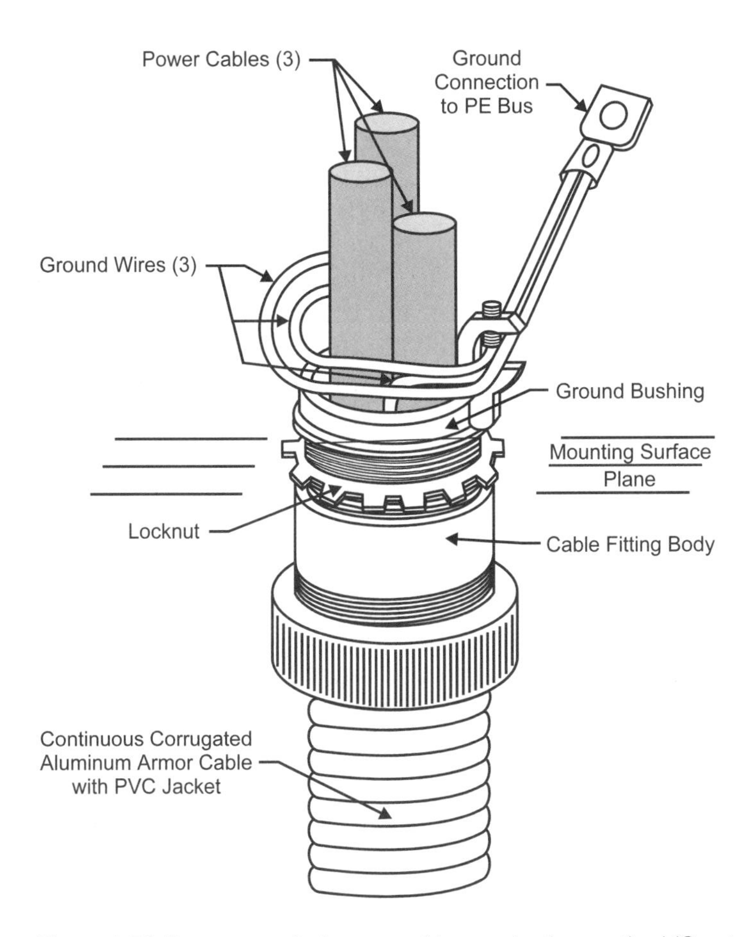

Figure 4-54. Recommended motor cable termination method (Courtesy of ABB Inc.)

Never install motor cables (e.g., 460 VAC) and control wiring (e.g., 4–20 mA or 0–10 VDC) in the same conduit or cable tray. It is also recommended that control wiring be shielded cable (for signals less than 24 V). Even though shielded control cable is used, the PWM output can have adverse effects on the low-power control signals. Unstable operating conditions can develop. It is further recommended that the control wiring be installed in its own individual conduit. In essence, the best installation procedure would be three separate, grounded, metallic conduits: one conduit for input power to the drive, one conduit for output power to the motor, and one conduit for control wiring. If EMI could be a serious issue with the installation, the use of ferrous metallic conduit rather than aluminum can help. The traditional steel conduit contains a certain amount of iron that can provide additional shielding against stray EMI signals.

If control wiring and power wiring are not in separate conduits, then the control wiring must be kept a minimum of 12 inches away from power wiring. The crossing of control and power wiring at 90° angles will reduce the EMI effects if the sets of cables must be close to each other. The previously indicated grounding techniques are also required to reduce EMI. Process control sensors and equipment must also be connected using shielded cable. The shield should be grounded only at the drive end, with the shield at the signal end cut back and taped to avoid contact with ground. This will avoid the possibility of ground loops that could cause EMI.

On any installation that is to conform to EMC compliance, the manufacturer's recommendations must be strictly followed. Their documentation indicates that the required research was conducted. If their instructions are followed, the complete installation will be EMC-compliant. This includes the use of shielded cable and CE-rated equipment, as well as specific cable-termination techniques. Any deviations from their guidelines would void the compliance.

Radio frequency interference (RFI) can be an irritating problem, just like EMI. RFI could be considered *electrical noise* and would take the form of *conducted* or *radiated.*

Conducted noise is noise that is conducted or reflected back onto the line supply. Since the AC VFD generates a carrier frequency, it could be considered a radio station, with the power input cable being the transmitter antenna. The simple procedure of installing power input and output cable in separate conduits will reduce the possibility of RFI. RFI can have serious effects on other control equipment connected to the same line input, especially if the equipment is frequency controlled (e.g., carrier current lighting, theft control, or security screening systems).

If RFI is not below a federally mandated level, the FCC has the authority to shut down the installation until compliance is proven. In cases where the interference is not reduced by separate input and output power conduit, the installation of RFI filters would be required. RFI filters are designed to reduce a specific frequency that is causing the disturbance to other equipment. The manufacturer of the drive can assist in identifying the proper filter, if required.

Radiated electrical noise is just as implied—the radiation of radio frequencies, much like the conducted noise that eventually radiates from the power input cables. Radiated noise is typically described as the radio frequencies emitting directly from the drive itself, without external connections. Any drive manufacturer that complies with CE ratings will have already designed the drive with radiated noise reduction in mind. The CE compliance standards contain stricter guidelines compared with those of the United States, related to AC, VFD design. The point to keep in mind is that if the drive is designed to meet certain RFI standards, it must be installed, grounded, and shielded per the manufacturer's requirements. Otherwise, it would be in violation of the standards and would be subject to penalties or shut down until remedies are installed.

Drives (AC)—Innovations and Technology Improvements

AC drives have been sold in increasing numbers during recent years. Up until the 1950s and early 1960s, the reliability of some AC drives was questionable, at best. The failure rate of some AC drives, out of the box, was 20% or more. Many drive service technicians always came with a package of spare parts. It was assumed that something would go wrong during startup. Fortunately, those days are behind us as industrial and HVAC drive consumers. The reliability and intelligence of AC drives from all major manufacturers has increased dramatically over the past 30 years. AC drives are fast becoming more and more a commodity item for simple applications like pumps, fans, and conveyors. The more complex AC drive applications are now accomplished with AC drives, but with modifications in drive software—which some manufacturers call "firmware."

The AC drive, with its high-speed microprocessor and PLC compatibility, is viewed as a critical piece of the automation system. The ability to connect to a variety of industrial networks makes the AC drive a viable variable-speed choice for years to come. The sizes and shapes of AC drives have been reduced over recent years. On the other hand, the power density (per square inch of chassis space) has increased dramatically. IGBT technology and high-speed application chips and processors have made the AC drive a true competitor to that of the traditional DC drive system. In this age of efficiency and network control, AC drives have emerged as a prominent choice. The emphasis is now on less motor maintenance and increased energy savings, with the ability to communicate to a variety of network systems. With these benefits in mind, the AC drive will continue to gain acceptance in applications that have been traditionally fixed speed or DC variable speed.

To make intelligent applications choices, it is necessary to review the improvements made in AC drive technology. The following sections will outline, in general and specific terms, improvements in AC drive design and control. In certain cases, AC drive improvements have paralleled that of DC drives. This section is meant to generate ideas as to where AC drives and motors can be applied, with little additional equipment required.

Compact Package Design

The AC drive systems of today include all of the needed components to operate, troubleshoot, and maintain the system. Because of the use of microprocessors and IGBTs, a 1-HP drive of today is about 1/3 the size of a 1-HP drive 10 years ago. This size reduction is also attributed to the surface mount technology used to assemble components to circuit boards. Twice as many components are possible on one board because of the placement of components on both sides of the board. The entire unit can be operational with three wires in (power input) and three wires out (power output). An additional set of wires would also be needed if optional external control is used.

AC drive designs of today are more compact with little documentation required to troubleshoot (many diagnostic features are visible in software), and have less parts that require replacement. In most cases, packaged AC drives of approximately 50 HP or less use only two circuit boards—control board and motor control board. In short, AC drives of today are more reliable than their ancestors of 30 years ago. Figure 4-55 illustrates this type of package design.

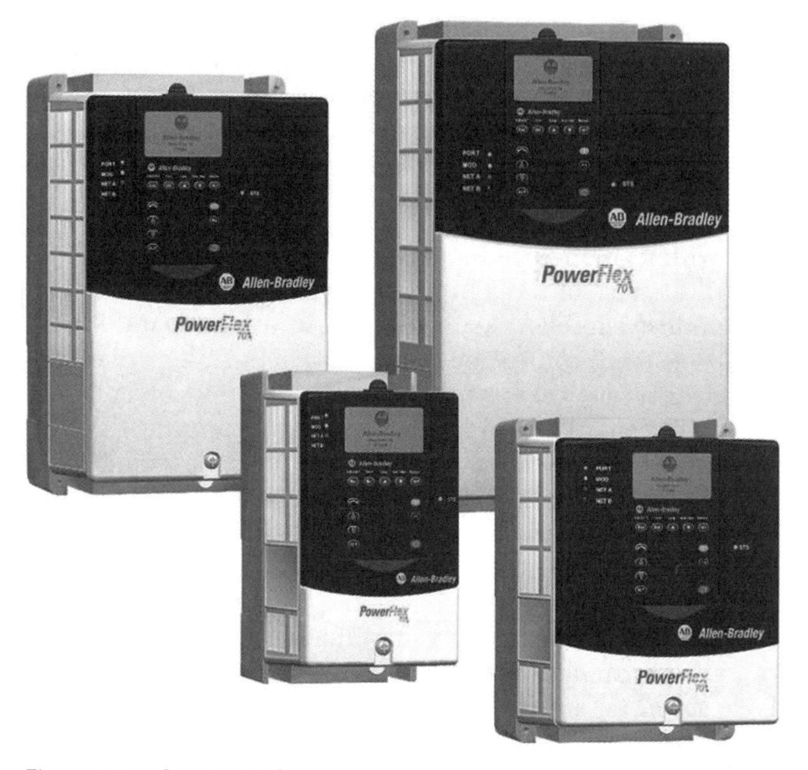

Figure 4-55. Standard AC drive package (Courtesy of Rockwell Automation, Inc.)

Digital I/O (Inputs/Outputs)

AC digital drives allow for simple programming and a high degree of application flexibility. The idea is to connect all control and power wiring and set up the drive for the application, through software programming. If the application is altered, the drive functions can quickly be reprogrammed through software, instead of rewiring the drive. The programming is typically done with a removable keypad or remote operator panel. Both AC and DC drives of today share in this technology improvement.

In earlier versions of AC drives, the drive had to be shut down and the control terminal block rewired for the new application. Downtime is costly. The less time a system is shut down, the more productivity is obtained.

Typically, the control wiring section of an AC drive will contain analog inputs (AI's for speed reference), digital inputs (DI's for controls such as start/stop, reverse, etc.), AO's (analog outputs) (connection for an auxiliary meter), and relay outputs (RO's for devices such as fault relays, at-speed relays, etc.). The digital inputs and outputs would typically operate on ±10 or 12 VDC or ±24 VDC logic. A software function would operate if the assigned terminal voltage is high (meaning 8 V or higher on a 10-VDC control). Any voltage less than that would indicate a digital logic "low" and the function would not operate.

In addition to the standard start/stop speed reference inputs, the drive would also include I/O for diagnostics such as auxiliary fault, motor overload, and communications status. Many of the drive manufacturers include a section in software called I/O status. This section of software is dedicated to the monitoring and viewing of drive inputs and outputs. When a DI is "high," it would register as an "I" on the LCD display. If "low," it would register as a "0."

Note: *High and low are relative terms in digital technology. A "high" would mean that a high control voltage is applied to a circuit. A "low" would indicate that a low control voltage is applied to a circuit. For example, in a 24-V control system, a "high" value might mean 20–24 V. On the other hand, a "low" value might mean 5 V or less.*

The same type of display would be seen for analog signals, with a true readout appearing. By viewing the I/O status section of software, it can quickly be determined if the drive has a problem or some interconnection device in the system, outside of the drive.

IGBT Technology

IGBT technology has been successfully applied to AC drives since the late 1980s. Before IGBTs, bipolar transistors and SCRs were the standard output power conversion devices. IGBTs can be turned on and off with a small milliamp signal. Smaller control driver circuits are required because of the smaller control signals needed compared with SCRs. Smaller control circuitry also means a smaller sized control circuit boards, which translates to less cost.

Multi-Language Programming Panel

Many of the programming panels (touch keypads) are removable and may or may not include a panel extension cord. Up until the last decade and a half, programming panels required continuous attachment to the drive control board. Storage of parameter values was a function of the control board and associated memory circuits.

With the latest advancements in E^2PROM™s and flash PROMs, the programming panel can be removed from power. Values can now be stored for an indefinite period of time with no batteries required for backup. This type of capability allows for a backup plan in case any or all parameter values are lost because of a drive malfunction or electrical damage due to lightning.

Drive panels are in many cases back-lit, meaning that the LCD digits have an illuminated background that can increase or decrease in intensity. This is helpful when the drive is installed in a brightly or dimly lit room. Many programming panels allow for individual display of several different languages. This is very helpful when the drive is mounted onto a machine and shipped to another country. The programming setup can be accomplished in English, for example, and then the language changed to Spanish before shipment to Mexico. Figure 4-56 indicates a typical programming keypad.

Additional functions of the modern-day drive panels include "soft keys" similar to that of a cell phone. The function of these keys change depending on the mode of the keypad (e.g., operating, programming, local/remote, menu, etc.).

The ability of the keypad to guide the user through a multitude of situations is also the trend of current drives. Inherent programs such as a "Start-up Assistant," guide the user through the required steps to start up a drive for the first time. The "Diagnostic Assistant" aids the user in providing suggestions as to where to correct a fault situation. The "Maintenance Assistant" can be programmed to alert the user when routine maintenance is suggested (e.g., checking or replacing the heatsink fan).

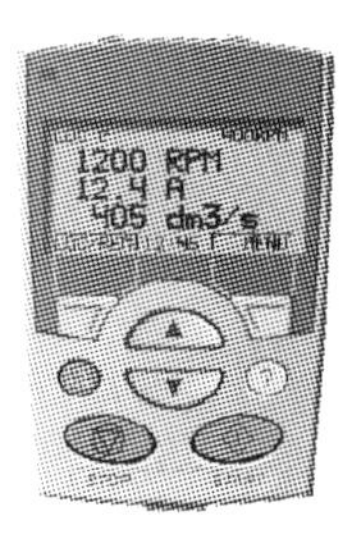

Advanced Control
Panel

Figure 4-56. AC drive programming keypad (Courtesy of ABB, Inc.)

Programming Macros

Because of the digital design, many of the AC drive parameters are preprogrammed in software before shipment from the factory. During drive startup, the operator need only load motor data values and values to customize the drive to the application. In most cases, an operator can install parameters and start up a drive in a matter of minutes, compared with an hour or two for analog AC drives.

Many AC drive manufacturers use pre-assigned values to each of the parameters, in what would be known as default values. The values would not exactly match the motor and application, but would allow the drive to operate a motor. In addition to defaults, several manufacturers include preprogrammed sets of values, known as macros. Individual macros would allow the operator to match the drive parameters and diagnostics to the motor and application that it is connected to. In many cases, all of the parameters can be set in a matter of seconds, rather than individually set parameters, which could take more than an hour. Macros such as hand–auto, three-wire control, torque control, and PID are available for easy configuration and set up of the drive.

Several drive manufacturers offer a macro or default setup for proportional integral derivative (PID) control. Proportional integral derivative is essentially the automatic control of drive speed by receiving a controlling input such as temperature, pressure, humidity, or tank level. Because of the microprocessor power in today's AC drives, much of the mathematical functions are now standard features of the drive's control board. A water treatment application would be a prime candidate for PID control and is illustrated in Figure 4-57.

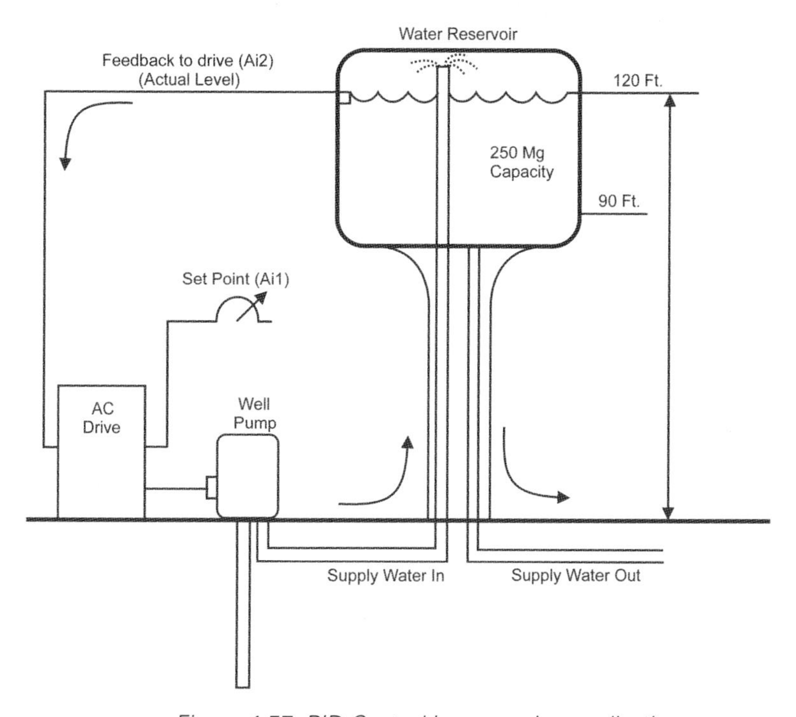

Figure 4-57. PID Control in a pumping application

A simple principle of PID is to keep the error (difference between set point and feedback) at zero. AI1 would be the set point or desired value—in this case 120 ft, which would be changed to voltage or current signal. The drive takes that signal and matches it with the transducer feedback signal (AI2) from inside the tank. This actual level would also be converted to a feedback signal current (milliamp). The PID controller takes the resulting error signal and increases the speed of the well pump to match the demand. When the level in the water reservoir goes down, the drive speeds up.

In the past, PID controllers were separate units, which added $400–$500 to the installation costs. With the latest AC drives, the PID function resides in the software.

Note: *Some companies refer to software as "firmware" indicating that it is a software program firmly imbedded, into the drive memory – normally not user changeable.*

Several manufacturers include the software logic to engage fixed-speed lag pumps. Alarm circuits wired into the drive would warn an operator or automated system control when the level reached the danger low-level of 90 ft. If that would occur, another fixed-speed lag pump could be engaged to keep up with demand, not handled by the regulated drive pump.

Duplex and tri-plex pumping systems can easily be accomplished with software logic inherent to the drive.

Enhanced Programmability

Even though "pre-programmed" macros are a tremendous time-saver when setting up a drive to match an application, there are instances where a "customized" macro is required. Many drive manufacturers provide a "firmware customization" service for their customers. The innovative manufacturers provide the customer with a means to construct their own specialized macro. The capability of "function block programming" allows the user to reassign many I/O points of the software blocks that create the original firmware. Software blocks, such as the "AND" or "TIMER" block, can be found in PLC programs and high-performance DC drives. Now they have been brought into the programmable functions of the VFD. Figure 4-58 indicates an example of a function block program.

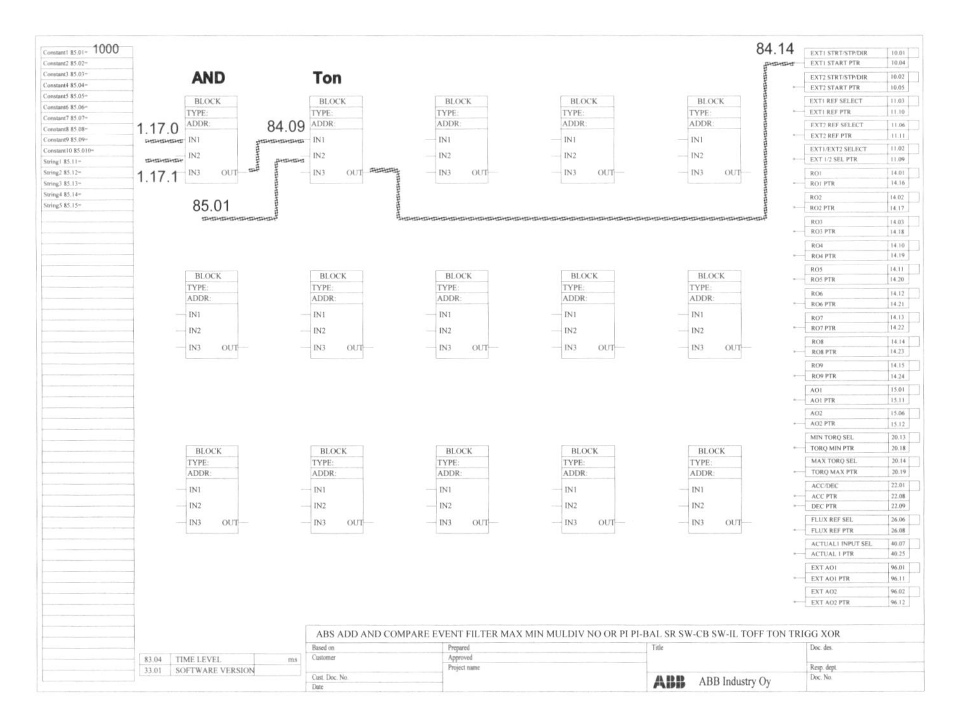

Figure 4-58. Function block programming

Sensorless Vector as a Standard Industrial Drive

The operation of V/Hz drives has been discussed, as well as the benefits of sensorless vector drives. The use of the sensorless vector drive has increased in industrial applications due to ease of set-up and the requirement to handle high-starting torques. V/Hz drives require the motor to "slip" in order for torque to be developed. With sensorless vector drives, full-rated motor torque is available at zero speed, with no slip required in the process.

Self-Tuning Speed and Torque Loops

A high-performance AC drive system normally requires tuning, once the standard software parameters are set in the drive. This would especially hold true for vector, flux vector, and DTC™ drives. The fine adjustments allow the drive to match the feedback loop with the speed and torque reference circuits. Through the tuning process, the operator is able to obtain efficient response times when accelerating, decelerating, and changing directions.

Some older AC drives require a manual tuning procedure. The operator must accelerate and decelerate the load, observe the behavior of the system, and make manual adjustments. In some drives, however, this tuning process is done automatically by the drive control circuitry. The response gains and recovery times are preloaded at the factory. When the drive sees dynamic adjustments occurring during commissioning, it adjusts the tuning parameters to match the outcome of a pre-assigned value set. Drive response times as low as 1 to 5 ms are possible with some systems.

Several manufacturers have reduced the guesswork during the process of dynamic speed and torque loop tuning. After the motor data is entered and when prompted by the drive, the operator conducts an identification run (ID). During this process, the motor is disconnected from the application. This is required so the drive can obtain a complete mental image of the motor characteristics (magnetic properties, hysteresis, thermal time constants, etc.). The drive conducts a 30–60 second program of fast accelerations and decelerations and full energizing of the stator windings to develop the complete mental image. Once the ID is done, the operator can install any standard parameter values required by the application (accel/decel times, digital and analog inputs and relay outputs).

Serial and Fiber-Optic Communications

Access to digital communications is a must in today's automated facilities. Drives used before the digital age required hard wiring to the control terminal block. This allowed only remote operation from a distance where control voltage or current loss could be kept to a minimum (maybe 25 feet or less). With today's serial and parallel mode of information transfer, the AC drive can accept control and speed commands from process equipment several thousand feet away. This allows the AC drive to be integrated into the factory automation environment, where process control equipment is located in a clean, dry control room.

Serial links (three wires plus a shield conductor) are more of the norm today, compared with a decade ago. Control and diagnostic data can be transferred to the upper level control system, at a rate of 100 ms. With only three wires for control connections, the drive "health" and operating statistics can be available at the touch of computer button. The communication speed of a serial link makes it ideal for simple process lines and general coordination of conveyors, where high-speed accuracy is not required.

Fiber-optic communications use long plastic or silica (glass fiber) and an intense light source to transmit data. With optical fiber, thousands of bits of information can be transmitted at a rate of 4 megabaud (4 million bits per second). An entire factory can be wired with high-speed fiber optics with very little, if any, electrical interference. This is due to the high frequency of light waves, as opposed to the lower frequency of a wire conductor serial link. With fiber-optic communications, steel processing, coating lines, and high-speed cut-to-length applications are possible. With small error signals fed back to the speed controller, the drive can immediately respond with a correction. This keeps the quality of the product very high, and the deviation in size very low.

Several drive manufacturers offer serial and fiber-optic software that installs directly to a laptop or desktop computer. With this software installed, all drive parameters are accessible from the stand-alone computer. This makes parameter changes simple and fast. Parameters can be changed in the computer, downloaded to the drive for verification, and saved in the computer as a file or macro. The file can then be easily transferred to other computers or a network or e-mailed to another factory with the same company. Hundreds, even thousands, of macros and file sets can be saved. The ultimate results are the ability to quickly respond to required changes in drive and application setup.

Serial and fiber-optic communications will be discussed in more detail later in Chapter 6. Figure 4-59 shows an operator interface scheme with fiber optic, serial, and hardwired connections.

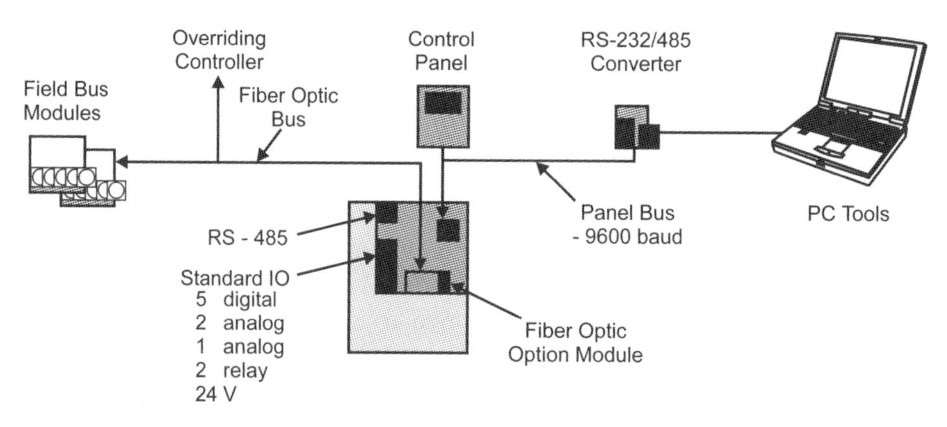

Figure 4-59. Operator interface scheme (communications)

Field Bus Communications (PLCs)

Some type of communication system is almost always specified with AC drives sold today. Data links to PLCs (programmable logic controllers) are common in many high-speed systems that process control and feedback information. PLCs provide the mathematical calculations, timing circuits, and software "and/or" logic signals required to process drive, sensor, and switch status.

Several manufacturers of PLCs offer a direct connection to many drive products. Because each PLC uses a specific programming language (usually ladder-logic programming), drive manufacturers are required to build an adapter box. This adapter (sometimes called a field bus module) is used to translate one language to another (called a protocol). Refer to Figure 4-59 for an example. The drive manufacturer installs one internal protocol, and the PLC installs another. Field bus modules allow for a smooth transfer of data to the PLC, and vice versa, with little loss of communication speed.

Drive Configurations

Many drive manufacturers offer out-of-the-box configurations. Several manufacturers offer *sensorless vector* drives that include the automatic tuning described above. In addition, some manufacturers offer a *vector-ready* configuration. The circuitry for a vector drive is included in the package, but the customer must add a feedback option to make the performance a reality. Because these products are packaged products, the drive vendor can offer very competitive pricing. Little to no additional optional devices are required to be installed at the job site.

Several manufacturers offer a variation of the standard six-pulse drive. An AC drive that is termed 12-pulse ready offers the optional feature of converting a standard six-pulse drive to a 12-pulse drive. As previously discussed, the 12-pulse drive does an impressive job of reducing the 5th and 7th harmonic content back to the power line. This type of drive includes 12 diodes in the converter section as standard. A delta-delta-wye transformer must be connected to the drive input to make the required phase shift possible. Depending on horsepower, this approach may require a slightly smaller initial investment compared with packaged 12-pulse drives. Active front-end drives that include two sets of IGBTs also make it possible for a packaged approach to harmonic mitigation.

The fact is harmonic reduction is a requirement in more applications today. Twelve-pulse or active front-end drives will increase in their importance, as EMI, RFI, and harmonics issues become more acute in the future.

Many AC drives are seen in centrifugal fan and pump applications. The energy savings realized is of major importance in this age of energy conservation. One of the features of AC drive technology is the ability to bypass the drive, if the drive stopped operating for any reason. This configuration, known as *bypass*, is used in many applications where the fan or pump must continue operating, even though it is at fixed speed. Figure 4-60 indicates a block diagram of the bypass drive.

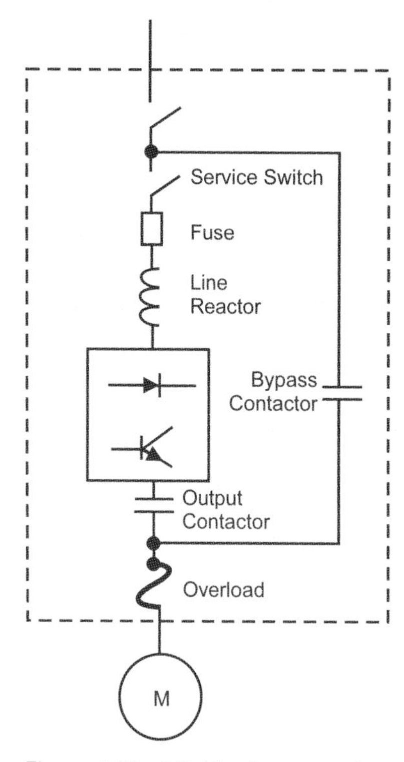

Figure 4-60. AC drive bypass unit

As seen in Figure 4-60, many bypass AC drives include all the features required for operation in drive or bypass mode. Many manufacturers include a *service switch* to allow for drive troubleshooting while the bypass contactor is closed—running the motor at full speed. The line reactor is also standard on many packaged units as is line input fusing.

One manufacturer in particular offers *electronic bypass* circuitry. An electronic circuit board operates all the diagnostics and logic required for an automatic transfer to bypass. Because of the electronic means of bypass control, information can be fed back to the drive and to a building automation system control. This would not be possible if the overload element was just a mechanical device. Light-emitting diodes are also a part of the bypass control board, allowing instant and clear indication of drive operation, bypass operation, and the run status. Building safety indications and *run enable* signals are also indicated with this type of bypass system.

Features/Software Enhancements

Additional features and innovations include a wide voltage input tolerance. Many manufacturers specify their drive as a 460-V drive, ±10% input voltage. However, several manufacturers offer a low and high value as part of the range of operation. The range of a 460-V drive may have input parameter values of 440, 460, 480, and 500 V, ±10%. This means that the drive input voltage could drop as low as 396 V or increase as high as 550 V. With this wide range of operation, the drive will continue to run and not trip offline because of a slight power dip or short-duration brown-out condition.

Along with this circuit, many manufacturers offer the capability of "power loss ride through." This circuit is standard from almost all drive manufacturers, but efficient handling of the power loss is not. One manufacturer, in particular, uses the regenerated voltage from the motor inertia to back-feed the DC bus voltage. Figure 4-61 indicates the effects of one such design.

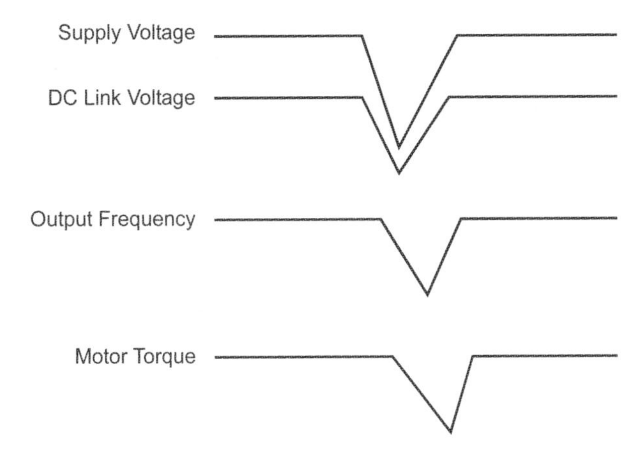

Figure 4-61. Power loss ride-through

The DC link (bus) voltage will drop slightly in response to the loss of supply voltage. When supply voltage is cut off, the drive control automatically reduces the speed reference command. The motor acts as a generator since, for a short period of time, it is rotating faster than the speed reference. The following example may illustrate this type of circuit.

A drive is set for a 60-Hz speed reference. The motor spins at the 60-Hz commanded speed. The building suffers a power outage. The drive immediately reduces the speed reference to 59 Hz. For a short period, the motor continues to spin at 60 Hz, which now causes regenerative voltage (the motor acts as a generator). The excess energy is fed back to the drive DC bus, and the microprocessor continues to operate. Eventually, the motor will coast down to 59 Hz.

Power has not returned to the building. The drive then responds with a speed reference of 58 Hz. The motor is spinning at 59 Hz, which causes regenerative voltage to be pumped back to the DC bus. The motor eventually coasts down to 58 Hz. If input power doesn't return, this same scenario is repeated until the drive DC bus drops below a minimum level (typically 65% of nominal value). At that point, the drive would shut down due to lack of DC bus voltage.

If the amount of motor inertia is high (as with a fan or flywheel), the "ride-through" time may be several seconds to over several minutes. This circuit has an advantage where short-duration power outages are common (and the application can tolerate automatic speed reduction while the drive stays operational).

Critical frequency or *skip frequency* is another circuit offered by many manufacturers. A *critical frequency* is a frequency that can cause severe mechanical vibration if the drive operates the application continuously at that speed. HVAC system cooling towers, some pumping applications, and certain machines have critical frequencies. Figure 4-62 shows this type of circuit.

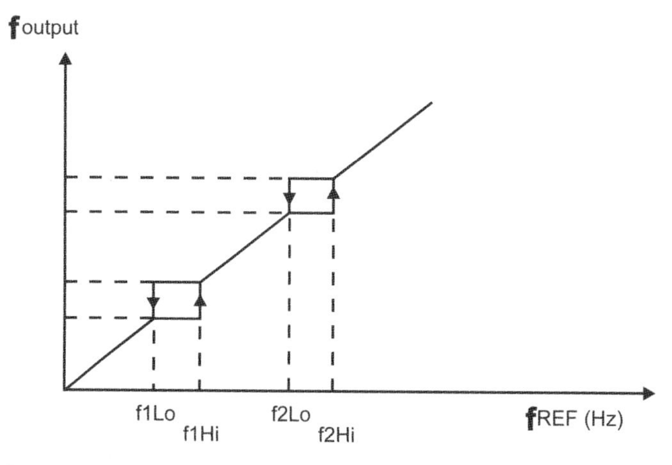

Figure 4-62. Critical frequency circuit

As an example, a critical frequency may appear at 32–34 Hz. When programmed, the drive would continue to output 32 Hz until there was enough speed reference to cause the drive to output 34 Hz. The drive would pass through that range, but the operator could not unknowingly set the drive to continuously operate at 33 Hz. When the operating speed was above 34 Hz, the critical frequency circuit would operate the same, only in reverse. The drive output would stay at 34 Hz until the speed reference was decreased below 32 Hz. This circuit causes less stress for mechanical equipment and is easily programmed in drives on the market today.

Chapter Review

Drives are at the heart of an automation system. They are the controlling element for DC and AC motors, which develop the torque to turn the wheels of industry.

In DC drive systems, an armature and field exciter are used to control the two separate elements in a shunt wound DC motor. SCRs are used to vary the DC voltage output, which has a direct bearing on the speed of the motor. The DC drive is the simplest of drive systems. The disadvantage of using SCRs for the drive power structure is the inherent nature of line notching. This notching is caused by the phasing on and off of the six SCRs located in the drive input section.

Digital DC drives are the latest entry into DC drive technology. With digital technology, precise control of speed and torque can be realized. Speed and current controller circuits use feedback to make small changes in armature supply and field exciter operation. Measuring and scaling circuits sample the actual speed and current output. Summing circuits take the error signal and translate those signals into corrective actions. Higher speed accuracy (<1% regulation) is obtained by the use of a tachometer generator or tach. When operated in the speed regulation mode, the drive closely monitors the speed-feedback signal. Armature voltage (or EMF) control would give a 1–2% regulation characteristic. IR compensation will improve the drooping speed due to load. When operated in the current regulation mode, the drive closely monitors the value of the current measuring circuit. The drive ignores the speed controls and calculates the current (torque) required by the load. The drive will automatically operate at the speed required to allow the motor to develop the desired torque.

Field exciters are constructed of SCRs or the newer IGBT power semiconductor technology. Some supplies are powered by single-phase or two-phase power and have the ability to operate in field control mode. This mode is the weakening of the shunt field strength to allow above base speed operation. Form factor is the term used to compare the purity of the DC output from the armature or field exciters.

The operation of the DC drive can be compared with a relationship of quadrants. A four-quadrant drive would allow forward and reverse operation as well as regenerative capability (regenerating voltage back to AC line power). This type of armature supply includes 12 SCRs in a bridge configuration.

Braking methods include coast-to-stop and ramp-to-stop, which are typically the longest method of bringing a motor to a stop. Dynamic braking causes the back-fed voltage to be dissipated in heat through a high-wattage power resistor. The fastest electronic method of stopping a motor is through regenerative braking. This allows full voltage to be fed directly back to the AC line. Mechanical braking also allows fast braking of the motor armature through a brake pad assembly similar to that of an automobile.

A concern of DC drive use is the generation of harmonics, line distortion, and power factor. A line reactor is required ahead of the drive unit to reduce the distortion back to the utility system. To avoid the generation of RFI, shielded control and power cables are used. In addition, a shielded transformer is used ahead of the drive.

DC drives have been the object of technology improvements in recent years. An all-in-one package design allows users access to all the required circuitry within one location. Digital I/O and multi-function keypads make drive setup and adjustment easy, along with programming macros and setup routines called wizards by one manufacturer. The self-tuning of the armature circuit and the interface with PLCs make this new breed of DC drive much easier to commission compared with older analog designs.

There are three basic designs of AC VFDs: current source inverters, variable voltage inverters (input inverters), and pulse width modulation. All AC drives operate under the same characteristic. They change a fixed incoming voltage and frequency to a variable voltage and frequency output. Most of the AC VFDs built today are of the PWM variety. With PWM drives, the incoming voltage and frequency is rectified to a fixed DC voltage. That voltage is "inverted" back to AC, with the output, 0– 460 V and 0–60 Hz (or 0–230 V).

Braking methods for AC motors are similar to that of DC. In addition, the AC drive has the capability to "inject" DC voltage into the stator windings. In doing so, the drive sets up a definite n and s polarity in the motor, causing high reverse torque and bringing the rotor to a fast stop.

Torque control AC drives basically fall into two categories: flux vector (feedback required) and sensorless flux vector (no feedback required). Vector control drives have the capability of generating full torque at zero speed. The drive forces the motor to develop the torque required to effectively handle the load. Special circuits (DSPs and ASICs) perform calculations every 25 μs. They allow the flux reference controller to respond to very small changes in torque requirements at the shaft.

Since the introduction of IGBTs into the power technology ranks, the size of AC drives has been reduced to less than half of its counterpart 10 years ago. With this technology improvement comes a challenge in AC motors—high-voltage spikes caused by voltage reflection. PWM drives produce an inherent oscillation between the drive output and motor input. The oscillating voltage actually amplifies itself into a value that is beyond the voltage insulation strength of the stator windings. The windings either suffer a short circuit between windings or an open phase. Precautions to be taken against this motor damage possibility include use of inverter duty motors, output reactors, or DV/DT output filters.

Harmonics are generated back to the AC line because of the technology of pulling voltages in bursts. The rectifier that accomplishes this is termed a switch mode power supply. All electronic devices with this type of supply causes harmonics back to the utility system. The local utility is very concerned about TDD (demand distortion) that affects other users on the power system. Line reactors, harmonic trap filters, and higher pulse drives are a few of the corrections to the harmonics issue. Improper shielding and grounding of AC drives can cause bearing current damage after prolonged use and can cause immediate RFI and EMI. By using proper installation methods, drastic reduction in conducted and radiated noise can result.

Package designs, digital I/O, IGBT technology, and multi-function keypads make AC drives easy to set up. Programming panels are removable and are able to store all drive values in flash memory. Macros and software programs like PID allow the user to perform more functions within the drive unit, rather than require a separate PLC program. Self-tuning, communications, and bypass capability make the VFDs of today a cost-effective choice in variable speed.

Check Your Knowledge

1. What are the two main circuits in a DC drive unit?
2. What are the main power components used in each circuit, and what are the characteristics of each?
3. How is line notching corrected in a DC drive system?
4. Describe what the following circuits are used for in a DC drive:
   Summing circuit
   Current controller
   Current measuring/scaling
5. Explain the difference between single-, two-, and four-quadrant systems.
6. What is dynamic braking and how is it accomplished?
7. What is RFI and how is it controlled in a DC drive system?
8. What is a macro? Describe its use.
9. What is the difference between a VVI, CSI, and PWM AC drive?
10. What is the carrier frequency or switch frequency?
11. What is motor cogging? What causes it?
12. What is injection braking and how is it accomplished?
13. What is the difference between scalar and vector drives?
14. How do sensorless flux vector drives differ from standard flux vector drives?
15. What is voltage reflection and how is it corrected?
16. What are harmonics and what are the corrective actions to reduce them?
17. What are the effective shielding and grounding methods used with AC drives?
18. What is PID and how is it used?

NOTE: This page was omitted from the original bound text. ISA apologizes for the omission error.

Drive Control and Feedback Devices

In this section, open- and closed-loop control will be reviewed. Most of the information has been previously presented. However, the focus of this chapter will be on the external devices that connect to the drive. These external components allow the drive to interface to a system and provide the necessary speed and torque control to maximize efficiency.

External devices (peripherals) are a vital part of any drive system—whether operating as part of a remote operator station or part of an entire production system. There is such a wide variety of peripherals that are used in drive control that to include all possible combinations would be beyond the scope of this book. However, the major categories of devices and their use will be covered in this chapter.

Open-Loop Control

Open loop control was presented in Chapter 4, under the direct current (DC) and alternating current (AC) drive sections. A brief review is given here. Figure 5-1 indicates the basics of open-loop control.

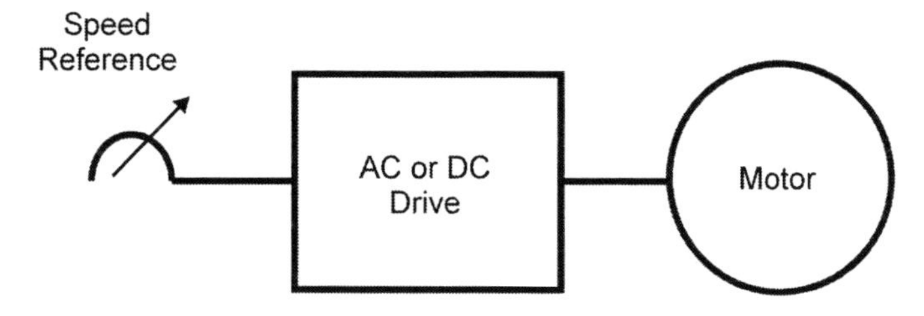

Figure 5-1. Open-loop control

The open-loop control is the simplest form of drive control. The drive operates the motor, given the speed reference that is delivered from the hand speed pot. If Figure 5-1 were of a DC drive, motor-speed regulation would be 5–7% higher. If the figure were of an AC drive, motor-speed regulation would be 3–5% higher, possibly higher depending on motor design.

Open-loop control is more typical in AC drives, where the inherent motor-speed regulation is acceptable in the 3–5% range. DC drives are almost never operated open loop because of the higher regulation characteristics. Some type of feedback is used, such as armature voltage feedback (EMF) or tach feedback. These methods will be discussed in greater detail later in this chapter. Before these methods are discussed, a review of closed-loop control is required. In addition, the types of devices involved will also be presented.

Closed-Loop Control

As indicated by the name, this type of control method requires the use of some peripheral device that closes the loop back to the drive. The device that is commonly used is the tachometer, or tach generator, as it is sometimes called. Figure 5-2 indicates a simple closed-loop control scheme.

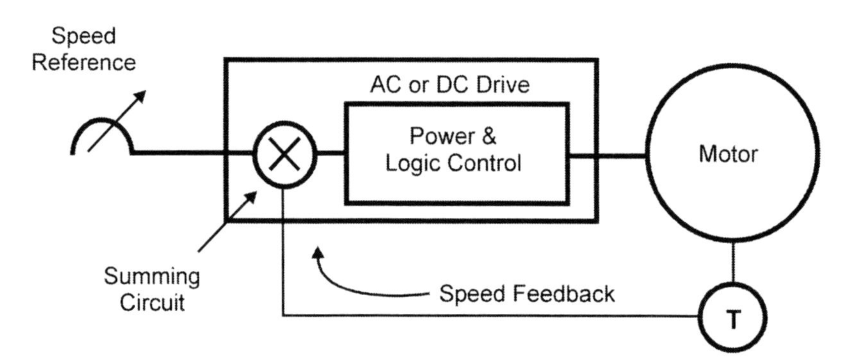

Figure 5-2. Closed-loop control

Closed-loop control is a bit more complex, but yields a great improvement in motor-speed regulation. The key to the success of this scheme is the tachometer (T) or feedback device. A speed reference is given to the AC or DC drive. The actual speed, determined by the tach, is fed back to the drive. Both the speed reference and feedback are combined into the summing circuit. The summing circuit produces an error signal. That error signal is now the speed reference that is sent to the power and logic control, which translates the signal into faster or slower motor speed.

If this happened to be an AC drive configured in torque-control mode, the feedback would be a current feedback instead of speed. If this was a position control, such as a servo controller, the feedback would be a position and use an encoder instead of a tach. The idea of this entire scheme is to have zero error on the output of the summing circuit. If error occurs, it must be corrected. How fast it is corrected is a function of the logic control in the drive.

The use of proportional integral derivative (PID) is critical to the success of the entire system. The PID controller will be programmed to correct for the error immediately or over a period of time. It will also be programmed as to how much error should be corrected over a period of time. The dynamics and stability of the system is dictated by the responsiveness or sloppiness of the feedback loop and control system. As with any type of control system, it is only as good as the weakest link. The remainder of this chapter will be devoted to closed-loop components, their accuracy, and how the responsiveness of the system will be affected.

Tachometers

A tachometer generator or tach is an electromechanical device that translates the rotational speed of a shaft to an electrical signal. An analog tach generator is a small generator that produces an output voltage whose magnitude is linearly proportional to shaft speed. An AC tach produces an AC voltage and a DC tach produces a DC voltage. DC tachs produce a negative voltage to indicate reverse rotation as shown in Figure 5-3.

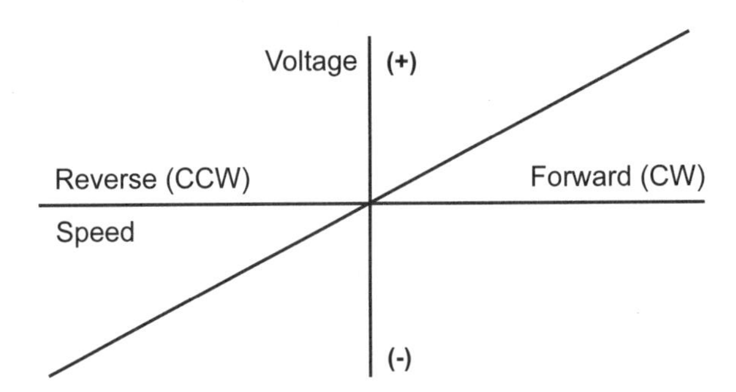

Figure 5-3. DC tach output voltage vs. speed

DC tachs are the most popular type of analog tach, since AC tachs do not indicate direction and are generally less accurate than DC tachs. The output of an analog tach is typically specified in volts per 1000 rpm. The V/1000 rpm voltage constant is the slope of the output voltage versus speed line.

Digital tachs, or pulse tachs as they are sometimes called, produce a series of pulses. The frequency of those pulses is proportional to shaft speed. This can be seen in Figure 5-4.

The output of a digital tach is typically specified in pulses per revolution (PPR). Most pulse tachs are magnetic devices in which pulses are generated by gear teeth passing by a magnetic pickup.

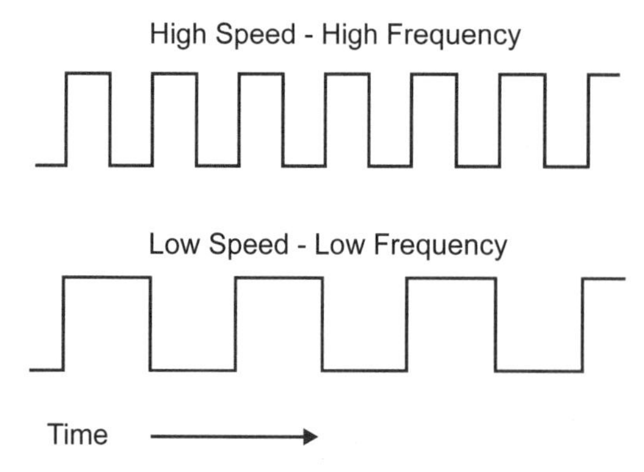

Figure 5-4. Pulse tach output

Encoders

An *encoder* is an electromechanical device that translates mechanical position and/or velocity into electrical signals. A *shaft encoder* or *rotary encoder* translates rotational or angular position and/or velocity into electrical signals.

An *incremental encoder* provides a signal that indicates position change or incremental position rather than absolute position. In principle, an incremental encoder is essentially the same type of device as a pulse tach, previously discussed. The term encoder usually implies a device with more advanced features and performance. Terms such as incremental encoder, encoder, pulse tach, and digital tachometer are basically used for the same type of device. In industry, they are often used interchangeably.

Optical encoders, on the other hand, are devices that use pulses for rotational signal generation. A light beam is transmitted through transparent stripes or slots in a rotating disk. The *photo detector* picks up those light beams and converts them into a series of pulses, sometimes called a pulse train. Figure 5-5 shows this process.

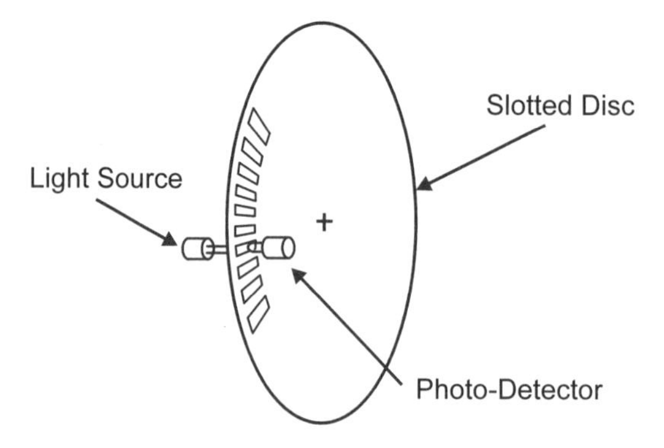

Figure 5-5. Optical encoder characteristics

Optical encoders are the most widely used types of encoder. They are capable of providing very high resolution.

Magnetoresistive encoders have a wheel or disk with numerous small magnetic poles imprinted on the disk surface in alternating north/south pairs. Incremental position is indicated by a sensing element consisting of a combination of resistors that change resistance on the basis of a magnetic field. The sensing element provides input to electronic circuitry, which generate pulses corresponding to each individual imprinted magnetic pole.

An *absolute encoder* produces a number of binary outputs that can be read as a binary word, which indicate the absolute angular position of the shaft relative to some unique index position. This type of encoder would be used primarily in a system where position feedback would be required (e.g., cut-to-length servo system).

This book is primarily concerned with motor speed or velocity in drive systems. Therefore, the focus will be on the incremental encoder or pulse tach, rather than on absolute encoders devices.

Encoder Characteristic

The following paragraphs explain several encoder features that provide functions and performance that go beyond simply indicating shaft speed.

An encoder with a single output cannot indicate direction of rotation. Quadrature outputs are two outputs with a 90° phase displacement, as shown in Figure 5-6.

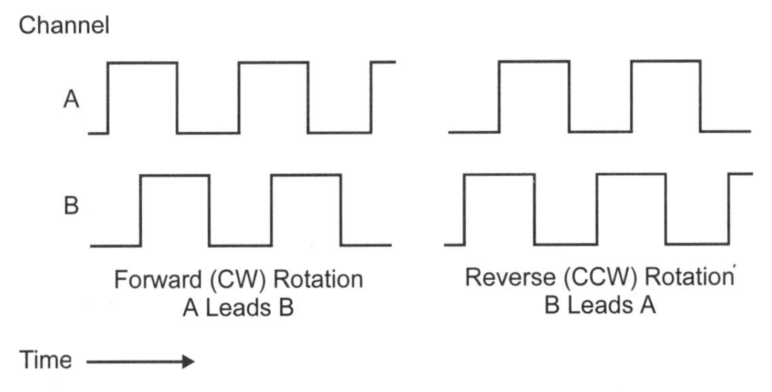

Figure 5-6. Quadrature outputs of a pulse tach (encoder)

As shown in Figure 5-6, quadrature outputs can be used to determine direction of rotation by detecting which of the two output signals is leading. The low-to-high transitions of the leading signal occur before the low-to-high transitions of the lagging signal.

Incremental encoders can be used to indicate when the shaft is in one particular "index" position. This is done by using an *index pulse* or *marker pulse* that occurs only once per revolution at the index position. Figure 5-7 shows this procedure. The width and phase relationship of the index pulse may vary among encoder models.

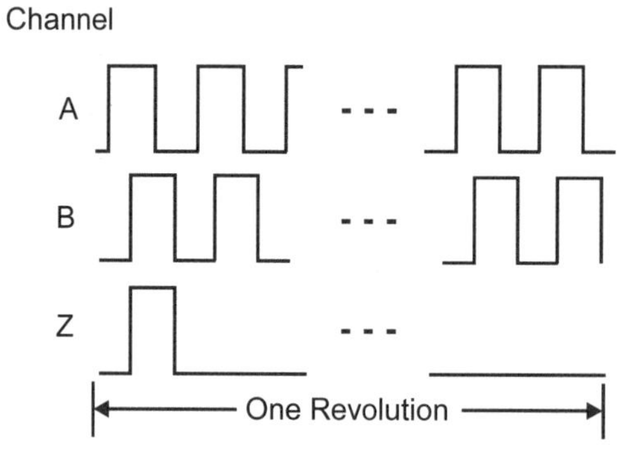

Figure 5-7. Encoder marker pulses of index positions

Figure 5-8 indicates *complementary* or *differential outputs*. Complementary outputs are pairs of outputs that are configured in such a way that one output (A) is high whenever its complement ($\overline{A}$) is low.

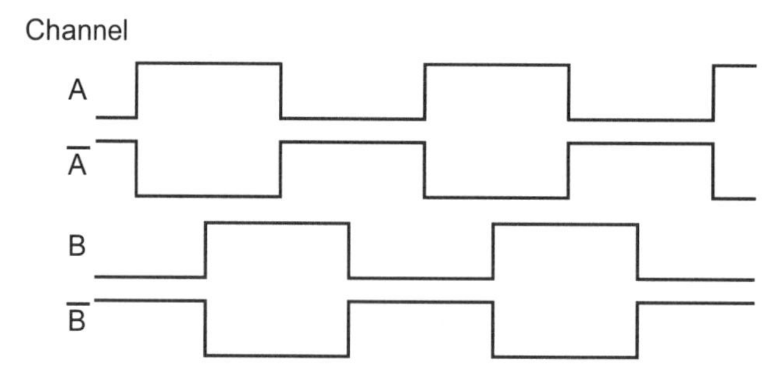

Figure 5-8. Complementary or differential outputs

A and $\overline{A}$ represent the signal voltages with respect to circuit common. The voltage between the A output and the $\overline{A}$ output is the voltage difference, or differential, between the A and $\overline{A}$-voltages. An encoder output signal that does not include the complementary $\overline{A}$ and $\overline{B}$ signals is called a *single-ended output*.

Differential signals have better noise immunity than single-ended signals. Figure 5-9 indicates a differential line driver and receiver connected by a twisted pair of shielded wires—a transmission line.

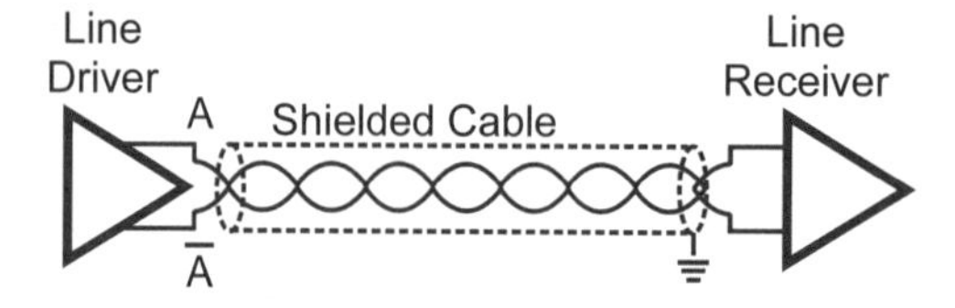

Figure 5-9. Differential line driver and receiver diagram

The use of a differential line driver and receiver protects against common mode noise between the transmitting and receiving locations. The use of a shielded, twisted-pair transmission line protects the signal from electromagnetic fields that might interfere with signal transmission.

The *resolution* of an encoder is determined by the number of pulses per revolution of the encoder shaft. The resolution determines the smallest amount of shaft rotation that the encoder is able to indicate. If an encoder generates 1024 pulses per revolution, it can indicate a movement of 1/1024 of a revolution or 0.35 degrees of rotation. The effective resolution of an encoder can be improved by using pulse multiplication. This procedure is shown in Figure 5-10.

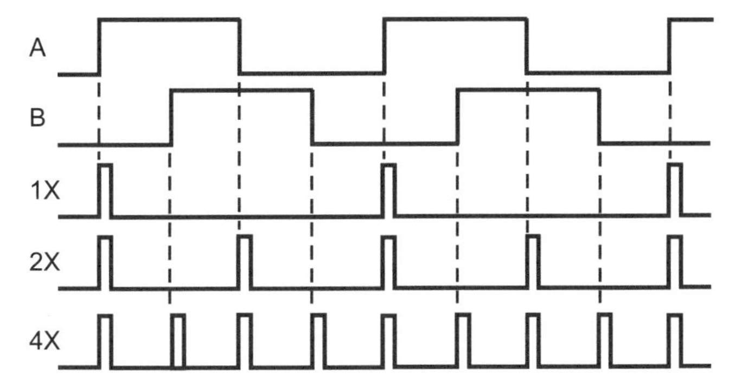

Figure 5-10. Encoder pulse multiplication

The A and B signals shown in Figure 5-10 are the outputs of a quadrature encoder. The 1X signal is a series of narrow pulses corresponding to the low-to-high transitions of the A signal. These pulses are typically generated by the device that receives or uses the encoder signal.

The resolution of the 1X signal is equal to the encoder PPR. The 2X signal contains pulses corresponding to both the low-to-high transitions and the high-to-low transitions of the A signal. The resolution of the 2X signal is twice the encoder PPR. The 4X signal contains pulses corresponding to the low-to-high and high-to-low transitions of both the A and the B signals. The effective resolution of the 4X signal is four times the encoder PPR.

To correctly apply encoders, the specifications of the encoder must be determined. Then the applications specifics can be matched to the encoder that would best meet the requirements. At this point, a review of typical encoder specifications is in order.

Encoder Specifications

The most basic encoder specification is the resolution or number of pulses per revolution of the encoder shaft. In general, using the highest possible pulses per revolution allows the best possible drive performance. High PPR allows speed to be measured more accurately and sampled more frequently. The pulse frequency is determined by the encoder-operating speed and the resolution according to the following formula:

$$\text{Pulse Frequency (Hz)} = \frac{\text{Speed (rpm)} \times \text{Resolution (PPR)}}{60}$$

The following example illustrates the pulse-frequency calculation for a 2048 PPR encoder operating at 1800 rpm. Note that the pulse frequency unit of measurement, hertz, is equivalent to pulses per second. The minute and revolution units cancel, leaving pulses-per-second or hertz as the units of measurement.

$$\frac{1800\dfrac{\mathit{revolutions}}{\mathit{minute}} \times 2048\dfrac{\mathit{pulses}}{\mathit{revolution}}}{60\dfrac{\mathit{seconds}}{\mathit{minute}}} = 61440\frac{\mathit{pulses}}{\mathit{second}}(\mathit{Hz})$$

The encoder PPR must be selected so that the pulse frequency is high enough to allow the required performance at the minimum operating speed. At the maximum operating speed, the pulse frequency must not exceed the maximum output frequency capability of the encoder. It also must not exceed the maximum input frequency capability of the circuitry that receives the signal.

Some drives can be adjusted to accept any PPR value within a specified range. Other drives accept only specific PPR values, such as 1024 PPR or 2048 PPR. The accuracy of an encoder is the maximum percentage variation between the actual positions of the pulse edges or transitions and the theoretical correct positions. The encoder accuracy is not the only factor that determines the speed-measurement accuracy. Speed-measurement accuracy is influenced by the encoder timing and counting accuracy. It is also influenced by the mechanical backlash in the coupling to the machine.

The measurement method may improve upon the encoder accuracy by averaging a number of pulses in each measurement. When speed is averaged over an extended period of time, the measurement accuracy will be determined entirely by the timing and counting accuracy.

The basic specification for the output signals indicates whether the encoder has a single output or quadrature output and whether or not a zero marker is provided. If complementary output signals are provided, the encoder specification may identify the IC-type number for the line driver. The output voltage and current ratings should also be specified. Single-ended outputs are often open collector, current sinking outputs. Most encoders provide square-wave outputs (50% duty cycle), but some models may be available with a fixed-pulse width.

Output specifications must be checked for compatibility with the circuitry that will receive the signal. Encoders require an external power source. The most common requirements are 12 and 24 VDC. Encoders are also available for operation at 5 VDC. However, these encoders are not recommended for installations requiring a long cable distance between the encoder and the drive.

Most encoders require a regulated input supply voltage and provide an output at the same voltage level as the input voltage. If the encoder has its own voltage regulator, its output signal level will be considerably lower than the input supply voltage. If the drive is designed to provide a regulated encoder supply voltage, it may not accept an encoder signal at a voltage level that is significantly below the supply voltage.

Before installation, the user should verify that the output voltage of the encoder is compatible with the input voltage range of the drive's encoder input. In addition, all encoders have minimum and maximum operating temperature ratings. If the encoder is subjected to temperatures outside the specified limits, it may not operate correctly and can ultimately be damaged. A possible source of encoder damage is heat. Heat is very likely to be conducted to the encoder housing through the mounting structure from motor or machine. An encoder should be selected with an operating temperature rating that is suitable for the location and mounting method.

A variety of mechanical specifications define the type of encoder housing available and the type of mounting arrangement possible. Encoders are available with various degrees of protection from moisture and environmental contaminants. The degree of protection is determined by the encoder housing type and material, the shaft material, the type of shaft seal, etc. Explosion-proof models are available for use in areas where fire or explosion hazards may exist because of flammable gases or vapors. Various bearing ratings are available to accommodate a wide range of radial and axial loads that might be subjected to the shaft of the encoder.

There will also be a maximum operating speed determined by the mechanical construction of the encoder. For each PPR rating, there will be a maximum speed corresponding to the encoder's maximum output frequency capability as described in a previous paragraph. The encoder manufacturer's installation and alignment procedures must always be carefully followed to ensure reliable operation.

Once the encoder is properly installed, it must be wired to the specifications of both the encoder and drive manufacturer. Careful attention to wiring is essential to ensure that a drive with encoder feedback performs properly. The following recommendations cover the most common requirements.

Each encoder output channel and the power supply should be connected using an individually shielded twisted pair of wires. Encoder wiring and a connection scheme are shown in Figure 5-11.

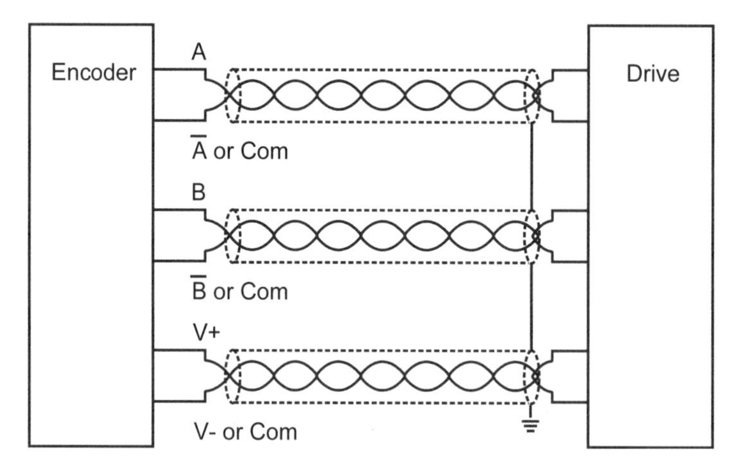

Figure 5-11. Encoder wiring diagram

Three individual cables or a three-pair cable can be used. If a three-pair cable is used, be sure that each pair of wires is individually shielded. The shields are to be grounded as recommended by the drive instruction material. Shielded cable is grounded at only one point to prevent ground loops or circulating currents through the shield conductor. The best ground location is usually at the drive. The encoder cable must be run in a steel conduit. Cables from more than one encoder can be run in the same conduit, but the conduit cannot carry power wiring.

Encoder cable should be a low-capacitance type of cable, designed for high-speed digital signals such as RS-422/485 serial communications signals.

Since the relationship between encoder shaft rotation and quadrature signal phasing is not standardized, this relationship can vary among encoder models. The instruction material furnished with the encoder is the best source of determining the encoder phasing. Phasing corresponds to the selected motor direction. If the drive does not operate properly upon initial startup, encoder phasing could be a suspect. It may be necessary to determine proper phasing by trial and error.

Note: *Today's microprocessor-based adjustable-speed drives are designed for use with incremental encoders rather than analog tachometer generators. Although some models may accept a feedback signal from a DC tach, the best performance is obtained by using an encoder. Analog tachometer generators have better EMI immunity compared with encoders. However, with the use of differential signals and careful attention to wiring, EMI immunity of an encoder can be equal or better than that of an analog tach.*

If an analog tach is used, it is necessary to determine what range of signals are compatible with the drive circuitry that it will be connected to. The circuit must be designed for either a DC or AC tach. The maximum input voltage and tach-generating voltage at maximum speed are factors to consider before purchasing a tach. Using a tach with the maximum compatible volts per 1000 rpm will provide the best performance over a wide speed range.

Resolvers

A resolver is a "position" transducer, with characteristics that resemble a small motor. This type of feedback device would be used mainly with servo motor applications where precise feedback of rotor position is critical to system accuracy. For example, in cut-to-length applications, linear position of a sliding table or cutting arm would be a function of the position of the rotor. Figure 5-12 shows a diagram of a resolver.

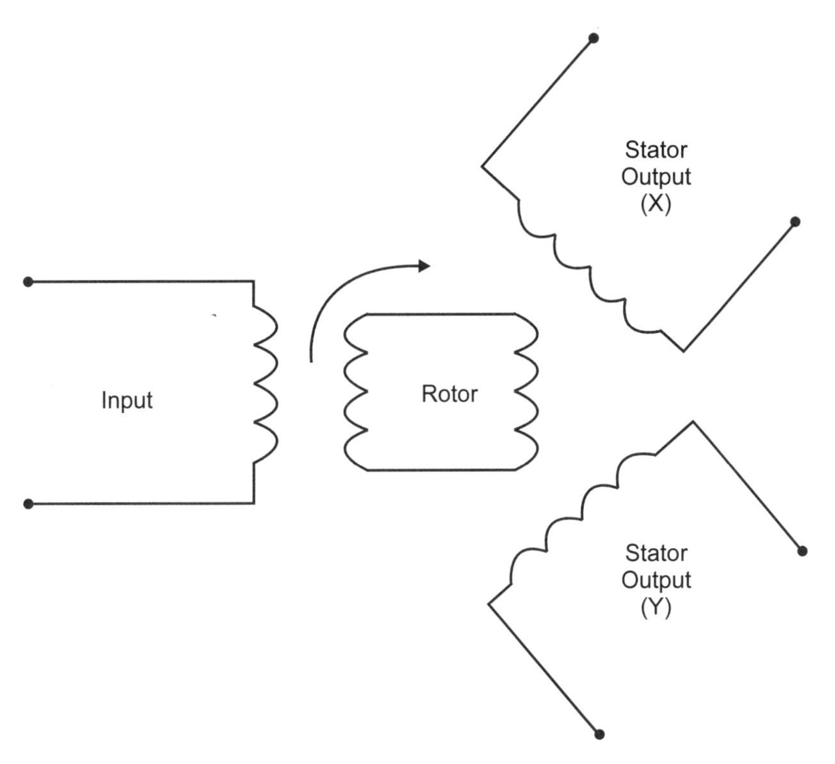

Figure 5-12. Resolver diagram

A resolver is very similar to an AC induction motor. A resolver contains a single winding rotor that rotates inside fixed coils of wire, called *stators*. A reference voltage is typically applied to the rotor winding. This rotating winding has a magnetic field that induces a voltage in the stator windings, which produce an analog output. This analog output is proportional to shaft (rotor) rotation.

Basically, the resolver is a rotating transformer. The rotating primary (rotor) induces a voltage in the fixed winding secondaries (stator windings). The analog output is what is fed back to the drive as an actual speed signal, or what would be considered a position signal.

Because there are no electronics involved with resolvers, they are better suited for dirty environments than encoders. Also, the resolver is a device that is an absolute measuring instrument. It can retain its exact location during a power outage. Typically the resolver can transmit information over distances up to 1000 feet with little effect from electrical noise. The resolution of some resolvers can be rated as high as 16,384 counts (14 bit or 2^{14}).

Drive Control Methods: DC

As stated earlier, the commonly used methods of speed control are open and closed loop. If speed regulation is not a factor, then a DC motor can be operated in open-loop control. However, most applications require some type of regulation to gain the most efficient use of the mechanics of the system. Therefore, a means of sending the drive an actual speed signal is essential to speed regulation. In DC drives there are basically two forms of closed-loop control—tach feedback and armature voltage feedback (EMF control). Though armature voltage feedback does not use an external device, it is termed *feedback* and can be considered a form of closed-loop control.

Armature Voltage Feedback (EMF Control, Speed Regulation)

Figure 5-13 shows an armature voltage feedback control scheme.

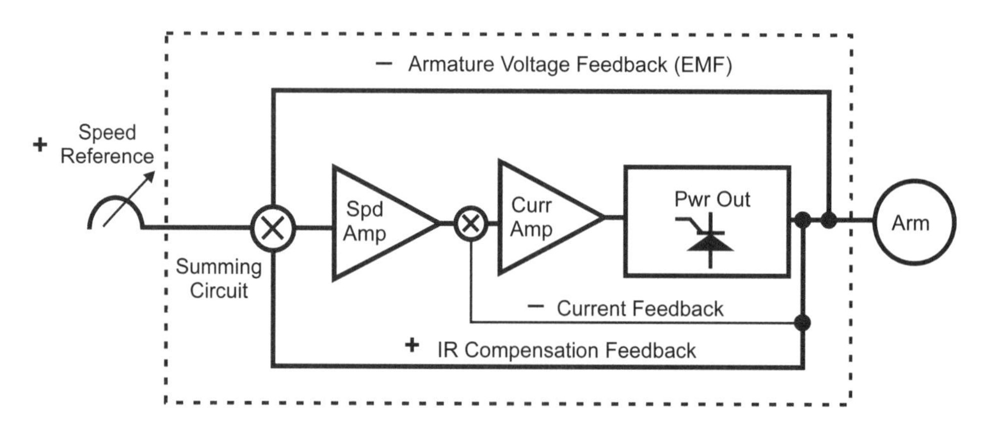

Figure 5-13. Armature voltage feedback (EMF control)

As shown in Figure 5-13, the drive requires a speed reference signal and a feedback signal of opposite polarity. The feedback is used to balance the control when the desired output speed is reached. All of the drive control systems are within the dotted lines.

A speed reference is sent to the summing circuit. By sensing the armature voltage at the drive output, the drive can sense the CEMF (Counter Electromotive Force) of the motor. This CEMF signal (negative polarity) is sent as feedback to the summing circuit. When the error is at zero, the drive will stabilize at the desired speed.

Another summing circuit is located after the speed amplifier and before the current amplifier. This summing circuit would use a shunt or other device to sense the armature current. The negative current feedback is sent to the summing circuit, with the resulting signal used to limit the amount of current output. If the current level is within limits, then the speed signal will be in control. But if the current exceeds the limits, it will lower the speed control until the current is reduced to a safe level.

With armature voltage feedback, motor speed tends to droop between full-load and no-load situations. To help compensate for this speed "droop," a feedback called IR compensation (an acronym for "current resistance" compensation due to a voltage drop across the armature due to load – E=IXR, Ohm's Law) is included in the drive. This circuit senses the armature current and feeds a small additional signal back to the speed amplifier.

At the summing circuit, three signals exist: positive speed reference, negative armature voltage feedback (EMF), and positive IR compensation. The IR compensation signal adds to the speed reference signal to compensate for speed droop created by the load.

With three signals summing at the same point, there is a possibility for instability. To set up IR compensation properly, speed and armature voltage feedback adjustments should be made with the IR compensation off. While observing the motor during speed step changes, IR compensation is gradually increased until oscillation occurs. Then IR compensation is decreased until the oscillation (instability) stops. Speed regulation of 2–3% is possible with this type of feedback control.

Armature Voltage Feedback (EMF Control, Torque Regulation)

The relationship between torque regulation and speed regulation in a standard DC drive configuration illustrates the importance of torque response. Since the armature current in a DC motor directly determines torque, the DC controller is configured as a closed-loop current regulator, using armature voltage feedback (EMF). The speed regulator then commands the current regulator to produce whatever torque is required to maintain the desired speed.

Torque-regulating drives are often used in load-sharing applications where a speed-regulating drive controls the speed of the driven machine, while a torque-regulated "helper" drive provides a controlled level of torque at some other location on the machine. If the load does not restrict the speed of a torque-regulated drive, the drive speed could exceed the safe operating limit. Therefore torque-regulating drives must have a speed-limiting mechanism that prevents the speed from exceeding a safe limit if the torque presented by the driven machine drops to zero.

With a DC drive, torque can be regulated directly by regulating armature current. In any motor, torque is the result of the force between two magnetic fields. In a motor (DC), torque is easily and directly regulated by regulating the currents that control the flux in the two magnetic fields. The field winding flux is the motor's magnetizing flux, which is held constant by providing a constant field current. The motor's torque-producing flux is the flux created by the armature current, which is controlled to regulate torque. The torque produced at any speed is given by:

$$\text{Torque} = K \times \Phi \times I_A$$

where:

K = a constant

Φ = the magnetic flux produced by the stator field

I_A = the armature current

Tachometer Feedback

When DC motor speed is of primary concern, it can be measured with a transducer and regulated with a closed-loop regulator as shown if Figure 5-14.

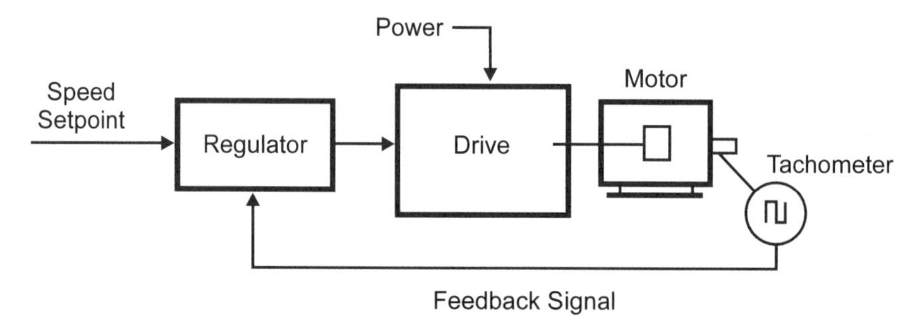

Figure 5-14. Closed-loop speed regulation—tach feedback

The transducer in Figure 5-14 is a tachometer generator. As previously reviewed, a tach is a small generator that produces an output voltage that is very accurately determined by its operating speed. There are also pulse tachs, which provide a train of voltage pulses at an average frequency that is exactly proportional to average speed.

The closed-loop speed regulator compensates for any changes in the characteristics of the drive caused by changes in load or by outside influences such as line voltage and ambient temperature. With a closed-loop speed regulator, the most important characteristic of the drive is its ability to rapidly respond to changes in requirements for torque.

The transducer devices already presented would be involved in generating the actual speed feedback signal. The accuracy of the system will be dictated by the regulation of the feedback device and the responsiveness of the drive control.

Drive Control Methods: AC

The characteristics of open- and closed-loop control have already been discussed. In this section, the focus will be on AC drive control, with commonly used peripheral devices such as transducers, sensors, and other control inputs. In addition, the performance (static and dynamic) and stability of the system will be explored.

Closed-loop regulation can be used with an adjustable-speed drive to regulate a variety of processes. Figure 5-15 shows the regulation of air pressure in the duct of a ventilation system.

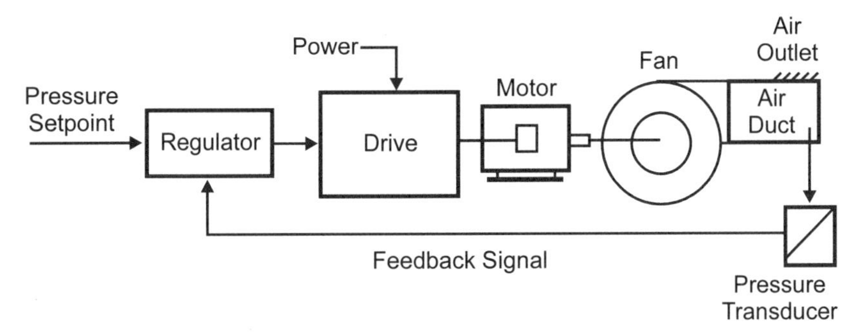

Figure 5-15. Armature voltage feedback (EMF control)

As air-outlet dampers are opened and closed, the speed of the fan must be increased or decreased to match the demand for air flow and maintain a constant static pressure in the duct. The closed-loop control system uses a pressure transducer in the duct to measure the static pressure. The air-pressure feedback is sent to the drive, which adjusts the speed of the fan as required. The regulator control loop not only adjusts for changes in air-flow requirements but also compensates the characteristics of all of the equipment such as the drive motor and fan that are "inside the loop."

When an adjustable-speed drive is inside the loop in a closed-loop control system, the speed-regulating accuracy of the drive is not the critical element. The movement of air or water volume is not an "exacting science." An exact amount of flow (measured in cubic feet per minute [cfm]) is not required in this particular application. The drive may have to pump air for a few more seconds to meet the demand. In this type of a closed-loop control system, the drive needs only to provide the required torque and respond to speed-correcting commands from the regulator.

However, if this were an application where drive speed directly determines the accuracy of the process, then the drive would be a critical part of the system. Such an application could be a coating line that processes paper stock into 12-ounce coffee cups. Precision control is needed to ensure that the cups are manufactured to the exact dimensions for 12-ounce capacity.

Feedback and Performance

The feedback devices of tachometers, encoders, and resolvers have already been presented. This section will be devoted to the overall performance of the AC drive system. The terminology will be presented and the performance characteristics reviewed.

In earlier sections, only *steady-state,* or *static,* performance has been reviewed. Static operation is where there are no changes in conditions. Figure 5-16 shows a drive's static and dynamic speed-regulating performance.

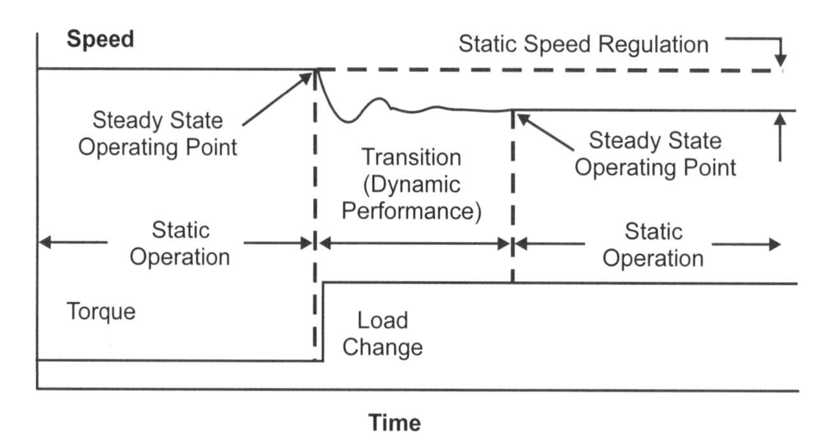

Figure 5-16. Static and dynamic performance of a system

The figure indicates static operating conditions before and after a load change with a transition period of dynamic performance immediately after the change. *Static speed regulation* is the change in steady-state speed that is caused by a load change. *Static performance* measures the difference between two operating points, without considering the performance during the transition from one point to the other. At each point, operation is measured only after the system has been operating at that point for some length of time. Sufficient time is allowed so no further change will occur in operation related to the transition from one point to another.

Dynamic performance describes the operation during the transition from one operating point to another. The dynamic performance capability of a system defines the system's ability to respond to a load change or a reference change.

Figure 5-17 is an enlarged view of Figure 5-16, showing the parameters that quantify both the static response and the dynamic response to a step change in load.

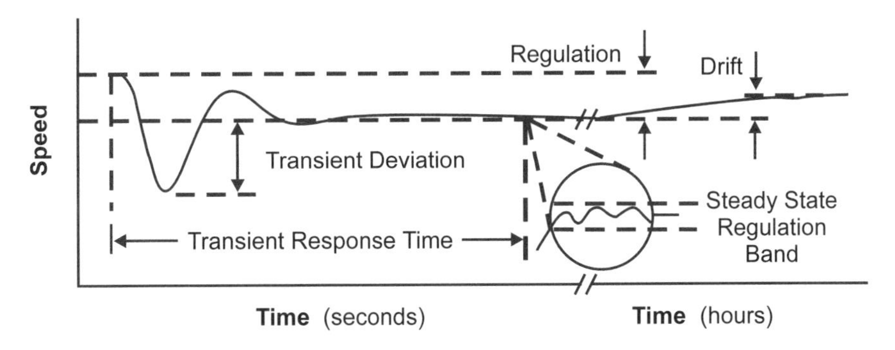

Figure 5-17. Step changes of load and the response

The *transient deviation* is the maximum deviation from set point immediately following the load change. The *transient-response time* is time required for the output to return to the steady-state regulation band after going through a period of damped oscillation. The *steady-state regulation band* is a small "dead band" of output variation that is not recognized by the regulator as a change. The regulation dead band is caused by regulator and transducer resolution limitations. The steady-state *regulation* is the change in steady-state output resulting from a load change. *Drift* is the change in steady-state output because of temperature changes and other long-term influencing factors. Drift is usually specified for a 24-hour period.

It is difficult to use transient-response time to compare the performance of two types of drives because total-system response time is determined by load inertia. Figure 5-18 shows another way of quantifying the dynamic change in output speed because of a step change in load torque.

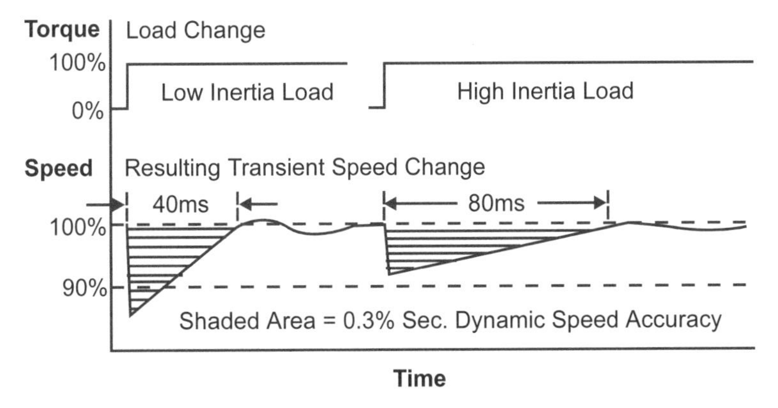

Figure 5-18. Dynamic speed accuracy

The *dynamic speed accuracy* is the area under the transient-response curve measured in percent-seconds.

For the low-inertia load, the figure shows that the maximum transient speed deviation is 15% and the response time is 40 ms. The dynamic speed accuracy is the area of the shaded triangle or 15% x 40 ms/2 = 0.3%-seconds. For the high-inertia load, the dynamic speed accuracy is 7.5% x 80 ms/2 = 0.3%-seconds. This example shows that the dynamic speed accuracy is about the same for a low-inertia load as it is for a high-inertia load.

Figure 5-19 shows the dynamic response of a drive resulting from a step change in reference.

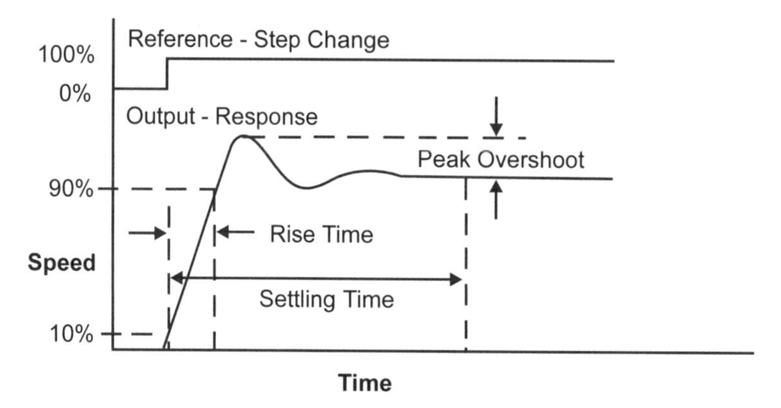

Figure 5-19. Reference step change and response

The parameters that quantify the performance are rise time, peak overshoot, and settling time. The *rise time* is the time required for the output to rise from 10 to 90% of its final value. The *peak overshoot* is the maximum amount by which the output overshoots the final value. The *settling time* is the rise time plus the time required for the output to reach a steady value after going through a period of damped oscillation.

In many applications, it is important for a drive to accurately follow a speed reference during acceleration and deceleration. In a web processing machine for example, the speeds of the various machine sections must match each other as a continuous web of material travels from one section to another. When the master speed reference is increased or decreased, the drives for each machine section must accurately follow the change. Figure 5-20 shows the *dynamic deviation* that occurs whenever the speed reference changes.

Bandwidth, or *small-signal bandwidth,* is another parameter that is sometimes used to quantify a drive's capability for accurately following a changing reference signal. Small-signal bandwidth is measured by applying a small sinusoidal variation to the regulator reference and observing the effect on the output. The bandwidth is the maximum frequency range of input signal that the output can follow. Another name for bandwidth is *frequency response.*

The bandwidth can be given in radians per second (ω) or in hertz (Hz). The relationship between radians/sec and Hz is $\omega = 2\pi f$. Bandwidth is inversely

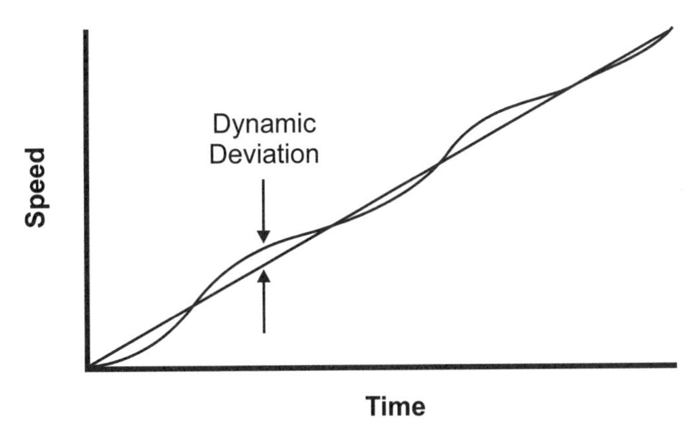

Figure 5-20. Dynamic deviation

proportional to the system *time constant* (t) or "Response Time" (ω= 1/t). The response time is similar to the rise time shown in Figure 5-19. The response time is the time required for the output to rise from 0 to 63% of its final value.

The bandwidth of a drive defines the maximum capability of the controller/motor combination with nothing connected to the motor shaft. The bandwidth of a controller defines the maximum electrical output capability of the controller without a motor connected to the output terminals. The bandwidth of a system is the actual operating performance of the drive and load when the drive is adjusted for optimum performance with that specific load.

High-performance control systems often have multiple control loops as shown in Figure 5-21.

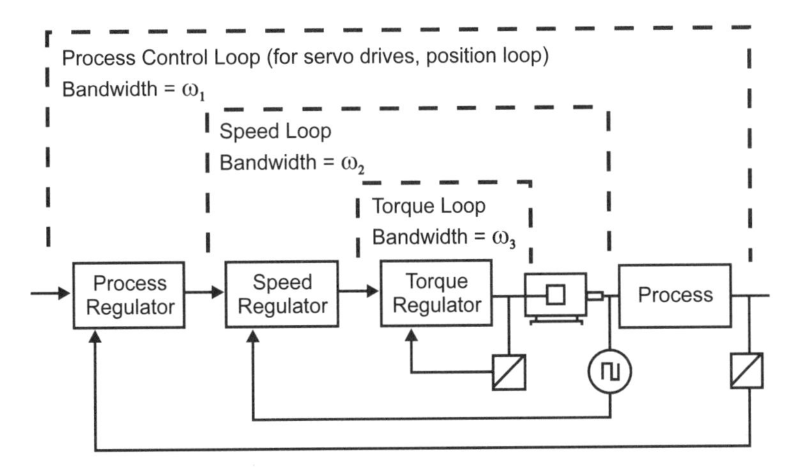

Figure 5-21. Bandwidth relationships in control loops

The outermost control loop regulates the process variable. An example of this would be a position control loop in servo drive systems. A general-purpose drive system might have a dancer position regulator that ultimately controls the tension of a web or filament. The speed-regulator loop is inside the process-regulator loop, and the torque-regulator loop is the innermost loop.

To provide stable performance, each inner regulator loop must be 3–10 times faster than the next outer loop. That is, ω2 = 3–10 times ω1 and ω3 = 3–10 times ω2. If the process is subject to fast changes, ω1 is large. A high-performance drive is required, and ω2 and ω3 must be large. Conversely, if the driven machine has a high inertia or other characteristics that dictate that its final output can change only slowly, then the drive does not need to have wide speed- and torque-regulator bandwidths.

Stability of the System

The performance examples presented all have stable performance characteristics. When the performance of a system is stable, the output is at a steady value, except during periods of transition from one operating point to another. During transitions, the output may oscillate, but the oscillation is damped and rapidly decreases to a low value. In unstable systems, the output may oscillate continuously for an extended period of time. Figure 5-22 illustrates responses to a step change in reference for a stable and unstable system.

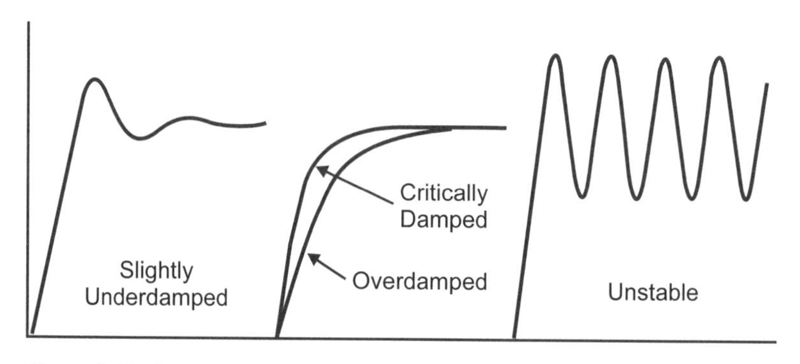

Figure 5-22. System responses—stable and unstable operation

Systems are usually adjusted for slightly *under-damped* or *critically damped* operation. A system is critically damped when it responds with the fastest rise time that is possible, without any overshoot.

System performance is determined by the interaction among all of the components of the system. The components of a control system include both the controlling system and the controlled system. An adjustable-speed drive system includes the adjustable-speed controller, the motor, all feedback and accessory devices, and the driven machine. The characteristics of the driven machine, or load, are an essential factor in determining the dynamic performance of an adjustable-speed drive system. Figure 5-23 shows the load torque versus speed for a driven machine compared with the torque capability of a drive.

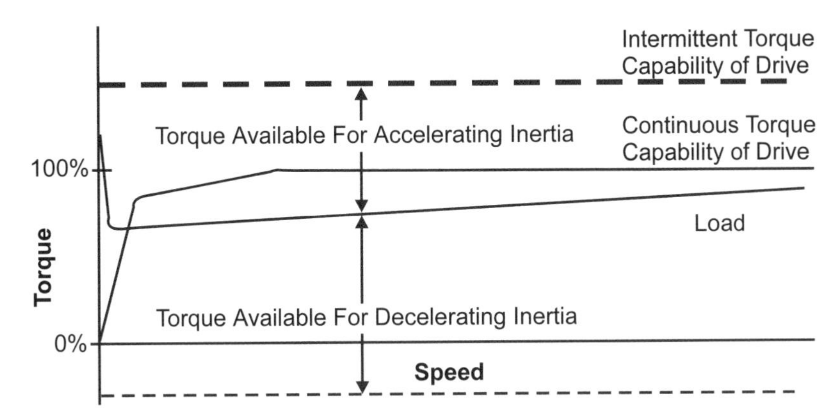

Figure 5-23. Accelerating and decelerating torque

The difference between the load torque and the intermittent torque capability of the drive is the torque available to accelerate or decelerate inertia. The reflected load inertia, plus the motor inertia and the torque available for acceleration or deceleration, determines the time to accelerate and decelerate. The acceleration and deceleration time are the main components of the drive's response to a step change in speed reference.

Acceleration or deceleration time is given by:

$$\text{Time} = \frac{(\text{Load Inertia} + \text{Motor Inertia}) \times \text{Speed Change}}{\text{K} \times \text{Torque}}$$

If the load inertia is expressed as WK^2 (lb-ft^2), speed change is given in rpm, and torque is given in lb-ft, then the constant, K, is 308 for calculating time in seconds.

The drive's torque response is a very important factor in determining the drive's dynamic performance. When the load torque increases suddenly, or when the speed set point is suddenly changed, the drive is asked to instantaneously change the level of torque that the motor is providing. The drive's torque response is the response time (typically milliseconds) required for the drive to respond to a step increase of 0 to 100% torque demand.

Accurately predicting the complete performance of a drive system and driven machine requires detailed information. Drive and machine characteristics must be known. To achieve optimum performance, the drive must be adjusted (tuned) to the characteristics of the driven machine. One aspect of tuning is to set the speed regulator gain adjustments for the best regulation that can be achieved without getting too close to unstable operation. The system bandwidth must be tuned to a frequency that is below any mechanical resonance frequencies of the driven machine.

For existing machine designs, drives can be selected based on comparing the capabilities of available drives with the capabilities of drives that have been successfully used in the past. For new machines, the keys to success include experience with similar machines and close cooperation between the machine design engineers and the drive manufacturer.

Sensors and Controls

A variety of sensors and controls are used to interface with the drive unit, either AC or DC. In this section, attention will be given to the more common devices that control a drive or give information to the drive, in the form of feedback.

Transducers

A transducer is a device that senses the condition, state, or value of an item to be controlled and produces an output that reflects that condition, state, or value. The following is a listing of typical transducers and sensors used to feed information back to the drive. In some cases, the transducer itself is the controlling element (determining a speed reference or set point).

Temperature

Thermocouple and thermistor. This device changes resistance per the change in temperature. Some thermocouples are mounted directly on machines actually inside tanks to monitor temperature. This temperature is then fed back to the drive to change the controlled value (increase or decrease the flow of heat).

Flow

Electromagnetic flow meter. This device uses an electromagnet and fluid motion to register an output. The moving fluid provides movement. An EMF is detected by two electrodes embedded in the wall of the tube. The electrodes are insulated from the liquid being measured.

Differential pressure flow meter. The fluid flow causes motion within the measuring unit. A restriction in the orifice or pipeline causes an increase in velocity and a decrease in pressure. This decrease is a rate of flow, and is the controlling element.

Tension, Force, or Strain

Resistance gage. There are several forms of resistance gages. The ultimate result is that the output is a change of resistance, per the unit being measured. A *tension gage* changes resistance per the tension applied to the sensor. A *strain gage* changes resistance per the stretching of the wires inside the sensor. This sensor type needs a power source to feedback a voltage signal to the drive.

Displacement of Position

Potentiometers, proximity sensors, photo cells. These sensors change output resistance per the controlling element. Potentiometers change resistance per the location of the wiper arm or shaft. Linear pots are constructed in a linear fashion with a slider arm, as opposed to a rotary arm as in a standard pot. Proximity sensors consist of two plates that change capacitance per how close they are to the controlling element. Photo cells are available as photovoltaic, which sends out a voltage per the amount of the controlling element. There are also photoconductive and photoresistive devices. Photoresistive devices change resistance per the amount of light sensed by a light-sensitive base plate.

Pressure

Diaphragm or bourdon tube. These are used to sense fluid pressures. The movement of the internal device is proportional to the pressure changes. The output is a variable resistance, which requires a voltage source to provide feedback to the drive. Three to fifteen PSI or static pressure transducers are commonly used in the HVAC industry to monitor the static pressure in the heating or cooling ducts. These devices use the principle listed above, but include an actual transmitter that would deliver a 4- to 20-mA output. That output would be accepted directly into the drive feedback circuit, with no additional power source needed. Pressure transducers (4–20 mA) can effectively transmit signals several hundred feet back to the drive with little loss of signal.

Level

Level transducers. Level transducers are available in a variety of controlling element styles. A float device is nothing more than a variable resistor, with the wiper arm connected to a flotation device that sits directly on top of the fluid being monitored. Some photoelectric level transducers change the voltage output per the density of the fluid being monitored. Capacitive-type sensors change the amount of capacitance per the proximity of the fluid to the sensing plates. A certain amount of conductivity would be needed in the fluid being monitored.

Thickness

X-ray and ultrasonic. These devices change the output voltage or current per the amount of material being sensed. An X-ray sensor has to monitor X-ray-sensitive materials for the sensing element to be effective. Ultrasonic sensors use an electronic oscillator to sense the thickness of the material. A receiver–transmitter is used for this purpose, along with a bridge circuit that does voltage comparisons.

Humidity

Hygrometer. This device uses a medium that changes dimensions according to the amount of humidity in the atmosphere. A hair hygrometer uses strands of human hair attached to a pivot arm. As the humidity changes, the pivot arm moves because of changes in hair length. The pivot arm is attached to a variable resistor, which can be connected to a power source to generate a voltage feedback signal.

Density

Float devices. These devices change the amount of voltage output per the density of the fluid being monitored. A rod (moveable core) is attached to a float device that moves up or down, depending on material density. The moveable core fits inside a linear differential transformer. The transformer is energized with AC voltage, with the output changing value, depending on how high or low the moveable core slides into the differential transformer. Some sort of rectification is needed before this type of signal could be fed back to the drive.

There are a variety of other sensors and feedback devices not mentioned above. The point to remember is that the drive needs an electrical feedback or reference signal to change speed or torque (current) output. All drives accept a standard analog input value of 0–10 VDC or 4–20 mA DC. These values could be a set point (reference) or a feedback. The drive can respond to the analog input signals of the voltage or current values stated above. The drive does not care what the controlling element is, as long as the analog input is of the value and type it can respond to.

Chapter Review

The two types of drive control methods are open and closed loop. Open loop is operating a motor directly from the drive unit. Closed loop includes some type of feedback device that is connected directly to the motor shaft. The speed regulation of the system can be improved by using a feedback device.

Typical drive feedback devices include tachometers (tachs), encoders (or pulse tachs), and resolvers. Tachometers are available in AC or DC versions. DC tachs are used in a variety of industrial applications, since they are able to indicate direction and are generally more accurate than AC tachs.

Encoders use a system of light beams directed toward a light sensor. The light beams are created by shining a light source through a rotating, slotted disk. The disk is connected to the encoder shaft, which is connected directly to the motor shaft through a coupling.

Resolvers are position-type devices. These devices are typically used on servo applications, where precise feedback of the rotor position is required. Resolvers are similar to an AC induction motor, as well as acting like a revolving transformer.

DC drive control methods include closed-loop control using a tach feedback device. It also includes armature voltage feedback or EMF control. With EMF control, a sampling of the output voltage is used as feedback to correct for output speed and current (torque).

AC drive control methods also include tach or encoder feedback, as well as operating the VFD by open-loop methods. A variety of transducers can be used as feedback devices. Pressure, flow, level, temperature, and humidity are just a few of the controlling elements sensed by transducers.

Dynamic and static speed regulation are part of the setup process of the performance drive application. The accuracy of the speed or torque is dependent on the feedback device, as well as the closed-loop control circuit within the drive. The amount of dampening will determine if the system will be stable or produce oscillations.

Check Your Knowledge

1. Describe open-loop vs. closed-loop control.
2. What is a pulse tach and how does it work?
3. What is the difference between an AC and a DC tach?
4. How is the resolution of an encoder indicated?
5. Describe the EMF, current, and IR compensation feedback loops in a DC drive system.
6. How is a pressure transducer used in a closed-loop AC drive system?
7. Describe the difference between static and dynamic performance of a closed-loop system.
8. What is bandwidth?
9. How is stable operation obtained with an AC drive system?
10. What is the operating principle of temperature and humidity sensors?

Drive System Control Methods

Introduction

Up to this point, basic drive theory, component hardware, and interface devices have been discussed. It is now time to put the basics to work to develop a drive system. The following information will help tie the components together into a coordinated control system. All systems configurations would be closed loop because of the precise speed and torque regulation required.

In actuality, there would be many more pieces to the system "puzzle" than what is presented here. However, this section is meant to present a general outline of drive systems and how the pieces work together in an automated environment.

Coordinated Drive Systems

It is helpful to start with what could be considered a "simple" system and move to the more complex. Figure 6-1 indicates one such simple closed-loop system.

As seen in Figure 6-1, this is a "widget" manufacturing facility. This section is the "finishing" section of the system, with proximity sensors strategically placed along the out-feed conveyor. All of the sensors are connected to an amplifier unit that sends *contact* signals to the drive. The drive needs to know where the widget is at all stages of the system. Therefore, the job of the proximity sensor is to send a *contact closure* signal to the drive. This would be considered a digital input (DI). In this case, the drive does not need to know how big, or how long the widget is, just that fact that it has arrived at a particular station on the conveyor. Once the drive has determined the widget has finished all processes, it can then send a *relay output* signal to the warehouse, alerting that the widget is on its way.

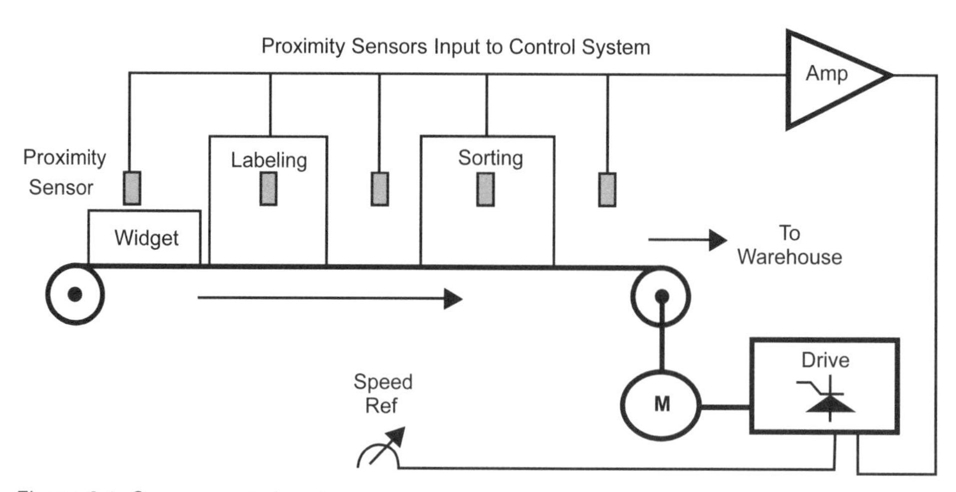

Figure 6-1. Sensor control system

In this case, the operator sends a speed reference to the drive. The drive operates the motor at that speed until the widget reaches the first proximity sensor. At that point, the contact closure signal indicates the widget has arrived at the labeling section. The drive takes the contact closure and operates at a preset speed 1 (slower speed), so the label section has time to perform its function. Once the widget exits the label section, another proximity sensor "opens" the preset speed contact, and the conveyor returns to normal speed.

The process is repeated when the widget enters the sorting section. At this point, another digital input is closed, which signals the drive to switch to preset speed 2. At the output of the sorting section, another proximity sensor closes. This indicates that the widget is ready for the warehouse, and the drive returns the conveyor to normal speed.

This is a somewhat crude system but could be considered a *coordinated system*. The drive could be either DC or AC, along with the corresponding motor. Similar configurations would be seen on packaging systems, food processing systems, and any application where process speed may differ from part movement speed. Later in this chapter, a view of a more automated system will be presented.

Figure 6-2 indicates a simple automatic AC drive pumping system. The heart of this system is proportional integral derivative (PID) control.

In Figure 6-2, the high level is set for 10 feet and the low level (danger) is set for 2 feet. This automatic pumping system would be set to have a constant level of 10 feet at all times. If the actual value (level) is less than 10 feet, the drive responds to the corresponding "error" signal and activates the pump at a designated speed. In this case, the level is only at 90%, with a feedback voltage of –9 V, indicating a 1-V error and a corresponding increase in speed. Once the error is at zero (feedback at –10 V), the drive slows to zero speed, meaning no pumping action is required.

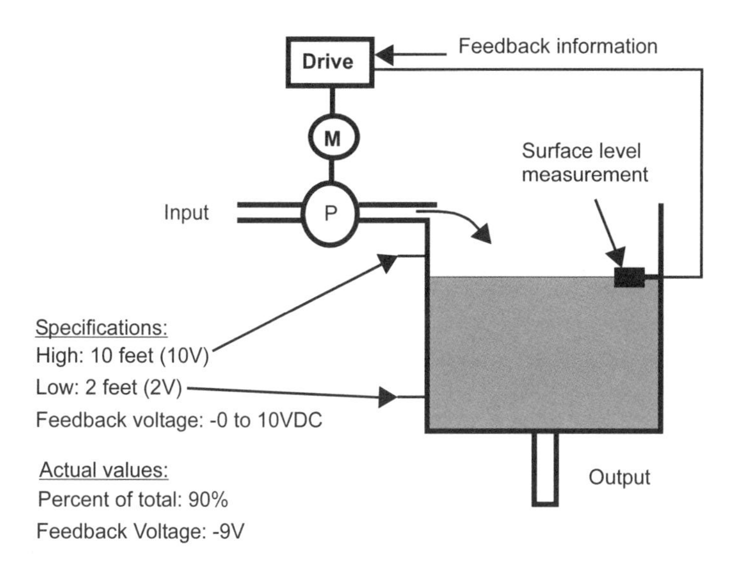

Figure 6-2. Automated pumping application—PID

If this were a duplex pumping system, the drive could be programmed to bring online a fixed-speed "lag" pump, if the demand required it. Several of the latest AC drives on the market include the software intelligence to operate this type of system automatically. Relay outputs can be programmed for a low-level pump start and a high-level pump stop. In addition, a *sleep* function can be set when the drive stops pumping. The sleep function would cause the drive to release the start command but keep the microprocessor alive, waiting for the next pumping cycle. This function saves additional energy, since the IGBTs are off, as well as any other power electronics circuits.

In Figure 6-2, when the level reached a "critical" stage (2-foot level), the drive could be programmed to take emergency action, such as sound an alarm. Some type of level sensor would be set at the 2-foot level. It would send a contact closure to a digital input that would be programmed for an emergency function (e.g., sound an alarm, engage full speed pumping, etc.). The sensor could also send a contact closure to a programmable logic controller (PLC), if that's what was controlling the application.

In Chapter 5, information on PID control was presented. Figure 6-3 is a graphic representation of PID system response and how it might be programmed for the drive shown in Figure 6-2.

Though indicating meters instead of feet, the graph indicates the response of the drive to a feedback error signal. If the drive was programmed as seen in the graph, it would take about 1 s for the drive/pump to stabilize. A combination of gain, integration time, and derivative rate are needed to effectively tune this pumping system. By looking at the graph, the drive gain may be set too high, causing the pump to overspeed (overshoot) the desired level. An oscillation would occur until the system stabilized in about 1 s. The *integration* time would also need review, since the drive may

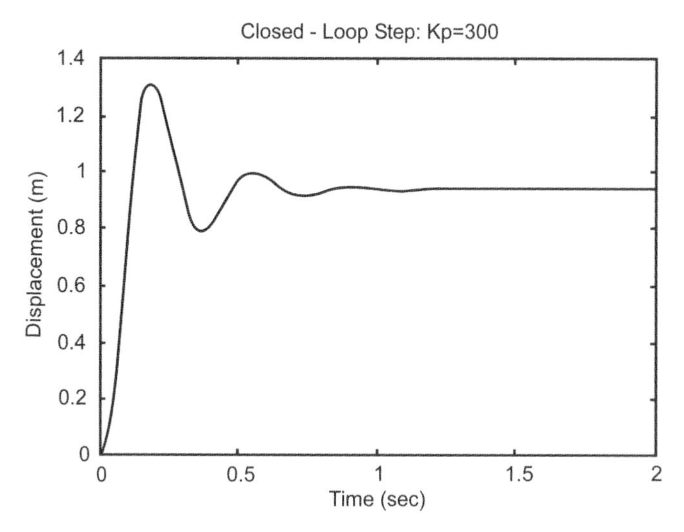

Figure 6-3. PID control—system response

be set to achieve the desired level too quickly for the conditions that exist. The derivative function could also be reviewed, since it dictates how the amount of error is to be corrected per unit time (i.e., 10% correction per second).

Figure 6-4 indicates a device called a *scanner* used to check the quality of output from a paper machine. The scanner would check paper-quality items such as thickness, coloration, moisture content, surface smoothness, and fiber content.

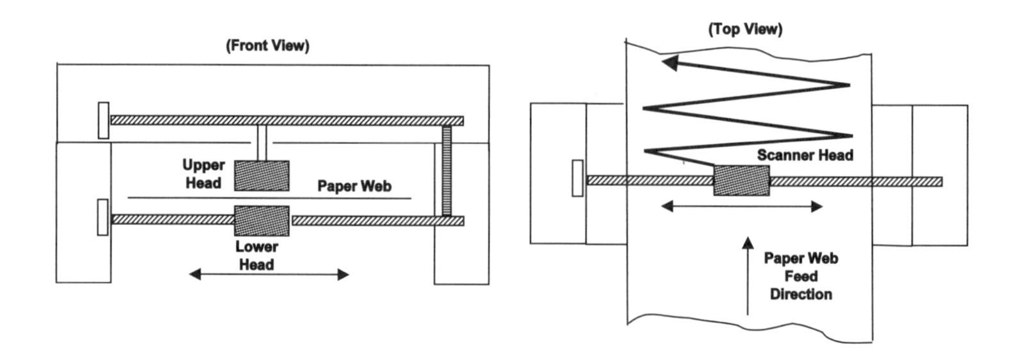

Figure 6-4. Paper machine scanner system

As one unit, the scanner could be considered a sensor that feeds vital information back to the main system control. The scanner would be the input device to the main control, which would signal the drives to change speed- or torque-control output to correct for errors in quality.

Included in the scanner assembly would be a small AC drive that controls the scanner head. The scanner head-speed rate (back and forth motion) would be controlled by the small AC drive (as low as 1 HP). The upper and lower head are connected through mechanical linkages that cause both pieces to move together. The transmitting devices would be in the upper head, and the receiving sensors would be in the lower head, for example.

Tension Control

Before the web of paper arrived at this point, a series of coordinated devices would be in action. Paper, plastic, foil, or any other type of web system would require the use of tension control. Figure 6-5 illustrates a basic tension-control system.

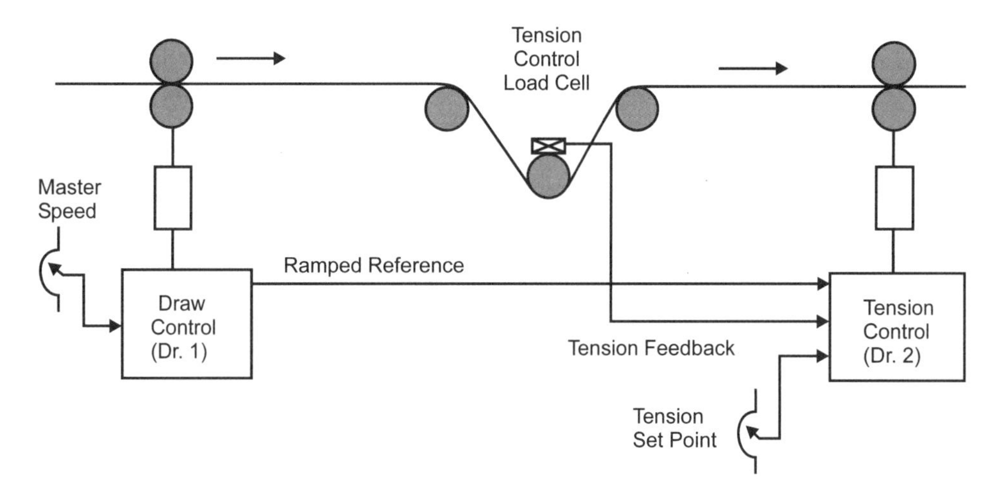

Figure 6-5. Tension-control characteristics

The tension control system shown Figure 6-5 would be part of a web-winding system, just ahead of a winder unit. The web material is fed through the in-feed rollers, under the tension control load cell and out through the out-feed rollers.

The purpose of tension regulation is to control the surface web tension as material is wound. The same would be true if the material was being unwound. Tension regulation is achieved by using load cell tension feedback. A *load cell* is a pressure-sensitive sensor that decreases in resistance as pressure on the cell increases.

Differences between the tension set point and the load-cell feedback allow the tension PI regulator (proportional integral) to develop the error correction needed to maintain tension by trimming either speed or torque of the driven section. The tension PI regulator is updated in millisecond time-frames to produce very responsive trim (fine tuning). The *proportional gain* of the tension regulator can be adapted to accommodate changes in roll diameter.

As the diameter of the roll increases, the proportional gain can be set to increase from a minimum gain at core diameter, to a maximum gain at full roll. A winder application is operated in torque control. The torque-control drive will operate at any speed necessary, as long as the torque (tension) of the web is satisfied. When operating in torque control an encoder is typically required. When using this type of control, accurate web material information is required for calculating the WK^2 torque value of the roll. These calculations will vary depending on the density and tensile strength of materials. If tuned properly, torque control may result in stable steady-state performance.

Dancer control is similar to tension control. The dancer unit changes output resistance according to the tension on the web that is wrapped over the dancer roll. The changes in resistance and corresponding voltage change are fed back to the drive so proper torque control adjustments can be made. Figure 6-6 shows a dancer-control scheme.

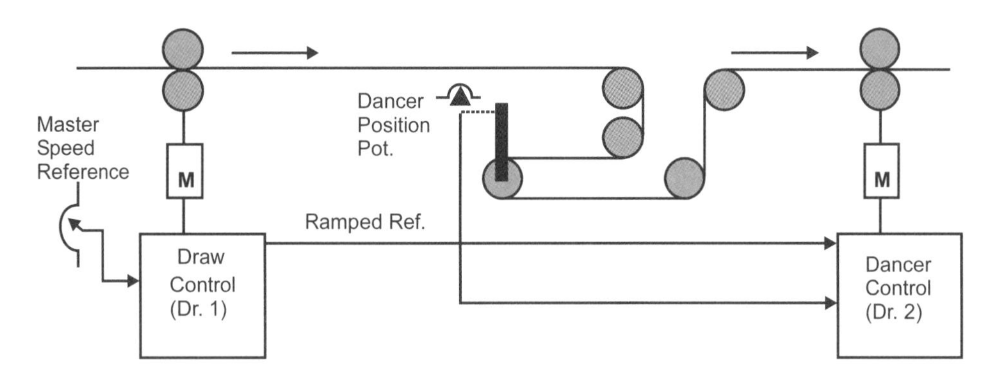

Figure 6-6. Dancer position (tension) control

The purpose of dancer regulation is to control the surface-web tension as material is wound or unwound. This is done by monitoring the position of the dancer feedback device, similar to a variable resistor or pot. The dancer is loaded with web material from the in-feed rolls or from another area of the system. The load on the dancer is monitored with the feedback sent to the dancer control drive. The output of the drive is automatically adjusted to achieve desired web tension at the out-feed rolls of the system.

Web tension variations are absorbed by the dancer and cause the position of the dancer to change. The difference in dancer position feedback and the dancer position set point allow the dancer PI regulator (drive 2) to develop the error correction needed to return the dancer to the set point position by trimming the speed of the section. The proportional gain of the dancer regulator can be adapted for roll diameter changes.

As the diameter of the roll increases, the proportional gain can be set to increase from a minimum gain at core diameter to a maximum gain at full roll. The set point position for the dancer is defaulted to the center of the total dancer movement. The regulation position of the dancer can be adjusted by the operator by way of a drive parameter.

The dancer PI regulator is updated in millisecond timeframes to produce very responsive trim (fine tuning). This allows for very stable dancer position control over the entire speed range.

Remote Operator Interface

In many cases, the actual drive must be located at a distance from the motor and driven machine. This is because the drive must reside in a somewhat clean atmosphere, free from dust particles and other contaminants that may be present in the factory. Also, in many cases, the operator needs to be close to the application to verify system operation or to make machine adjustments under safe conditions.

For these reasons, some type of remote-control capability is more often than not necessary. The simplest remote operator device would be a remote start/stop pushbutton, along with an analog speed pot. A step up from the simplest devices would be an operator console, with pushbuttons for preset speeds, jog, forward/reverse, drive reset, speed increase, and speed decrease. It could be as elaborate as pilot lights to indicate each production stage, status indicators, and a full-color monitor and touch screen to enable the complete system.

For purposes of this text, the focus will be on standard hardwired control devices, followed by automated controls with serial and fiber optic communications.

Figure 6-7 indicates a remote operator station and an operator console.

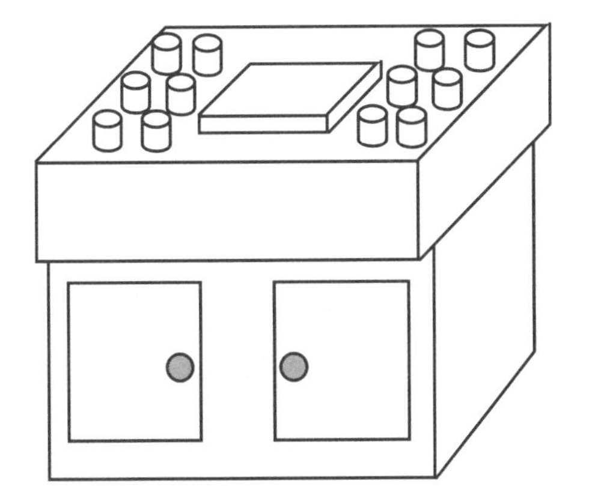

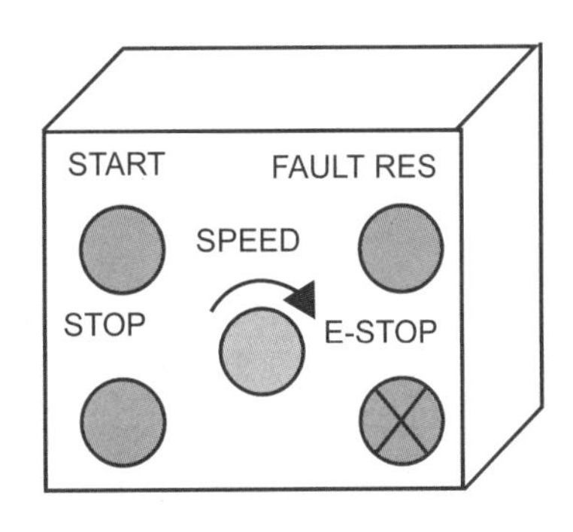

Figure 6-7. Remote operator controls

Any drive, AC or DC, needs two items to be satisfied—start command and speed reference. These remote devices would be wired into the drive's digital input and analog input terminals. Additional controls may be needed such as the ones listed above, but basic drive operation would require start and speed command signals.

Most drives have a control terminal block where standard I/O is connected. In addition, terminals or a removable connector or terminal block may be available for future connection to serial communications. Figure 6-8 indicates standard drive I/O connections.

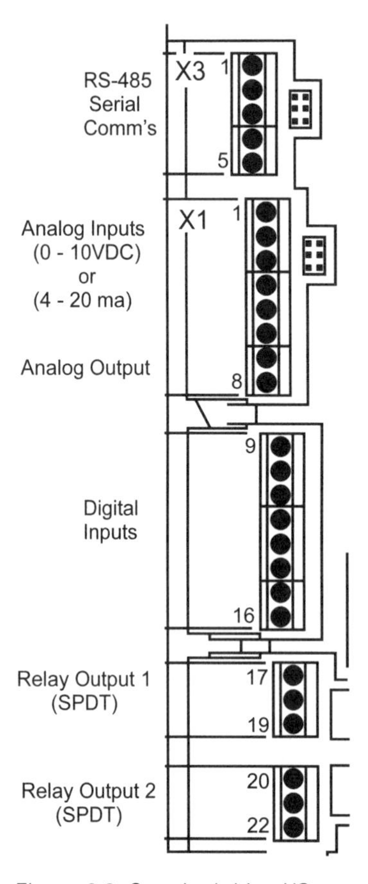

Figure 6-8. Standard drive I/O connections

As shown in Figure 6-8, in many cases the control connections are easily identified and are laid out on the control board in a logical manner in a sequential number scheme. The analog input circuit must be matched with the signal type that is connected. In many cases, small terminal jumpers function to match either voltage-reference or current-reference inputs. Some drives include a DIP switch or rocker switch for signal matching. To function properly, this matching jumper or switch must be located in the proper location. If it is not, unstable control could result, or in the worst case, the drive would operate at maximum speed, with no speed control. The user's manual and the silk screen indication on the board are the likely places to find the correct settings.

The analog output is normally a connection for an external analog meter. This meter could be a separately purchased and mounted device or an item included on an operator console. The normal output would be 0–20 mA and scalable to many types of values.

Digital inputs receive their name from the fact that the input is either on or off. Some drives operate on 12 VDC logic, some on 24 VDC, and still others use a 120 VAC interface option. Typically all the drive needs to see at a digital input terminal is control voltage, which is accomplished through a contact closure (a manual switch, limit switch, auxiliary contact, etc.). Once the drive sees the control-logic voltage at the terminal, the drive performs the operation connected with that digital input (i.e., start, stop, preset speed, reverse, etc.). When control voltage is removed from that terminal, the function stops.

A word about control logic would be appropriate here. Many drives use what is called *source* control. That is, the terminals on the control board must see a control voltage before a function occurs. In other words, voltage must be sourced to the drive. Some drive manufacturers term this control "PNP" logic, in reference to the transistor regulator types involved with the control logic inside the drive. Figure 6-9 illustrates this type of logic control.

In source logic, all of the circuit *commons* are tied together. The circuit is complete when the control voltage is applied to an appropriate DI.

The converse logic control is termed *sink* control. In this type of control, the logic voltage is actually tied to circuit common. The control logic voltage sinks to circuit common. When a contact closure is made with a DI, a circuit is closed between the terminal and circuit ground. The internal control logic energizes the function. This type of control is required by some PLC controllers, where TTL (Transistor-Transistor Logic) outputs, or external voltage sources, must be applied for control. This is also used where circuit ground is something other than earth ground. Figure 6-10 shows this type of control logic.

If there is a possibility for unsafe condition to exist, it would be in the fact that inadvertent grounding (connecting to common) of an external DI switch or contact would cause a function to occur. If for some reason the start switch was connected to ground during routine maintenance of the drive, the drive would accidentally start. Many codes or industrial control schemes require a positive voltage at the terminal block before any operation occurs. In source logic, if the start switch were connected to ground, the logic voltage would be shorted to ground and the operation would stop.

It should be noted that some drive manufacturers include a logic-control power supply on the control board. No external power source is needed, only a contact closure to engage a function. If an external source is required by the drive, care must be taken to ensure that polarity and

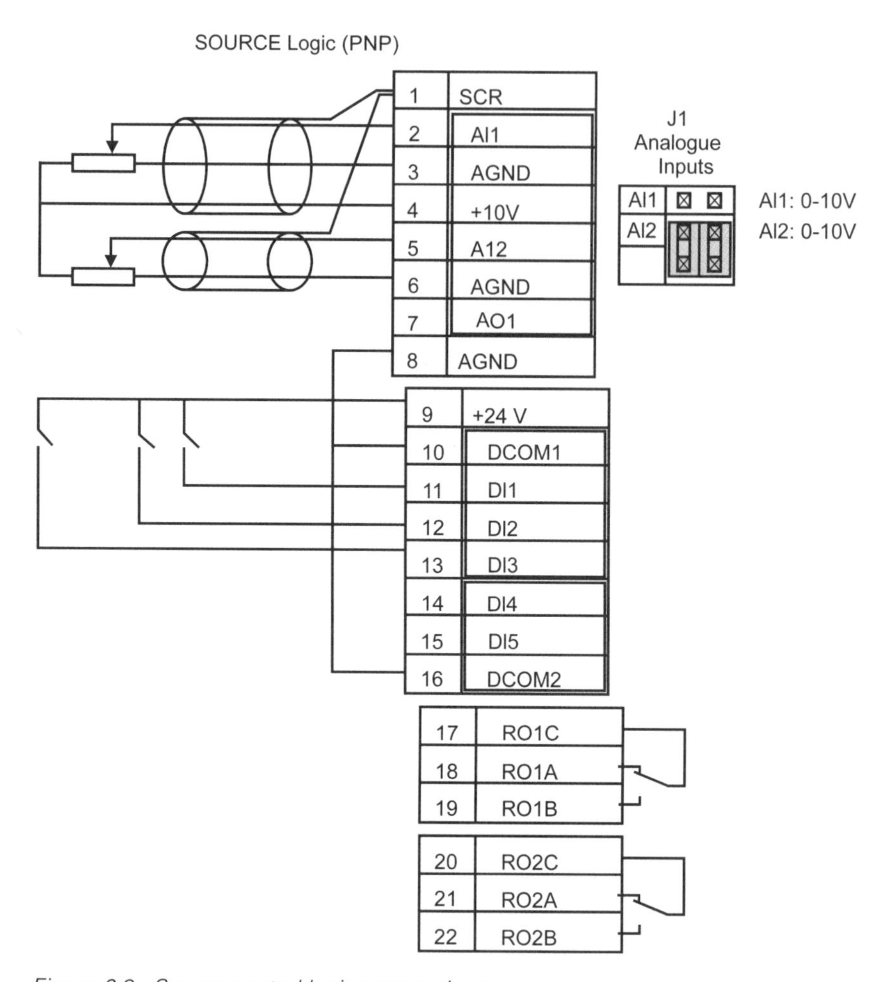

Figure 6-9. Source control logic connections

grounding of the external source matches that of the drive. Ground loops and voltage mismatch can cause many aggravating situations, especially at the low voltage or current values being used.

Many drives include several relay outputs as external-control contacts. These contacts may be *dry* (not carrying a voltage) or *Form C* contacts. They can be programmed for a multitude of operations. For example, the contacts may be programmed to close when a preset speed is selected, or a set speed is reached, or reverse is commanded. In addition, some drives have the capability of monitoring any type of read only information using the relay outputs.

Some manufacturers call this the *supervision* function. Quantities such as current, hertz, output voltage, DC bus voltage, and calculated torque can be internally connected to a relay output. When a programmed value is obtained, or exceeded, the relay would change state or energize. The SPDT (Single Pole, Double Throw) contact can be wired into an indicator light, an alarm circuit, or fed back to a system controller like a PLC. With this type of function, the drive can actually be used as a monitoring tool. It has

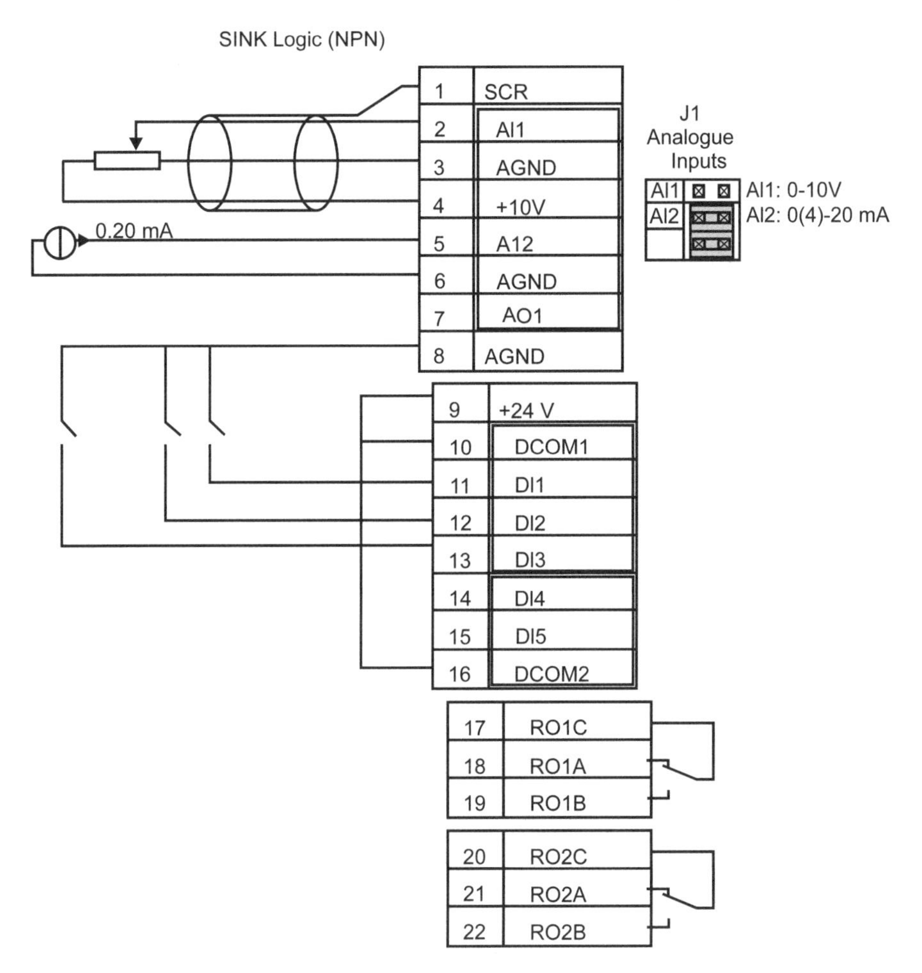

Figure 6-10. Sink control logic connections

the intelligence to compare values and make indications when values are not reached, when they are exceeded, or when they occur.

Some manufacturers use digital outputs instead of relay outputs. A digital output would supply a voltage or current value to an external device, when a programmed value is met.

Serial and Ethernet Communications

During recent years, the push has been to automate many operations to improve product quality or to maximize the efficiency of the system. Communications is a necessary factor in automated systems. Generally speaking, the most common type of drive communication is through a serial link. In this scheme, the data is transmitted in a serial fashion (bits are transferred sequentially, one after the other). When talking about drive communications, three modes currently apply: serial, fiber optic, and Ethernet (intranet) communications. The drive control schemes using each of these modes will be explored, as well as their connections to higher level control systems.

Since serial communications involves sequentially transmitted data, it would not be considered high-speed. Typical communication rates include 4800, 9600, and 19,200 baud (bits per second). This transmission speed is acceptable when communicating with an air-handling unit, which moves volumes of air in and out of the building. This speed would not be acceptable in a paper machine, where high-speed data transmission is critical to the success of paper density, coating, and composition. In many cases, this type of communication is ideal for 24-hour monitoring of drive operation. Figure 6-11 indicates this type of monitoring function.

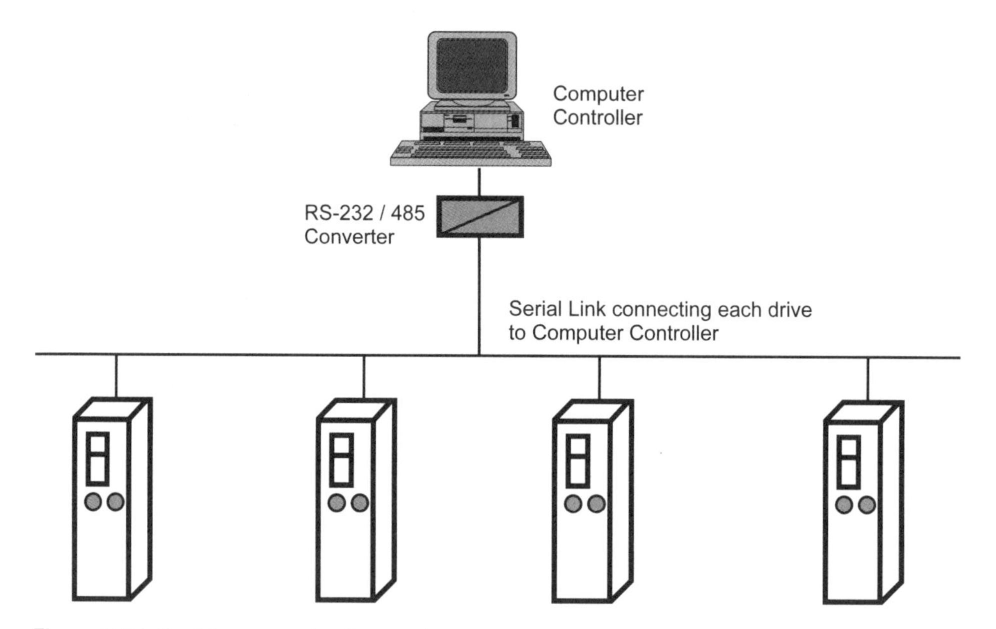

Figure 6-11. Serial communications setup

In most cases, the drive serial link is an RS-485 configuration. With this type of connection, the total communication network length can be ~4000 feet. To accomplish this network matching, the computer must have an RS-485 output. If it does not, then a converter such as the one listed in Figure 6-11 would be needed.

There are many different languages (protocols) available for industrial applications. The HVAC industry also has several protocols available specifically designed for air handling, cooling tower, chiller, and pumping applications. Several companies have been pioneers in the PLC market and have developed their own specific protocol. The drives pictured in Figure 6-11 have the same protocol as that available in the computer. If the protocol matches, then communication is possible after the computer and all drives are programmed to accept serial communications.

In many cases, because of transmission speed and protocol limitations, the total number of drives on a serial link may be as high as 32. In practical terms, if communication speed is at issue, the total number of drives may be around half of that. With a 9600 baud rate, the communication speed starts at 100 ms and would drop from that point, with every drive added to the network.

Typical programming for the drive would include ID number, baud rate, protocol selection, fault function, and communication time out. The computer would also be programmed in a similar fashion to match the drive communication speed and inputs.

Connection to a building's Ethernet or network system is now becoming more popular. There are definite advantages to this type of communication connection. Information gathered from the drives can be easily downloaded to a mainframe network computer. Trends can be identified and analysis can quickly be done, as opposed to transferring data to an independent system and then transferring to the network. In addition, connecting to a building's drive system can easily be accomplished though the Internet, which would be available through a modem connection.

Several software companies offer software that allows the user to develop customized screens that indicate parts of the process. This would include drive operation, inputs to the system, and outputs from the system. Color graphics are fast becoming the interface media of choice. Figure 6-12 gives an example of this type of network/drive communications.

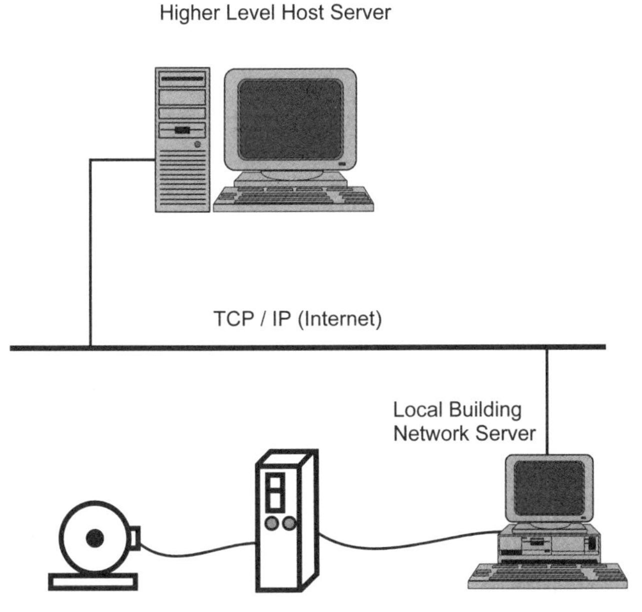

Figure 6-12. Ethernet/drive communications

The Ethernet or network communication speed is higher than that of the serial link. Though the network speed is high (in the low mega-baud range), that doesn't necessarily indicate a rapid transfer of data from network to drive, or vice versa. Information from the network must be transmitted to the drive, and the drive's microprocessor must be able to efficiently decode the information. With the drive's slower serial link rate, only a limited amount of information can be handled per second. The processing speed of many drives would be in the 25- to 50-MHz range, with 2–5 MB of memory available. By today's computer standards, this rate would be extremely slow. However, by today's drive microprocessor standards, this speed is quite adequate for processing all internal drive information. As drive microprocessor technology improves, internal processing speed will also improve.

When connecting the serial link to the drive, it is done in a "daisy chain" fashion. Figure 6-13 indicates this procedure.

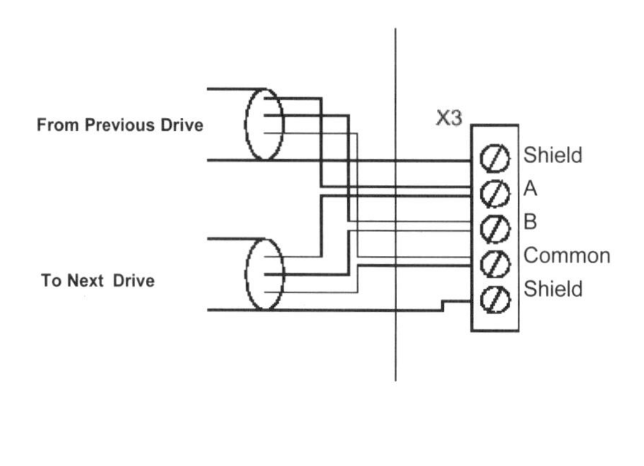

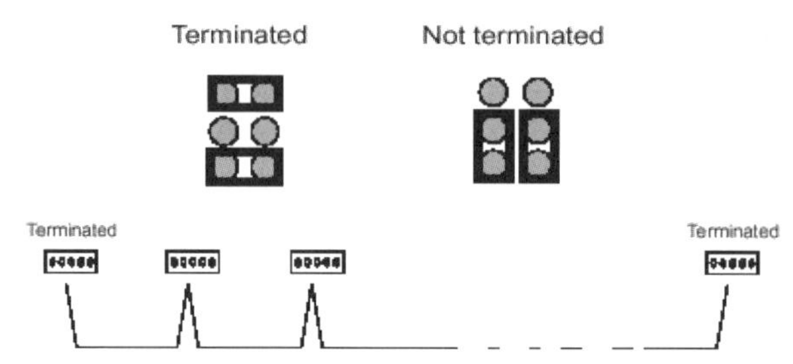

Figure 6-13. Serial link connections

When wiring the drives, care should be taken not to "daisy chain" the shields. Many drive manufacturers include termination resistors on the control board. These resistors reduce electrical noise on the communication network. Termination resistors are to be included on the first and last drive in the network. The inner drives are not to be terminated. (Too many resistors in-series with the communications devices may cause the network to malfunction.) Termination resistors are typically placed "in circuit" by moving a pair of jumpers into position across several contact points.

Fiber-Optic Communications

The use of fiber-optic communications has steadily increased over the last few years. Optical fibers or "light pipes" are highly immune to electrical noise (EMI and RFI) and have the capability of transmitting data over long distances. Glass-constructed optical fibers, along with periodically placed amplifiers, would allow transmission over thousands of feet. The glass-type of optic fiber is quite costly compared with plastic. When comparing optical fiber with hard-wired control, the user must decide between high noise immunity and higher installation costs and lower immunity and lower installation costs.

In addition to drive-to-control fiber-optic communication, an increased use of optical fibers is seen in modern drive circuitry. The advantages of fiber optics for building communications certainly holds true for internal drive control and communications. Figure 6-14 illustrates this type of internal communications.

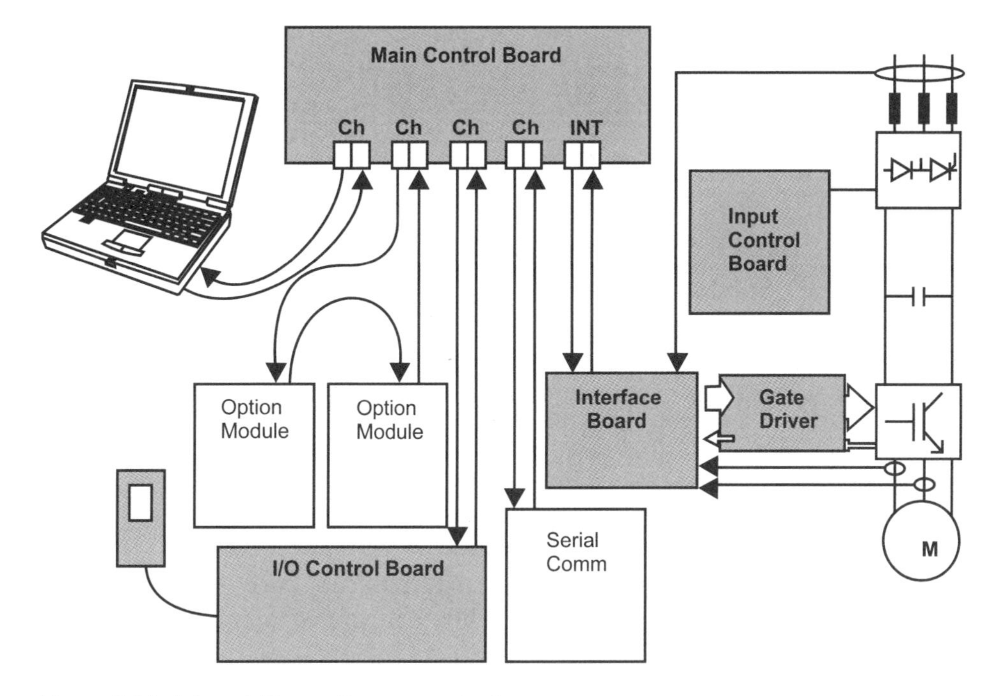

Figure 6-14. Internal fiber-optic communications

In Figure 6-14, the fiber-optic cables interconnect between the main control board and the other definite purpose boards. In addition to the internal communications, fiber optics can also be used to interface with monitor and programming software, as well as optional PLC modules.

In a higher-level system, fiber optics is the normal. Its high speed (~4+ mega baud) communication makes this format ideally suited for industrial applications. Figure 6-15 shows an external drive interface and a PLC.

As seen in Figure 6-15, the drives are connected by fiber optics in a "ring" structure. The fieldbus option module is purchased from the drive vendor. It changes the protocol of the PLC into a language that the drive can understand.

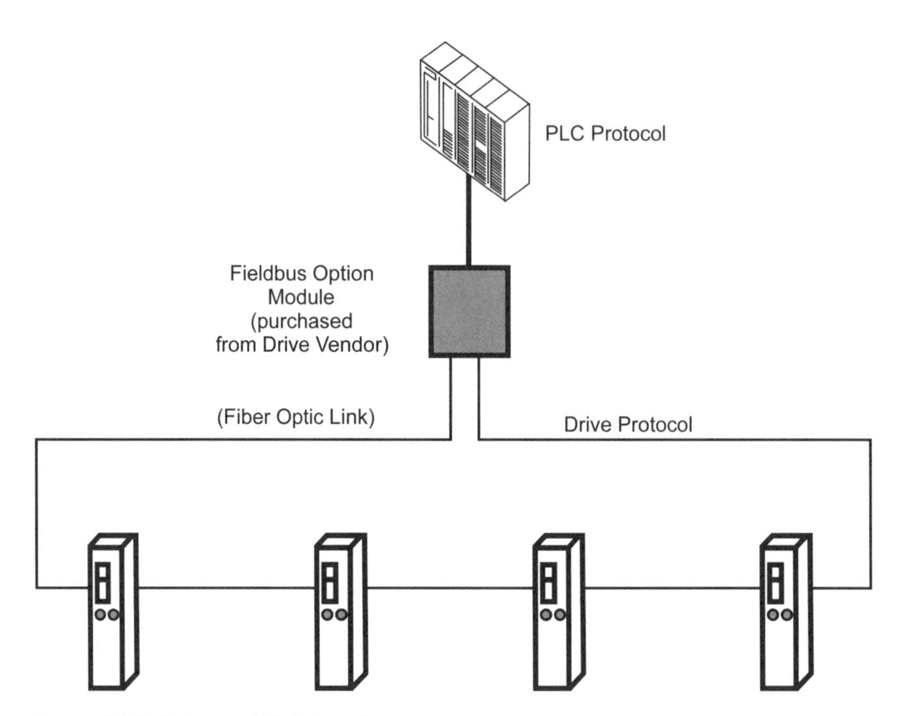

Figure 6-15. Drive and PLC interface

The only possible disadvantage to this type of communications is the fact that if one drive goes down on a fault, the entire communication network goes down with it.

Programming is similar to that of serial communications. Each drive on the network needs a unique ID, as well as baud rate, communication fault function, and communication time out.

When installing a fieldbus module to a network, care must be taken in connecting the *transmit* and *receive* fibers in the correct positions. Figure 6-16 illustrates this procedure.

In Figure 6-16, output from the drive (TX) must be the input to the Fieldbus module (RX). The same holds true for the receiving optic cable. Also be sure that the cable plugs are completely seated into the receptacle by listening for the "snap" action. This allows for the maximum transfer of "light" data into the receptacle.

DC Systems

The basics of DC drives have already been covered. At this point, it would be helpful to review several DC applications and summarize the characteristics of each system.

Printing Press

Figure 6-17 is a simplified diagram of a printing press, using a DC motor and drive system.

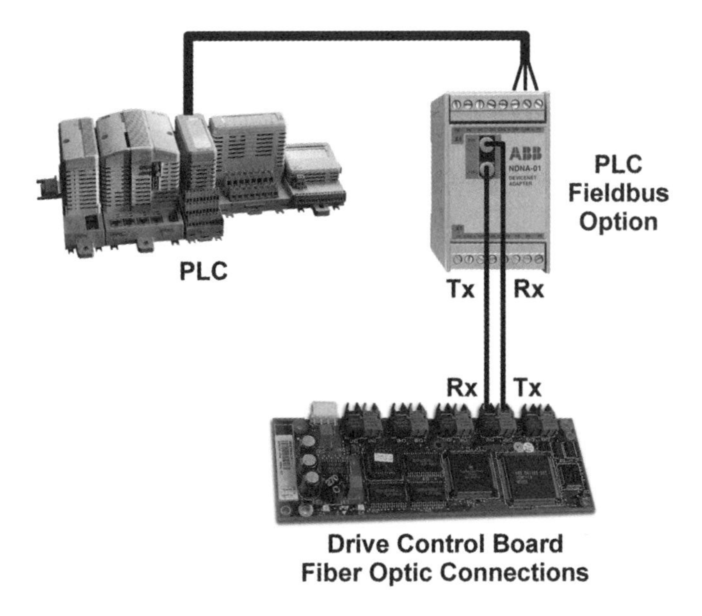

Figure 6-16. Transmit and receive fiber-optic connections (Courtesy of ABB Inc.)

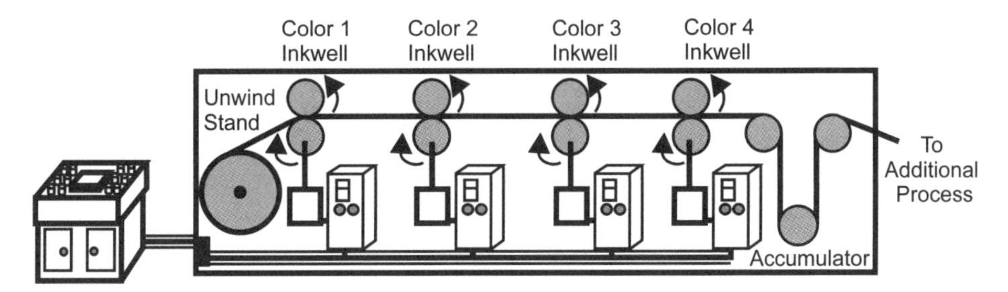

Figure 6-17. DC drive system in a printing press

DC drives have been traditionally used in applications that require high starting torque. Printing presses have long been a prime candidate for DC drives and motors.

Figure 6-17 is a very simplified drawing of a four-color offset press. In an actual press, more rollers would be seen, as well as a variety of sensors, limit switches, and transducers. In some cases, the press may be connected to a common line shaft (i.e., meaning only one motor, connected to a long shaft; each ink station would have a drive shaft connected to the common shaft by a gear box).

Each of the color stations impress a specific color onto the paper web. The key to the success of the press is the tension control and coordination between all of the stations. Each inkwell station and roller set is operated by an individual DC drive and motor. In many cases, the drive is located inside the machine, in a clean and dry cubicle with a constant stream of filtered air.

The lower pinch roll is operated by the drive, which is similar to how a surface-driven winder would be controlled. The upper roll carries the ink plate with the specific color. The accumulator is available to take up any slack in the web, before it moves to the next process (i.e., coating, folding, cutting, bundling, etc.).

This is a prime example of where high-speed fiber-optic communications is essential. Each drive needs to operate at a slightly faster speed than the previous drive. If that ratio of speed is done by each drive, the proper tension will be maintained on the web. If too much tension occurs, the web breaks and the machine must be stopped and re-threaded, which may take up to 1/2 hour to accomplish. If the web has too little tension, the web starts to bunch with the result being uneven ink transfer and wrinkled paper sent to the cutting process. In addition, the register could be off. (The synchronization of all colors means colors printing exactly where they are suppose to print. Off register printing leaves the "shadow" effect, with a blurry image.)

If the printing system is "tuned" properly, all the operator has to do is operate the system speed, to increase or decrease production. The entire coordination is in the automated electronics, not in manual manipulation of torque, speed, tension, and ink coloration.

As time goes on, some of the DC printing systems are being retrofitted with flux vector AC drive systems. As the technology of torque control with AC drives improves, this trend will continue for many years to come.

Ski Lifts

Another traditional DC drive system is that seen in ski lift units. These types of applications are also found at state fairs, theme parks, and any other location where above ground "people movers" are found. Figure 6-18 indicates a simplified version of a ski lift system.

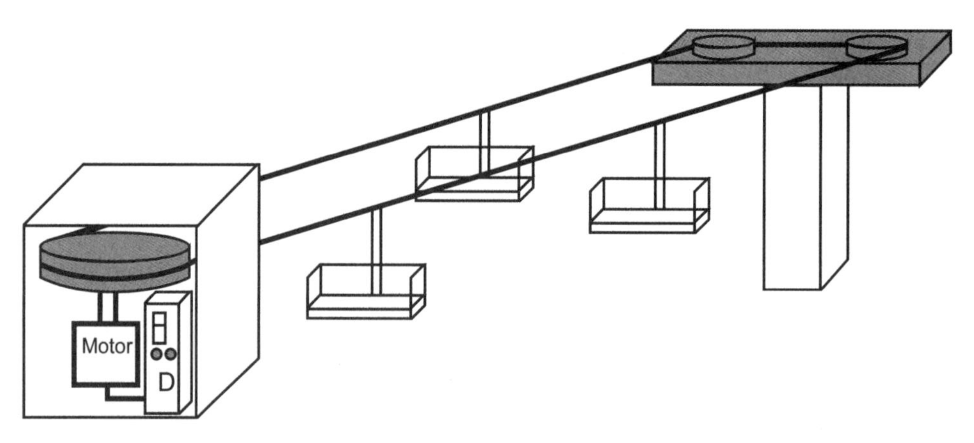

Figure 6-18. Ski lift system (chair lift)

Additional components are found in ski lift systems. Sensors, current limit devices, safety limit switches, and monitors are just a few of the additional items found in modern lift systems. Typically the drive is located inside a clean, dry, heated room, which may or may not be in the loading building.

Quite often, the drive system is asked to start up at full torque, with rated capacity of people on board the chairs. In some cases, the entire system is manually controlled by an operator located in the loading building or a control station. The operator's job is to observe the system and change speed if necessary. In other cases, the system is operated automatically from the control station (auto), or by remote, from another location—possibly at the drop-off point (hand). This is only one instance where hand/auto control is possible. There are a variety of other applications where hand/auto functions are required for convenience of the operators. Figure 6-19 indicates a diagram of hand/auto control.

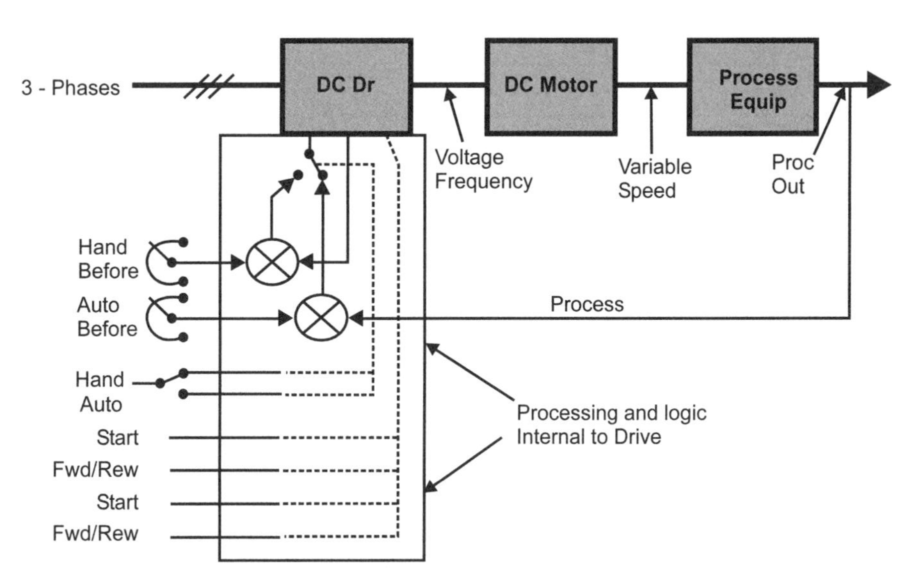

Figure 6-19. Hand/auto control

Another DC system application is found in material handling. Figure 6-20 shows a barge unloader application with coal being the material. Coal is delivered by ship and brought to the utility by barge, which can maneuver into tighter locations compared with a freighter. This application would be found at coal-fired power utility plants or at any factory where material is delivered by ship or barge.

As seen in Figure 6-20, the barge, connected by cable to a DC motor, is pulled into position by a DC drive. Another cable, connected to the other end of the barge, would also be operated by a DC motor and drive (not shown in the figure). The function of that drive is to stabilize the barge and to control back tension. As the barge moves in the direction indicated, the other DC drive slowly moves the motor in the opposite direction, maintaining tension at all times. As the barge is slowly moving, the coal

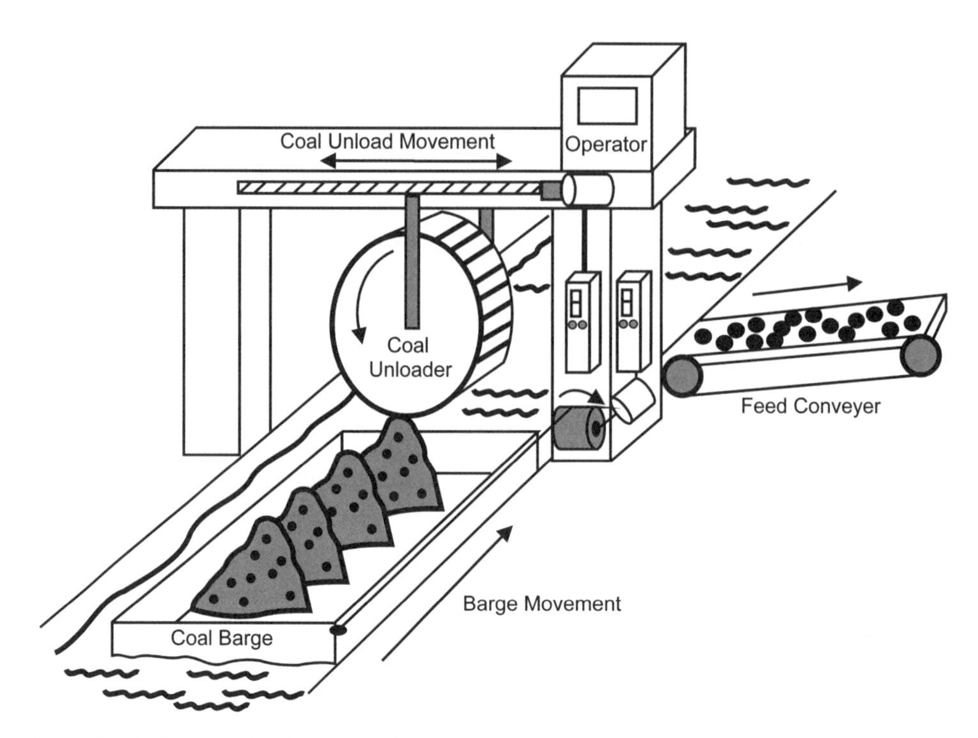

Figure 6-20. Barge unloader application

unloader rotates like a Ferris wheel, in the direction indicated. Using swivel-type scoops, coal is deposited onto the feed conveyor to be transported to the coal yard for storage or directly to the utility boiler system. The operator controls the process, manually moving the coal unloader up and down and the gantry back and forth, to achieve maximum removal.

In this application, DC drives and motors work well for tension control of the coal barge. In this case, 50- to 100-HP DC motors can operate the application satisfactorily. The gantry motor and drive can also be DC or even AC and as low as 50 HP. Since precise torque or tension control is not required in the gantry system, a standard AC PWM drive will perform the functions required. Limit switches and joystick control are standard manual operator devices. (Note: Joysticks have a center off position. When pushed away from the operator, the drive speed is forward. When the joystick is pulled toward the operator, the drive speed is reversed.)

This automated control comes where the two DC drives and motors have to slightly "fight" each other to provide adequate tension control. Therefore the DC drives have to coordinate in speed and torque reference to maintain the tension required. Too little torque could mean an unstable barge and coal not removed by the semi-automated process. Extra time and effort would be required to manually unload any remaining coal.

There are many more DC applications that use torque, tension, and precise speed control throughout the process. The above are only a few, but they do highlight the torque and tension capability of DC systems, as well as low-speed control.

AC Systems

The AC drive and motor system has gained acceptance in the coordinated system environment because of the improvements in power semiconductor technology. In addition, high-speed process control, microprocessor, and communications improvements make the AC drive look like another node on the process network. Steel and aluminum processing, converting lines, and paper machines all require precise speed and torque control.

The basics of AC drives have already been covered. At this point, it would be helpful to review several AC applications and summarize the characteristics of each system.

Many drive applications use multiple motors to provide coordinated control. In certain applications, one section of the machine may operate faster than commanded speed. In cases like these, and where overhauling loads are possible, a common DC bus configuration is able to regenerate energy back to the DC bus. That energy is then used by another inverter section to power a different section of the system. Figure 6-21 indicates a common DC bus configuration.

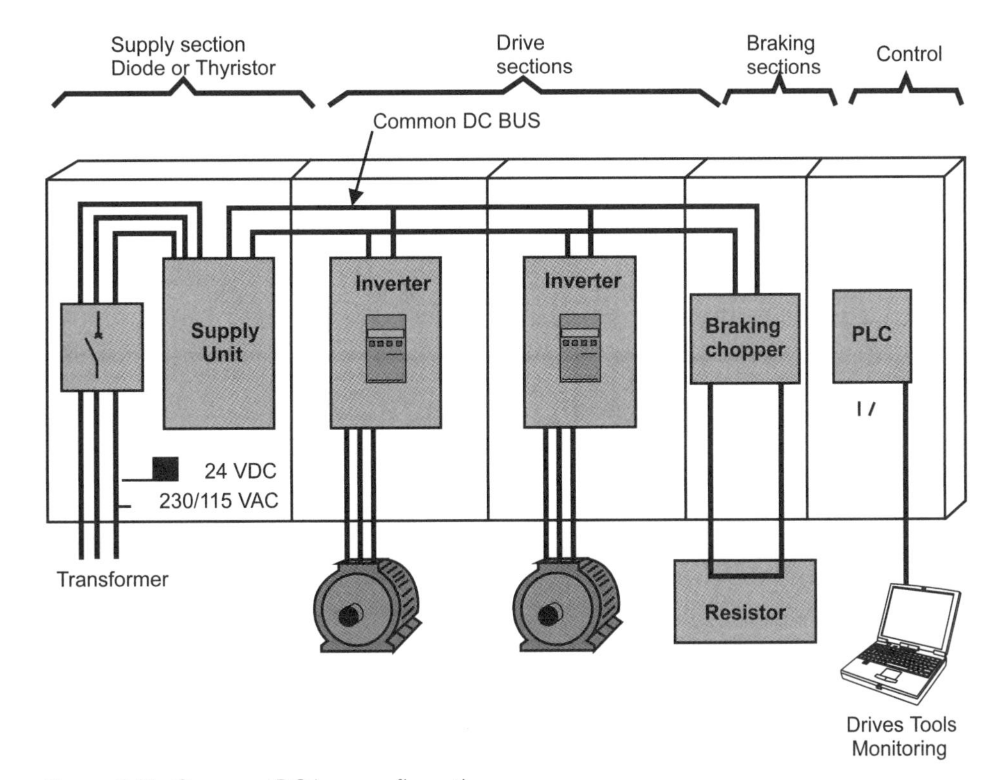

Figure 6-21. Common DC bus configuration

The supply section converts AC to DC through a fixed diode bridge rectifier. When horsepower is in the 1500- to 2000-HP range, the input converter section may be SCRs, to handle the high current. Reverse connected IGBT bridges may be used for full, four-quadrant regenerative braking. This scheme also has the capability of operating in a very low harmonic mode.

Several manufacturers offer water-cooled units, which allow for increased sizes of drives, using diode bridge rectifiers, in smaller sizes than non-water-cooled. The braking chopper is part of a DB, IGBT sensing circuit, that closes when a fast deceleration or stop is required. As in many cases with large horsepower, the controller unit is typically PLC mounted in a separate cabinet, along with other software and control devices.

Coal Classifier

As an AC coordinated system component, a coal classifier uses devices found in many control systems. This system is found in coal-fired power utility plants, but the principles are the same whether filtering coal, cement, sand, or any other medium. Figure 6-22 indicates this system.

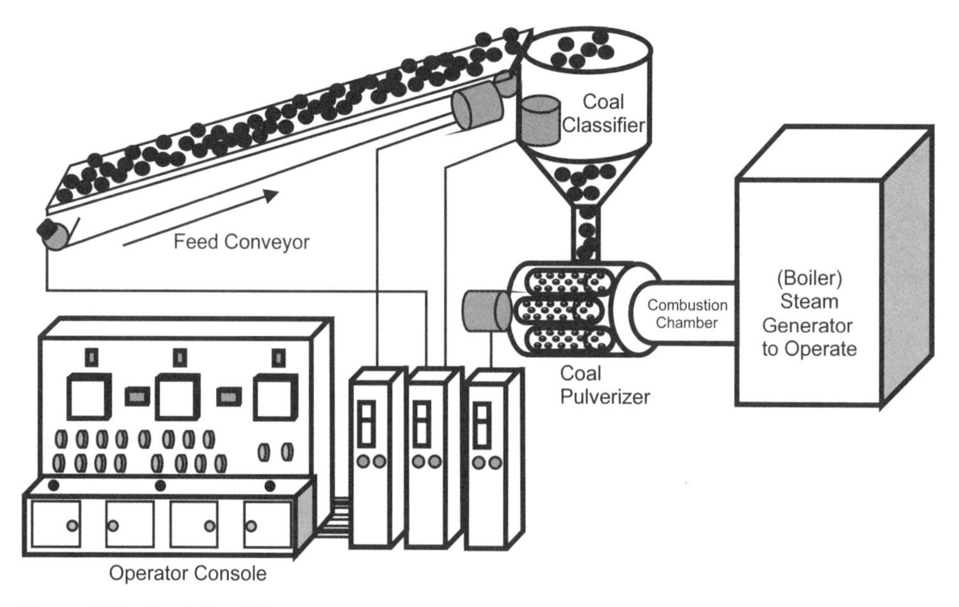

Figure 6-22. Coal classifier system

The classifier is part of a much larger, coordinated system. The output of the boiler /steam generator is dependent on the quality and purity of the coal powder that is burned as fuel.

Raw coal is loaded by conveyor into the hopper of the classifier. The classifier is operated by an AC motor and sifts through the coal particles, dropping the small pieces into the coal pulverizer. The output of the pulverizer is a fine coal dust that burns cleanly and evenly, with the highest BTU output possible. The powder is then forced into the combustion chamber, where it is used to fire the boiler and create steam for the turbine generator.

The classifier is operated as a closed-loop system. The plant operator controls the ultimate speed of the entire system. However, the classifier is part of that coordinated effort. A desired set point speed is entered at the operator console. The drive accepts that set point, and through PI control, looks at the actual speed feedback of the feed conveyor. The drive then makes speed corrections to power the classifier motor at the optimum speed. Too high of a speed would allow too many coal particles to enter the classifier, overloading the system. Too low of a speed would mean that few coal particles would enter the classifier and pulverizer. A lean burn would result in the combustion chamber, and BTU output would be reduced.

By means of PI control, this section of the system would operate at peak efficiency. The pulverizer unit would have a similar coordinated scheme, set up in the controller software.

HVAC Systems

AC variable-frequency drives (VFDs) are well known for their energy-saving capabilities. The savings can be quite substantial, as indicated in the next figures.

Assumptions:

- Full rated flow = 178,000 CFM @ 3″ of H_2O
- Fan/blower efficiency = 85%
- Motor efficiency = 94%
- Drive efficiency = 98%
- Rated shaft power = 100 HP
- Cost per KWH = $0.10

Figure 6-23 indicates an energy-use comparison of variable-speed AC drive use versus outlet damper control.

Figure 6-24 shows fan efficiency improvement using variable speed compared with outlet damper control.

Figure 6-25 shows the annual savings that a variable-speed fan can have compared with outlet damper control.

It is clear that the amount of energy savings is substantial. The greatest savings are available when the fan is operated at 40–70% flow for the majority of the operating time. Savings can be also realized with VFDs versus inlet guide vanes. However, the highest savings will be realized using VFDs with a flow rate of only 30% for the majority of time. Even at that

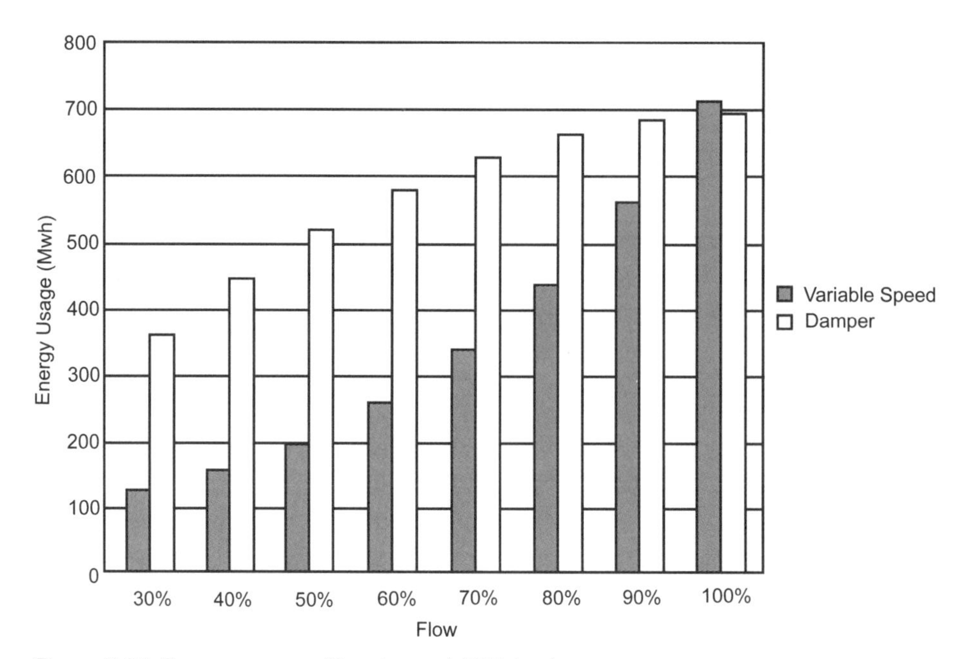

Figure 6-23. Fan energy use (Courtesy of ABB Inc.)

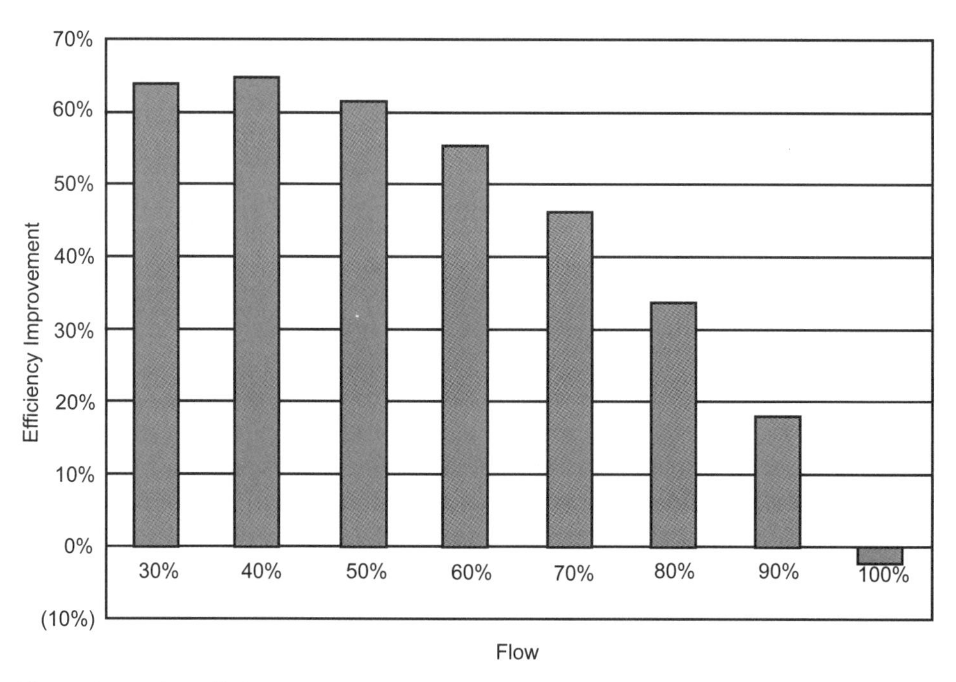

Figure 6-24. Fan efficiency improvement (Courtesy of ABB Inc.)

flow rate, a savings of less than $25,000 annually is seen, about the same as an outlet-damper system and at the same flow rate.

The system that enables the energy savings above is shown in Figure 6-26.

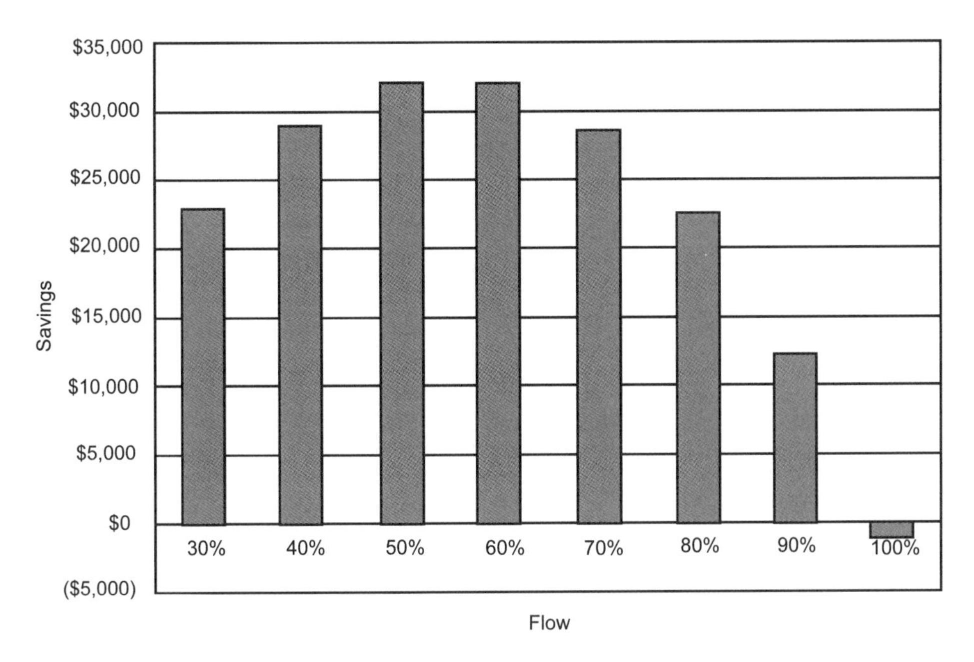

Figure 6-25. Annual savings for variable-speed fan (Courtesy of ABB Inc.)

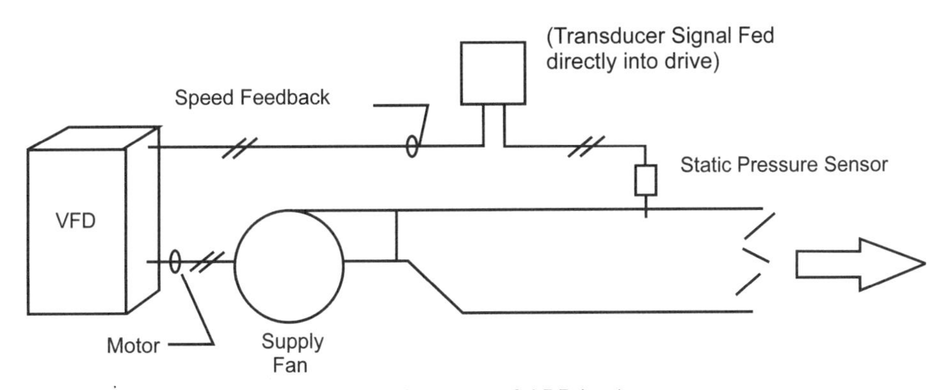

Figure 6-26. PI control using a VFD (Courtesy of ABB Inc.)

In this example, the energy savings would come as a result of completely opening the outlet damper. The drive then operates as a closed-loop controller, responding the static pressure feedback.

Cooling Towers

Another system that can realize substantial energy savings is a cooling tower. Figure 6-27 indicates how a cooling-tower system operates.

The speed of the cooling tower fan(s) is controlled by the VFD. In traditional systems, the fan would operate at full speed 24 hours per day, unless cooling water was not required. With the VFD, operating in PI control, the set point temperature is converted to a voltage set point. The feedback from a temperature transducer allows the drive to calculate temperature error and respond with increased or decreased fan speed, or zero speed.

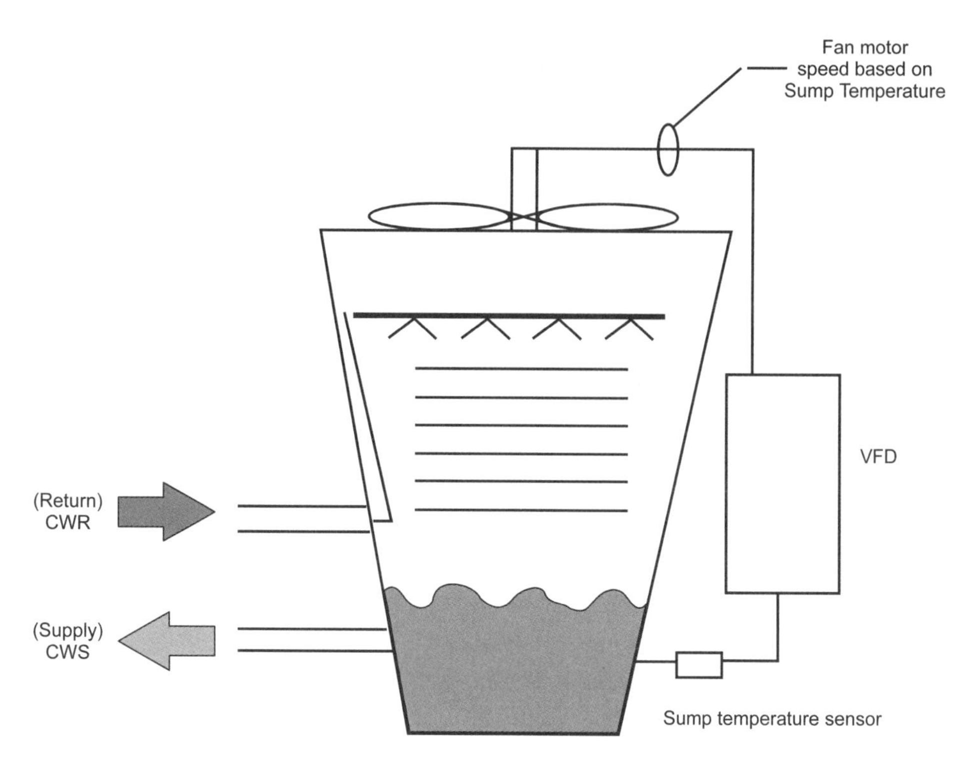

Figure 6-27. Cooling tower application (Courtesy of ABB Inc.)

HVAC is a systems environment for AC drives. Seldom, if ever, are AC drives manually operated in office buildings, schools, or any other location where temperature or humidity is critical for daily operation. A typical VFD system connected to a building automation system is shown in figure 6-28.

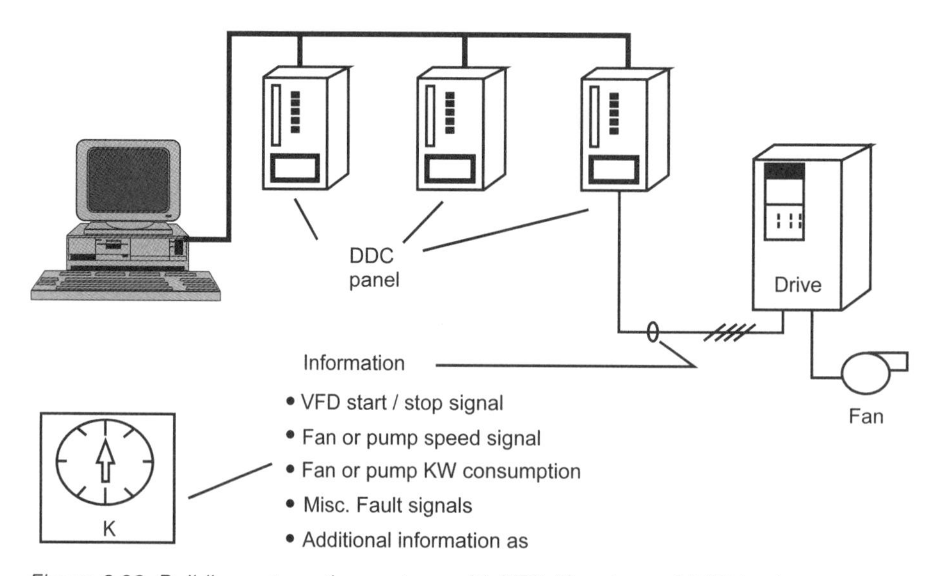

Figure 6-28. Building automation system with VFD (Courtesy of ABB Inc.)

Distributed digital control (DDC) provides the automated set points to the drives. The drive's on-board PI control provides motor speed appropriate to control the medium required. In return, the DDC systems can poll the drive for important operating information, such as start/stop, faults, KW consumption, and more.

Using the systems that are on the market today, it is possible to connect to a variety of building automation systems, using almost any manufacturer's drive. However, comparisons should be made between vendors, to verify how much and what type of information can be obtained by the DDC system. Some drives only allow start/stop and speed reference signals to be transmitted. A very few manufacturers will allow up to 60 parameters (points) to be viewed by the building automation system. In this age of timely information, the easier it is to acquire operating information, the more efficient building operators can be.

AC versus DC Drive Systems

An adequate economic comparison between two types of drives requires an analysis of all of the costs incurred over the entire life cycle of the equipment. In addition to the purchase price of the drives and related equipment, this includes all of the material and labor costs required to obtain and install the equipment. It also requires an analysis of the costs to put the drive into operation, plus all of the costs to operate and maintain the equipment during the entire time it is expected to be in service.

The best way to determine which is the most economical system is to perform a detailed analysis. There are no rules of thumb that will consistently and accurately predict the outcome of an analysis. Since the introduction of AFDs (Adjustable Frequency Drives) in the late 1960s, these drives have been slowly proving to be the most economical choice in an increasing variety of applications, but individual application details can often tip the balance either way.

The following is an outline of elements typically included in total life cycle cost. The items marked with an asterisk are the most significant items.

- Procurement expenses
- Project engineering expenses of selecting and specifying the equipment
- Purchasing department expenses
- Freight and receiving expenses
- Cost of equipment and installation materials
- Controller options and accessories
- Motor, options, and accessories *

- Operator interface equipment
- Supervisory control equipment
- Machine interface equipment
- Transformer and other power distribution equipment*
- Power factor and harmonic correction equipment*
- Wire, cable, conduit, etc.*
- Installation and commissioning expenses*
- Operating expenses*
- Electric power
- Periodic maintenance
- Planned downtime
- Unplanned downtime
- Cost of routine or major anticipated repairs
- Spare and/or replacement parts and equipment

In addition to the above, the following factors should be considered when analyzing AC versus DC systems.

Technology

Because it is relatively easy and economical to control the speed and torque of a DC motor, DC drives have long been the adjustable-speed drive of choice. However most drive users prefer to use VFDs wherever possible because AC motors are much more rugged and reliable than DC motors and they require less maintenance.

For many years, drive manufacturers have been working to develop adjustable-frequency drives that will allow AC motors to be controlled as effectively and economically as DC motors. It is evident that this development effort would result in an overall shift in drive use from DC drives toward AC drives. The motor is the controlling element of a DC drive system, while the electronic controller is the controlling element of an AC drive system. Since the emphasis on technology advancement is primarily electronic rather than electromechanical, the overall progress in technology has a greater impact on AC drives.

Performance Capabilities

With the introduction of flux vector drives, there are virtually no fundamental performance limitations that would prevent a VFD from being used in any application where DC drives are used. Using the latest control techniques, the performance available from AC motors equals or exceeds the performance available from DC motors.

In areas such as high-speed operation, the inherent capability of AC motors exceeds the capability of DC motors. Several manufacturers now offer inverter duty motors that are specifically designed for use with VFDs. Inverter-duty motors have speed-range capabilities that are equal to or above the capabilities of DC motors. In addition, DC motors usually require cooling air forced through the interior of the motor to operate over wide speed ranges. Totally enclosed AC motors are also available with wide speed range capabilities.

The only question should be one of availability of models in the required horsepower range or implementation of certain optional capabilities or special functions.

Motor Purchase Price

The price of the motor must be evaluated along with the cost of all of the other drive system equipment. Although DC motors are usually significantly more expensive than AC motors, the motor-drive package price for an VFD is often comparable to the price of a DC drive package. However, if spare motors are required, the package price tends to favor the VFD. Since AC motors are more reliable in a variety of situations and have a longer average life, the DC drive alternative may require a spare motor while the AC drive may not.

Since DC motors tend to be less efficient than AC motors, they generally require more elaborate cooling arrangements. Most AC motors are supplied in totally enclosed housings that are cooled by blowing air over the exterior surface which is in intimate contact with the stator core, the source of the majority of the losses.

Since cooling air does not enter the interior of the motor, dirt and contaminants in the air do not usually cause problems. Totally enclosed DC motors are usually very expensive because they must be over-sized to adequately dissipate heat because of losses in the armature.

DC motors are usually cooled by blowing air through the interior of the motor. At a minimum, this means that the motor will be equipped with a blower and filter box. If the atmosphere is particularly dirty or corrosive, clean air must be ducted in from a centralized cooling system. In evaluating the price of the motor, it is important to consider the cost of a cooling arrangement that is adequate for the application.

Cost of Motor Options

AC motors are available with a wide range of optional electrical and mechanical configurations and accessories. DC motors are generally less flexible and the optional features are generally more expensive. Optional mechanical configurations include various types of enclosures, special shafts, optional conduit box locations, special bearings, and other options.

Mounting options include vertical mounting and several types of flanged end brackets. Motor accessories include separately powered blowers or fans, tachometer generators or encoders, various types of temperature-sensing devices, space heaters, friction brakes, and other items. Some configurations such as explosion-proof enclosures are very expensive options for DC motors compared with AC motors.

A number of AC motor manufacturers have developed motors specifically designed for use with adjustable-frequency drives. As a result, AC motors are readily available with special cooling arrangements or enhanced thermal capacity for wide-speed ranges. Motor-mounted tachometer generators or encoders are also readily available.

A VFD without tach feedback can be used in some applications where DC drives typically require tach feedback. Since a tach generator or encoder adds significantly to the price of the motor, it is important to carefully consider whether or not it is required.

Additional System Component Costs

As mentioned earlier, a valid comparison of equipment prices must include the cost of all of the components of the drive system. Most DC drive installations require a drive-isolation transformer or input-line chokes. The transformer or chokes provide impedance, which reduces power line notching caused by the SCRs in the DC controller. Since PWM drives have a diode bridge input section, they do not cause line notching and therefore have less need for added input impedance.

Large DC drives, with motors rated 1000 HP or higher usually require rather costly armature circuit chokes to provide sufficient commutating reactance to ensure spark-free commutation and acceptable brush life. Large AC drives require no equivalent expenditure.

The cost of power factor and harmonic-correction equipment must also be considered as part of the total drive package price. As mentioned earlier, DC drives sometimes require a centralized cooling system that provides clean cooling air through ducts to the motor. Although a centralized cooling system is used to supply air to multiple motors, it is a drive-system component that must be considered in any cost comparison.

Summary

Expenses incurred in selecting and specifying drive systems tend to be lowest for the type of equipment that is the most familiar to the specifier. The equipment supplier can help to reduce this expense by providing application information and assistance. Ultimately, it is the user that must be satisfied with the purchase of the drive system. The most efficient use of system capabilities will be obtained if up-front time is taken to review the application, and match the system with the requirements.

Chapter Review

Drive systems operate in a coordinated fashion, with control between the controller (PLC) and the drive unit. A variety of sensors, switches, and transducers are a part of the overall scheme of automation.

Proportional integral derivative control is used when automatic control of some quantity is required. Temperature, pressure, and humidity levels are just a few of the items that can be conveniently controlled by PID.

Tension control is a major part of any coordinated system that processes web material. Dancer control is similar to tension control, in that a separate regulator signal is fed back to the drive for correction to take place. Proportional gain and integration time play a part in the tuning of a web system.

A variety of remote operator devices are available for interfacing signals to the drive unit. Remote-operator stations are the simplest form of remote control. Standard I/O would include start/stop, speed reference, digital inputs, analog outputs, and relay outputs. Both sinking and sourcing control are used in industry today.

Serial communications is the simplest form of communication link to a drive. Typically, multiple drives are controlled by one system controller, which could be a computer that is set up to talk to the protocol that is installed in the drive. Fiber-optic communications has the highest immunity to noise compared with other forms of drive communications. Optical fibers are connected in a ring structure and can be connected with plastic or glass fiber. Building automation systems or Ethernet systems are able to talk to many drives on the market today.

DC systems have traditionally been associated with printing press, ski lift, and material handling applications. A major benefit of DC is the high starting torque at zero speed. AC systems have their roots in energy-saving applications. Substantial energy savings can be realized using VFDs instead of fixed-speed outlet damper control. Additional applications for AC drives include conveyors, overhead gantry units, overhauling loads, etc.

A multitude of questions should be asked when comparing AC systems with DC systems. Initial procurement, operating, and maintenance costs need to be analyzed over the life of the equipment to be installed.

Check Your Knowledge

1. Name three or more devices that are used in closed-loop systems for set point or feedback conditions.
2. Why is proper tension control important in a web-fed system?
3. What is a dancer control?

4. What are jumpers or DIP switches used for when connected to analog input signals?
5. What is the difference between sinking and sourcing control logic?
6. What is meant by serial communications? How is it used with drives?
7. What are termination resistors and why are they used?
8. What is the advantage of using fiber optics instead of serial communications?
9. What is the benefit of using DC drives in applications such as printing and ski lifts (chair lifts)?
10. What is the common DC bus configuration and why is it used?
11. How is a VFD used to save energy in an outlet damper application?
12. What are the most significant items to be reviewed when evaluating AC or DC drive systems?

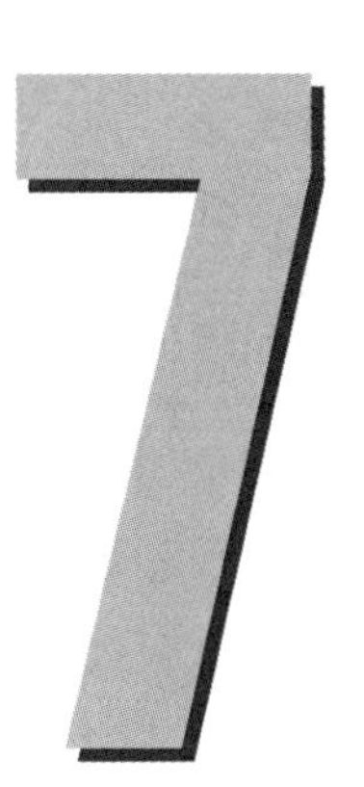

Maintenance and Troubleshooting of Drive Systems

Whether it be AC or DC drive systems, maintenance of the electronic equipment is rather easy if some basic steps are followed. In this chapter, the focus will be on the preventative maintenance of drive equipment. If a drive should malfunction, some practical tips will be presented on how to find the source of the problem.

First and foremost, the focus will be on how to avoid drive problems in the first place. By integrating some simple, logical steps into a preventative maintenance program, drives can provide many years of trouble-free service. Before looking at those steps, a quick review of variable-frequency drives (VFDs) is in order.

A VFD controls the speed, torque, and direction of an AC induction motor. It takes fixed-voltage and fixed-frequency AC input and converts it to a variable-voltage and variable-frequency AC output. In very small VFDs, a single power pack unit may contain the converter and inverter. Fairly involved control circuitry coordinates the switching of power devices, typically through a control board that dictates the firing of power components in the proper sequence. A microprocessor or digital signal processor (DSP) meets all the internal logic and decision requirements.

As seen in an earlier chapter 4 (Drive Types section) a VFD is basically a computer and power supply. The same safety and equipment precautions you would apply to a computer or a power supply apply here.

Routine Drive Maintenance

VFD maintenance requirements fall into three basic categories:

1. Keep it clean.

2. Keep it dry.

3. Keep the connections tight.

Keep It Clean

Most VFDs fall into the NEMA 1 category (side vents for cooling air flow) or NEMA 12 category (sealed, dust-tight enclosure). Drives that fall in the NEMA 1 category are susceptible to dust contamination. Dust on VFD hardware can cause a lack of airflow, resulting in diminished performance from heat sinks and circulating fans. Figure 7-1 illustrates this type of situation.

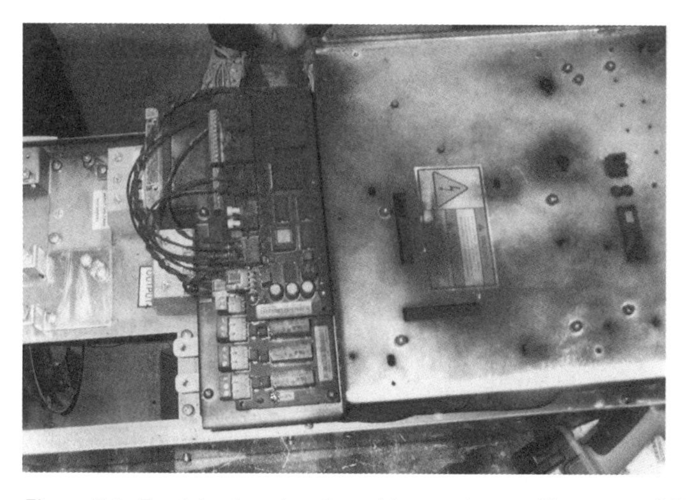

Figure 7-1. Fan injecting dust into drive enclosure (Courtesy of ABB Inc.)

Dust on an electronic device can cause malfunction or even failure. Dust absorbs moisture, which also contributes to failure. Periodically spraying air through the heat-sink fan is a good preventative-maintenance measure. Discharging compressed air into a VFD is a viable option in some environments, but typical industrial air contains oil and water. To use compressed air for cooling, you must use air that is oil-free and dry or you are likely to do more harm than good. That requires a specialized, dedicated, and expensive air supply. And you still run the risk of generating electrostatic charges (ESD).

A non-static-generating spray or a reverse-operated ESD vacuum will reduce static buildup. Common plastics are prime generators of static electricity. The material in ESD vacuum cases and fans is a special, non-static-generating plastic. These vacuums and cans of non-static-generating compressed air are available through companies that specialize in static-control equipment.

Keep It Dry

In Figure 7-2 you can see what happened to a control board periodically subjected to a moist environment.

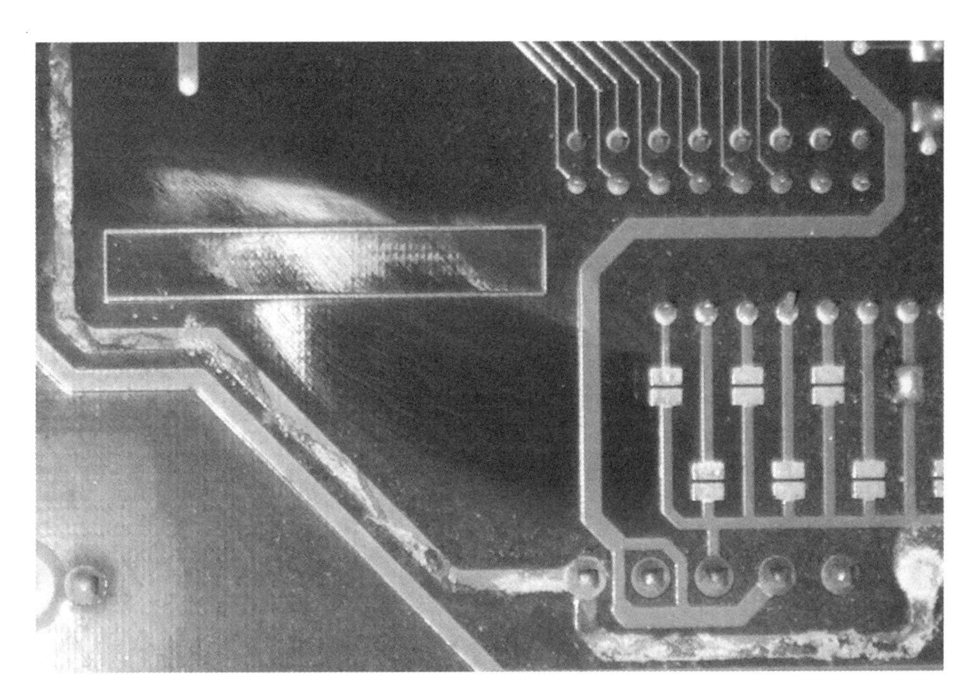

Figure 7-2. Corrosion on board traces caused by moisture (Courtesy of ABB Inc.)

Initially, the VFD in Figure 7-2 was wall-mounted in a clean, dry area of a mechanical room and moisture was not a problem. However, as is often the case, a well-meaning modification led to problems.

In this example, an area of the building required a dehumidifier close to the mechanical room. Since wall space was available above the VFD, this is where the dehumidifier went. Unfortunately, the VFD was a NEMA 1 enclosure style (side vents and no seal around the cover). The obvious result was water dripping from the dehumidifier into the drive. In six months, the VFD accumulated enough water to produce circuit board corrosion.

What about condensation? Some VFD manufacturers included a type of condensation protection on earlier product versions. When the temperature dropped below 32°F, the software logic would not allow the drive to start. VFDs seldom offer this protection today. If you operate the VFD all day every day, the normal radiant heat from the heatsink should prevent condensation. Unless the unit is in continuous operation, use a NEMA 12 enclosure and a thermostatically controlled space heater if you locate it where condensation is likely.

Keep Connections Tight

While this sounds basic, checking connections is a step many people miss or do incorrectly—and the requirement applies even in clean rooms. Heat cycles and mechanical vibration can lead to substandard connections, as can standard preventative-maintenance practices. Re-torquing screws is not a good idea, and further tightening an already tight connection can ruin the connection.

Here's why:

Although re-torquing as a way of checking tightness is common in many preventative-maintenance procedures, it violates basic mechanical principles and does more harm than good. A screw has maximum clamping power at a torque value specific to its size, shape, and composition. Exceeding that torque value permanently reduces the clamping power of that screw by reducing its elasticity and deforming it. Loosening and then re-torquing also reduce elasticity, which still means a loss of clamping power. Doing this to a lock washer results in a permanent 50% loss.

What should you do? Use an infrared thermometer to note hot connections. (A "hot connection" results when poor contact is made between two conductors, which causes increased resistance and an elevated temperature in the connection.) Check their torque (using a torque wrench, and matching the value against the manufacturer's installation recommendations). If they have merely worked loose, you can try re-tightening them. Note which screws were loose and be sure to give them an infrared check at the next preventative maintenance cycle. If they are loose again, replace them.

Finally, don't forget the "tug test." To do the "tug test" simply pull, with moderate pressure, on each of the wires inserted into terminal blocks. This should be done to both power and control terminal connections. This checks crimps, as well as screw connections. Do not do this with the drive online with the process, or you may cause some very expensive process disturbances.

Bad connections eventually lead to arcing. Arcing at the VFD input could result in nuisance over voltage faults, clearing of input fuses, or damage to protective components. Arcing at the VFD output could result in over-current faults or even damage to the power components. Figures 7-3 and 7-4 show what can happen.

Loose control-wiring connections can cause erratic operation. For example, a loose start/stop signal wire can cause uncontrollable VFD stops. A loose speed-reference wire can cause the drive speed to fluctuate, resulting in scrap, machine damage, or personal injury.

Additional Steps Beyond Routine

1. As part of a mechanical inspection procedure, don't overlook internal VFD components. Check circulating fans for signs of bearing failure or foreign objects—usually indicated by unusual noise or shafts that appear wobbly.

Figure 7-3. Arcing caused by loose input contacts (Courtesy of ABB Inc.)

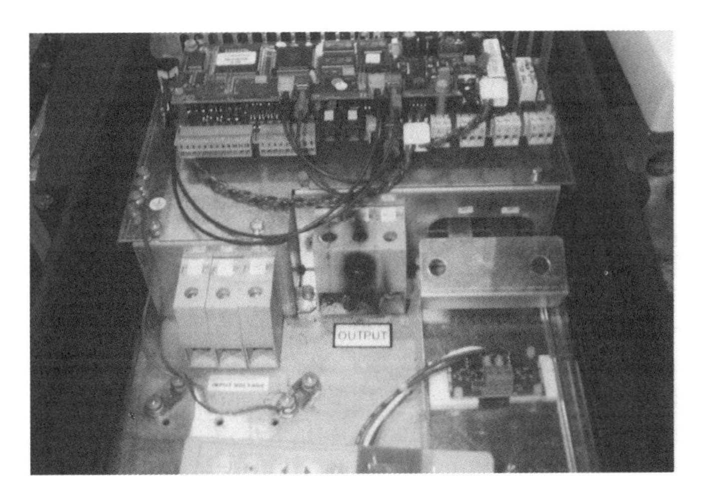

Figure 7-4. Arcing caused by loose output contacts (Courtesy of ABB Inc.)

2. Inspect DC bus capacitors for bulging and leakage. Either could be a sign of component stress or electrical misuse. Figures 7-5 and 7-6 show fan and capacitor stress problems.

3. Take voltage measurements while the VFD is in operation. Fluctuations in DC bus voltage measurements can indicate degradation of DC bus capacitors. One function of the capacitor bank is to act as a filter section (smoothing out any AC ripple voltage on the bus). Abnormal AC voltage on the DC bus indicates the capacitors are headed for trouble. Most VFD manufacturers have

Figure 7-5. Foreign object in fan (Courtesy of ABB Inc.)

Figure 7-6. Capacitor failure (Courtesy of ABB Inc.)

a special terminal block for this type of measurement and also for connection of the dynamic braking resistors. Measurements more than 4 VAC may indicate a capacitor-filtering problem or a possible problem with the diode bridge converter section (ahead of the bus). If you have such voltage levels, consult the VFD manufacturer before taking further action.

With the VFD in start and at zero speed, you should read output voltage of 40 VAC phase-to-phase or less. If you read more than this, you may have transistor leakage. At zero speed, the power components should not be operating. If your readings are 60 VAC or more, you can expect power component failure.

4. What should be done with spare VFDs? Store them in a clean, dry environment, with no condensation allowed. Place this unit in your preventative-maintenance system so you will remember

to power it up every 6 months or so to keep the DC bus capacitors at their peak-performance capability. Otherwise, their charging ability will significantly diminish. A capacitor is much like a battery—it needs to go into service soon after purchase, or it will suffer a loss of usable life.

5. Regularly monitor heat-sink temperatures. Most VFD manufacturers make this task easy by including a direct temperature readout on the keypad or display. Verify where this readout is and make checking it part of a weekly or monthly review of VFD operation.

You would not place your laptop computer outside on under (delete the word "on") the roof of a building or in direct sunlight where temperatures could reach 115°F or as low as –10°F. A VFD, which is basically a computer with a power supply, needs the same consideration. Some VFD manufacturers advertise 200,000 hours—almost 23 years—of mean time between failures (MTBF). Such impressive performance is easy to obtain, if you follow these simple procedures.

General Troubleshooting

Even if the steps outlined above are followed, there is still a possibility of a drive malfunction. If that does occur, the obvious questions about where you should start would be, "Check at the motor? Check at the drive input? Check at the drive display?" The answers are—yes.

There have been many books, articles, and pamphlets written about the proper troubleshooting techniques. Drives would certainly be no different than any other device, mechanical or electronic. However, the following simple tips may assist in troubleshooting a specific electronic drive problem. Some technicians identify a starting point at the source of torque development—the motor. Once the motor is cleared of any wrongdoing, then move backward to the drive, and then to the input to the drive.

Therefore, the logical place to start is at the motor. A simple but important question to ask is, "Should it be turning?" This may seem like a ridiculous statement, but the question does bear asking. Maybe the motor should not be turning because of a mechanical brake that didn't release. Maybe there is some other mechanical reason the motor is at a standstill. If the motor is supposed to be turning, then it is time to move backward and check the drive.

Standard drive questions are as follows: "Does the drive have power? Is the circuit breaker closed? Are the fuses OK? Is the disconnect operational? Is the display operational?" If the drive appears to have no power, do not assume that the drive is dead, with no power. A drive panel or display could be malfunctioning; connections to the panel could be broken. Always verify power to the drive by checking the input power terminals or DC bus terminals.

If the display is operational, then it is time to check the two items that satisfy a drive—a start command and speed reference. The easiest place to check it would be on the drive's I/O status section of parameters. This is a read-only section that some drive manufacturers include in the list of parameters. By viewing the display with I's and 0's, it is easy to see if the drive has a start command. It is also easy to see if the drive has a run-enable signal. Another place to look for drive status is in the operating data section. Some manufacturers include this section in parameters and include a multitude of items such as DC bus voltage, output volts and amps, heat-sink temperature, analog input values, reference input values, etc.

If the drive truly is receiving a start command and speed reference from an external source, then the problem is with the drive. If, through viewing the I/O status or operating data, it is determined that the drive is not receiving a start command and speed reference, the problem is with the external devices (e.g., operator station, PLC, auto-control system, etc.). The easiest way to tell if the drive is the problem is to operate the drive from keypad mode (no external connections). If the drive runs the motor up and down in speed from keypad mode, then the problem is external to the drive (wiring, sensors, and automated system). If the drive does not run the motor up and down in speed, then the problem lies with the drive. Further investigation into the drive is required.

The latest versions of drives on the market offer varying degrees of troubleshooting through software. Some manufacturers present a display with hints on where to check (e.g., "comm loss," "control bd error," etc.). Some manufacturers go one step further and offer a computer software support tool that identifies the source of the software or hardware problem. It then sends the user to a page that lists possible problems and the effective remedies.

In all cases, the drive manufacturer's user manual or installation and troubleshooting manual should be consulted for specific recommendations. The manufacturer is the best judge as to how far to go with repairs. Given the cost and simplicity of some fractional and low horsepower drives, one option may be to purchase a new drive rather than spend the time trying to repair a component on a very dense circuit board.

Chapter Review

To avoid having to troubleshoot a drive, there are several steps in maintaining a healthy drive:

Keep it clean and dry and keep the connections tight.

The heat sink should be routinely sprayed with compressed air to reduce any buildup of dust and particles on the chassis. Avoid inducing compressed air into the drive electronics unless it is ionized air or compresses air, specially packaged to reduce ESD contamination.

Ensure that the drive is not located in an area where moisture could be of concern. Less than 95% humidity with no condensation allowed is the standard rating for all drives. Moisture is a major enemy of electronics, as is excessive heat.

Check tightness of connections as part of a routine preventative maintenance procedure. Don't over-tighten power connections. Mechanically overstressing bolts or nuts could actually reduce their clamping power.

Routine inspection of the drive's electronic and mechanical parts is helpful. Periodic voltage measurements will indicate if the drive is headed for trouble in the near future. Be aware that even in start, with zero speed, the drive will have output voltage phase to ground—maybe as high as 40 V. If the reading exceeds 60 V, power-component failure could occur in the near future. Power up spare VFDs once every 6 months or so. The DC bus capacitors ability diminishes if it is not electrically stressed periodically.

In general troubleshooting, start at the motor and work backward. It must be determined first if the motor should be turning. Once that is determined, then move to the drive and verify the status. Verify that the drive operates the motor in keypad (drive-control mode). If the answer is "yes," then the drive is not the problem. The problem exists with equipment external to the drive. Check all interface wiring and components connected to the drive.

Check Your Knowledge

1. What are the three main procedures in maintaining a drive?
2. Why is accumulated dust on circuit boards a potential problem?
3. What is the procedure for removing accumulated dust on boards?
4. Why is it not a good idea to continually retighten a screw or nut?
5. What are specifics on checking capacitors?
6. What is the easiest method of determining if the drive has a problem?
7. Where would an operator look in a drive to obtain specific information on status or fault conditions?

Final Review & Closing Remarks

The following information will serve as a final book summary. This will assist the reader in preparing for the final "Check Your Knowledge" section that follows. For a thorough review and before the final "Check Your Knowledge" is taken, it would be helpful to review all chapter summaries and questions.

What is a Drive? Why Drives are Applied

There are many reasons to use variable speed drives, but basically they fall into three categories of efficiency gains, process changes and improvements, and system coordination. As an example, efficiency of AC motors can be quite high, which thereby reduces the overall monthly cost of operating the system. Variable speed drives also allow for changes in the process, as well as process improvements. Some processes operate at less than full speed, so optimum product quality can be achieved. System coordination is a major factor in today's industrial environment. AC and DC drive systems are typically applied in a manufacturing process. Computers control the entire process, from in feed rate to output of the machine.

A generic drive system includes the following components: machine, coupler, motor, drive, controller and power source. No matter what type of system is discussed, these main components are involved.

There are various types of variable speed drives available for use in industry. The basic categories are mechanical, hydraulic and electrical/electronic. Electronic drives can be further divided into the following categories of eddy current, rotating DC, DC converters and variable frequency AC.

Review of Basic Principles

All electrical circuits have three main factors: current, voltage and resistance. Current is the actual electrons that cause the work to happen in a circuit. Resistance is the opposition to current flow, which is present in any circuit (almost all electrical circuits have some resistance). Voltage is the electrical "pressure" that tries to overcome resistance.

The two types of voltage (electrical pressure) available are direct current (DC) and alternating current (AC) . DC is typically found in battery circuits, and its output value does not fluctuate, until the battery goes dead. AC is typically found as a power source for households and industrial operations. The output value fluctuates depending on the time base of transmission (positive to negative to positive output). Frequency is the number of times complete cycles are seen in a power system (e.g. 60 Hz). The two types of AC available are single phase and three phase.

Electromagnetism is the ability to produce a magnetic field through the use of a voltage and a coil. The devices that use this principle are inductors, relays, contactors, and transformers. Inductance is the ability to block AC voltage and allow DC to flow. Capacitance is the ability to block DC and allow AC to flow. Capacitance in an inductive circuit (motors) tends to improve the power factor of the entire system. *Power factor* is the measure of the efficient use of the current waveform; it is stated as a ratio between the utility generated voltage and current waveform.

Semiconductors are a mix between conductors and insulators – and need an electrical "push" to drive the device to conduct current. Typical semiconductor devices include diodes (allow current flow in one direction), thyristors (*silicon controlled rectifiers* [SCRs] that conduct current only when triggered ON), gate turn-off thyristors (GTOs can be latched on or off depending on the polarity of the gate signal), transistors (amount of current flow is determined by the amount of trigger signal), and insulated gate bipolar transistors (IGBTs are specialized transistors that have extremely high speed switch ON and OFF times).

There are three basic types of mechanical loads that are encountered by any AC or DC drive system: constant torque (e.g. conveyors), variable torque (e.g. centrifugal fans/pumps), and constant horsepower (e.g. machine tools).

Speed, torque, and horsepower (HP) play a major role in the operation of any application. Speed affects how much HP is required to perform the function; faster acceleration (more speed), requires more HP. Torque is a turning effort, and defines the ability of a system to start and keep moving at a specified rate. Inertia (WK^2 or WR^2) is the measurement of an object's resistance to change in speed. This measurement is needed to determine the acceleration time available from a drive system.

Gears, belts, pulleys (sheaves), chains, and sprockets all work to allow a smooth transmission of mechanical power, and in some cases, change speed and direction. Types of belts and pulleys include flat and V-belts, synchronous belts, and chains and sprockets.

Couplings, gearboxes, and speed reducers offer a positive connection point between the motor and application. Couplings are available in the following designs: flange, sleeve, and flexible (mechanically and elastically). Speed reducers offer an effective means of changing speed delivered to the application, as well as the torque developed by the motor.

Motors

AC and DC motors are the two major types used today in industrial and HVAC applications. These motors provide the speed, torque and HP necessary to operate the application. The motor changes one form of energy (electrical) to rotational or linear motion (mechanical).

The two major components of a DC motor are the *armature* and *field winding*. The armature is the rotating part that is physically connected to the shaft and develops magnetic flux around its windings. The field winding is the part of the stationary frame and provides the flux necessary to interact with the armature flux to produce rotation. The commutator acts as an electrical switch and always ensures that a repelling force is taking place in the armature flux circuit. This repelling force against the field winding flux causes rotation of the armature. Brushes are the devices that physically connect the voltage supply to the Armature circuit. Brushes are constructed of carbon material and require routine maintenance or replacement in order to reduce arching at the commutator segments.

Two separate voltage supplies are connected to the DC motor, one for the armature (variable DC voltage armature supply) and one for the field winding (fixed voltage field exciter). Speed of the DC motor is directly controlled by the magnitude of the armature supply voltage. Speed is also inversely proportional to the magnitude of the field flux. Torque is a direct result of the interaction of armature and field winding flux.

Various types of enclosures safeguard the DC motor against harm. For example, drip-proof motors provide a degree of protection against vertical falling materials, and also allows for the ventilation of cool outside air. Totally enclosed motor frames provide a higher degree of protection, but are not practical for large frame motors due to the inability to remove heat.

Motors are listed with many types of ratings that indicate the torque generating ability, altitude, heat capability, vibration, and electrical specifications. DC motors are constructed with several different types of field winding circuit: series wound, shunt (parallel wound), and compound wound.

AC motors are listed with one of two ratings: NEMA or IEC. All motors can be classified into single phase or polyphase categories. The main components of the AC motor are the *rotor* and *stator*. The rotor is the rotating part and the stator is the stationary part connected to the frame. Only one power source is required to set the rotor into motion. The stator windings create magnetic flux that causes a magnetic field (flux) to be induced in the rotor. The attracting forces of the rotor and stator flux produce torque and rotation of the rotor.

Speed of an AC induction motor is related to the frequency applied and the number of pole pairs. The number of pole pairs causes an inverse relationship in speed, but the frequency applied has a direct relationship to speed. The AC motor will always operate a speed less than synchronous. This is due to the requirement of magnetic flux in the rotor to be attracted to the rotating magnetic flux in the stator.

AC motors typically draw 600% inrush current upon start-up. Once the speed has increased to near synchronous, the current draw drops closely in line with the torque being produced. All AC motors are designed with a specific torque producing characteristic in mind (V/Hz). If the Volts per Hz relationship is kept constant, the motor will develop the rated torque it was designed to produce.

A common rating scale for AC Induction motors is that of a NEMA design classification: A, B, C, D, and E. Each classification indicates a different motor torque producing category. AC Induction motor nameplates have similar designs to DC motors, only referring to AC input power. A major indication of motor durability is the temperature class of the Stator windings. IEC ratings differ with NEMA in most categories.

AC motor types range from the standard induction motor, to wound rotor, synchronous, and multiple pole motors. Specialty motors include stepper, AC vector, servomotors, linear stepper, and linear motors.

Drives

In DC Drive systems, an armature and field exciter are used to control the two separate elements in a shunt wound DC motor. SCRs are used to vary the DC voltage output, which has a direct bearing on the speed of the motor. The DC Drive is the simplest of drive systems. The disadvantage of using SCRs for the drive power structure is the inherent nature of line notching. This notching is caused by the "phasing on and off" of the (6) SCRs located in the drive input section.

Digital DC drives are the latest major development in DC Drive technology. With digital technology, precise control of speed and torque can be realized. Speed and current controller circuits use feedback to make small changes in armature supply, and field exciter operation. Measuring and scaling circuits sample the actual speed and current output. Summing circuits take the error signal and translate those signals into corrective actions. Higher speed accuracy (< 1% regulation) is obtained by the use of a tachometer generator or tach. When operated in the speed regulation mode, the drive closely monitors the speed feedback signal. Armature voltage (or electromagnetic force or EMF) control would give a 1 to 2% regulation characteristic. Induction regulator (IR) compensation will improve the drooping speed due to load. When operated in the current regulation mode, the drive closely monitors the value of the current measuring circuit. The drive ignores the speed controls and calculates the current (torque) required by the load. The drive will automatically operate at the speed required to allow the motor to develop the desired torque.

Field exciters are constructed of SCRs or the newer IGBT power semiconductor technology. Some supplies are powered by single phase or 2-phase power and have the ability to operate in "field control" mode. This mode is the weakening of the shunt field strength, to allow above base speed operation. *Form factor* is the term used to compare the purity of the DC output from the armature or field exciters.

The operation of the DC drive can be compared to a relationship of "quadrants." A four quadrant drive would allow forward and reverse operation as well as regenerative capability (regenerating voltage back to AC line power.). This type of armature supply includes (12) SCRs in a bridge configuration.

Braking methods include coast and ramp to stop, which are typically the longest method of bringing a motor to a stop. Dynamic braking causes the back-fed voltage to be dissipated in heat, through a high wattage power resistor. The fastest "electronic" method of stopping a motor is through regenerative braking. This allows full voltage to be fed directly back to the AC line. Mechanical braking also allows fast braking of the motor armature, through a brake pad assembly similar to that of an automobile.

A concern of DC drive use is the generation of harmonics, line distortion, and power factor. A line reactor is required ahead of the drive unit to reduce the distortion back to the utility system. In order to avoid the generation of RFI, shielded control cable, and power cable are used. In addition, a shielded transformer is used ahead of the drive.

There are three basic designs of AC variable-frequency drives (VFDs): current source inverters, variable voltage inverters (input inverters), and pulse width modulation (PWM). All AC drives operate under the same characteristic. They change a fixed incoming voltage and frequency to a variable voltage and frequency output. With PWM drives, the incoming voltage and frequency is rectified to a fixed DC voltage. That voltage is "inverted" back to AC, with the output, 0–460V and 0–60 Hz (or 0–230V).

Braking methods for AC motors are similar to that of DC. In addition, the AC drive has the capability to "injecting" DC voltage into the stator windings. In doing so, the drive sets up a definite N and S polarity in the motor, causing high reverse torque, and bringing the rotor to a fast stop.

Torque control AC drives basically fall into two categories: flux vector (feedback required) and sensorless flux vector (no feedback required). Vector control drives have the capability of full torque at zero speed. The drive forces the motor to develop the torque required, to effectively handle the load.

Since the introduction of IGBTs into the power technology ranks, the size of AC drives has been reduced to less than half of its counterpart 10 years ago. With IGBT technology comes a challenge in AC motors—high voltage spikes caused by "voltage reflection." PWM drives produce an inherent oscillation between the drive output and motor input. Precautions to be taken against this motor damage possibility include: use of inverter duty motors, output reactors, or DV/DT output filters.

Harmonics are generated back to the AC line, due to the technology of pulling voltages in bursts. The rectifier that accomplishes this is termed a "switch mode power supply." All electronic devices with this type of supply cause harmonics back to the utility system. Line reactors, harmonic trap filters, and higher pulse drives are a few of the corrections to the harmonics issue. Improper shielding and grounding of AC drives can cause bearing current damage after prolonged use, and can cause immediate radio frequency interference (RFI) and electromagnetic interference (EMI). Proper installation methods drastically reduce in conducted and radiated noise.

Package designs, Digital I/O, IGBT technology and multi-function keypads make AC drives easy to set-up. Programming panels are removable and are able to store all drive values in flash memory.

Drive Control and Feedback Devices

The two types of drive control methods are *open-loop* and *closed- loop*. Open loop is operating a motor, directly from the drive unit. Closed loop would include some type of feedback device that is connected directly to the motor shaft. The speed regulation of the system can be improved by using a feedback device.

Typical drive feedback devices include tachometers (tachs), encoders (or pulse tachs), and resolvers. Tachometers are available in AC or DC versions. AC tachs are used in a variety of industrial applications, since they are able to indicate direction and are generally more accurate than AC Tachs.

Encoders use a system of light beams, directed toward a light sensor. The light beams are created by shining a light source through a rotating, slotted disc. The disc is connected to the encoder shaft, which is connected directly to the motor shaft, through a coupling.

Resolvers are position type devices. These devices are typically used on servo applications where precise feedback of the rotor position is required. Resolvers are similar to an AC induction motor, as well as acting like a revolving transformer.

DC drive control methods include closed loop control using a tach feedback device. It would also include armature voltage feedback or EMF control. With EMF control, a sampling of the output voltage is used as feedback to correct for output speed and current (torque).

AC drive control methods also include tach or encoder feedback, as well as operating the VFD by open loop methods. A variety of transducers can be used as feedback devices. Pressure, flow, level, temperature, and humidity are just a few of the controlling elements sensed by transducers.

Dynamic and static speed regulation are part of the set-up process of the performance drive application. The accuracy of the speed or torque is dependent on the feedback device, as well as the closed loop control circuit within the drive. The amount of "dampening" will determine if the system will be stable, or produce oscillations.

Drive Systems

Drive systems operate in a coordinated fashion—with control between the controller (PLC) and the drive unit. A variety of sensors, switches, and transducers are a part of the overall scheme of automation.

Proportional-integral-derivative (PID) control is used when automatic control of some quantity is required. Temperature, pressure, humidity, and level are just a few of the variables that can be conveniently controlled by PID.

Tension control is a major part of any coordinated system that processes web material. Dancer control is similar to tension control, in that a separate regulator signal is fed back to the drive in order for correction to take place. Proportional gain and integration time play a part in the tuning of a web system.

A variety of remote operator devices are available for interfacing signals to the drive unit. Remote operator stations are the simplest form of remote control. Standard inputs and outputs (I/O) would include start /stop, speed reference, digital inputs, analog outputs, and relay outputs. Both sinking and sourcing control are used in industry today.

Serial communications is the simplest form of communication link to a drive. Typically, multiple drives are controlled by one system controller, which could be a computer that is set up to talk to the protocol that is installed in the drive. Fiber optic communications has the highest immunity to noise, compared to other forms of drive communications. Optical fibers are connected in a ring structure, and can be connected with plastic or glass fiber. Building automation systems or Ethernet systems are able to talk to many drives on the market today.

Maintenance and Troubleshooting of Drive Systems

To avoid having to troubleshoot a drive, there are several steps in maintaining a "healthy" drive. Keep it clean, keep it dry, and keep the connections tight.

The heatsink should be routinely sprayed with compressed air to reduce any buildup of dust and particles on the chassis. Avoid inducing compressed air into the drive electronics, unless it is ionized air or compresses air, specially packaged to reduce electrostatic discharge (ESD) contamination.

Ensure that the drive is not located in an area where moisture could be of concern. Less than 95% humidity, no condensation allowed is the standard rating for all drives. Moisture is a major enemy of electronics, as is excessive heat.

Check tightness of connections as part of a routine periodic maintenance procedure. Don't over-tighten power connections. Mechanical overstress of the bolt or nut could actually reduce the clamping power of the device.

Routine inspection of the drives electronic and mechanical parts is helpful. Power up spare VFDs once every 6 months or so. The DC bus capacitor's ability diminishes if it is not electrically stressed periodically. In general troubleshooting, start at the motor and work backwards. It must be determined first, if the motor should be turning. Once that is determined, then move to the drive and verify the status.

Closing Remarks

The use of electronic motor speed controls has grown tremendously since the early 1960s. The increased use can be attributed to technology improvements not seen in years prior to the 1060s. Motor speed control is a multi-billion dollar industry worldwide. The use of AC and DC drives, brushless DC drives, permanent magnet AC drives, and stepper drives, all play a part in today' s industrial and HVAC marketplaces.

The use of electronic motor speed controls is expected to grow in non-traditional applications. Applications like automotive subsystems, household appliances, electric vehicles, people movers and marine propulsion units can all benefit from the technology drives offer.

As of this printing, AC drives (VFDs) comprise over 50% of the control method in use on standard induction AC motors. That trend will only increase in the years to come, due to increased focus on energy saving devices. The vast consumption of energy by fixed speed motors is an invitation for the installation of VFDs as part of an energy management program.

The trend in AC drives appears to include several factors that all users can benefit from. First of all, drives will continue to have increased intelligence. Drives of today and tomorrow are more than just a "motor turner." They are a mini-PLC and personal computer, rolled into one unit. The ability to customize drive functions is becoming easier, due to windows based development tools. Custom application software and custom programming tools will continue to be a trend in AC drive development.

Another trend in AC drives, is the use of communication options. If communications is used, the drive can be less reliant on its own intelligence. External control devices provide the drive with the information, I/O and feedback that it needs to control process variables in a closed loop system.

The use of micro-drives will also increase in the future. These types of drives will present increased functionality and tout the ability to be flexible during process changes. Industry demands the ability to make changes quickly and efficiently. This is no exception when micro-drives are in use. Since standard consumer products will continue to demand energy savings and flexibility during use, user-oriented programming tools will be the norm, rather than the exception.

As more consumers purchase vector and torque controlled drives, the retail cost will continue to decrease. The manufacturer will realize cost-effective techniques and the consumer will reap the benefits of technology improvement at a reduced price. Who knows where electronic adjustable speed drives will be in the future. The future is only limited by the imagination of results-oriented consumers.

Check Your Knowledge

This is the final exam for the book. Reviewing the "Check Your Knowledge" questions in each chapter would be helpful before taking this final set of questions.

1. How is line notching corrected in a DC drive system?
2. What is RFI and how is it controlled in a DC drive system?
3. What are harmonics and what are the corrective actions to reduce them?
4. What are the effective shielding and grounding methods used with AC drives?
5. What is PID and how is it used?
6. Name three factors that cause the efficiency of an AC motor to improve.
7. What are the two separate electrical circuits in a DC drive system?
8. What is the purpose of the commutator?
9. What is the V/Hz ratio?
10. Why are the laminations in the armature skewed?
11. Where would an operator look in a drive to obtain specific information on status or fault conditions?
12. For current to flow, what must be added to overcome resistance?
13. What is a pulse tach and how does it work?
14. Describe the difference between static and dynamic performance of a closed-loop system.

15. What is the difference between a series wound and shunt wound DC motor?

16. Why is proper tension control important in a web-fed system?

17. Describe what the following circuits are used for in a DC drive:

    summing circuit
    current controller
    current measuring/scaling

18. What NEMA design class would provide the highest amount of starting torque, when connected across line power?

19. What are the two main parts of a DC motor and what is the purpose of each?

20. What is the definition of base speed?

21. What is the difference between a DPFG and a TEFC motor?

22. How does a synchronous motor differ from a standard AC induction motor?

23. How is speed determined in an AC induction motor?

24. What is the purpose of compensation windings?

25. What is a dancer control?

26. What is the common DC bus configuration and why is it used?

27. What is meant by serial communications? How is it used with drives?

28. How is a VFD used to save energy in an outlet damper application?

29. What are jumpers or DIP switches used for, connected to analog input signals?

30. Name three or more devices that are used for set point or feedback conditions in closed loop systems.

31. If a speed reducer has a 10:1 ratio, with 3 lb-ft and 1200 rpm input shaft, what speed and torque would the output shaft be (assume 85% efficiency)?

32. How does an SCR operate?

33. What is a Darlington bipolar transistor?

34. What is electromagnetism?

35. What is power factor?
36. Give an example as to where inductance may be helpful.
37. What are the three main procedures in maintaining a drive?
38. Why is accumulated dust on circuit boards a potential problem?
39. What is the easiest method of determining if the drive has a problem?
40. Coordination of variable-speed drive systems in industry are typically controlled by what type of device?
41. What is dynamic braking, and how is it accomplished?
42. What is the difference between scalar and vector drives?
43. What is voltage reflection and how is it corrected?
44. Explain the difference between single-, two-, and four-quadrant systems.
45. What is the operating principle of temperature and humidity sensors?
46. What is meant by an encoder PPR?
47. Describe the EMF, current, and IR compensation feedback loops in a DC drive system.
48. Inductance has the ability to block _____ and let _____pass.
49. What is the definition of torque?
50. What is the procedure for removing accumulated dust on boards?

Appendix A: Check Your Knowledge - Answers

Chapter 1

1. A drive is a device that controls the speed, torque, direction, and resulting horsepower of a system.
2. Efficiency gains, process changes and improvements, and system coordination.
3. Motor load, the horsepower rating, and the speed of operation.
4. A programmable logic controller (PLC) or other computer device.
5. Machine—device that performs the work
   Coupler—connects the motor to the machine
   Motor—changes one form of energy to rotating
   Drive—controls the speed, torque, and direction of the motor
   Controller—generates and sends a reference to the drive
   Power Source—supplies power to operate the drive
6. Mechanical, hydraulic, and electric/electronic:
   Mechanical—device that uses belts, chains, and pulleys to change the output speed through increasing and decreasing of pulley diameters.
   Hydraulic—device that uses fluid and a pump to operate a hydraulic motor. Control of motor speed is done through a valve.
   Electric/electronic—device that controls the speed of an electric motor by means of converting one form of energy to another. (An AC drive converts fixed power to a variable-frequency output. A DC drive converts AC power to variable-voltage DC power.)
7. The armature supply and the field supply.
8. Changing AC power to a fixed-voltage DC power, filtering the DC waveform, and inverting fixed DC voltage to a variable voltage and frequency AC output.

Chapter 2

1. Voltage
2. Ammeter and voltmeter
3. Direct current (current flowing in one direction only; its value does fluctuate until the power supply is removed).
4. Magnetic flux is the relationship between the north and south poles of a magnet, with flux being the magnetic field itself.
5. The ability to produce a magnetic field through the use of a voltage and a coil.
6. 60 Hz refers to the number of complete cycles the AC waveform goes through during normal operations.
7. DC, AC
8. AC, DC
9. Inductance is useful in the DC bus circuit of an AC drive (filters out unwanted AC ripple) so that the voltage delivered to the next stage will be as clean.
10. Power factor, given in %, is the measurement of the phase difference between the utility-generated voltage, and current waveform.
11. It is used to reduce any surge current that may enter the input section of the drive due to a lightning strike or other high-voltage disturbance.
12. Control circuit and the power circuit.
13. With the alternating current, the coil is set-up where voltage is induced into the secondary part of the coil.
14. The alternating sequence of the AC allows the transfer of voltage through magnetism properties.
15. A diode conducts current in one direction only. The device continues to operate until the AC waveform goes into the negative direction, at which time the conducting of current stops.
16. An SCR conducts current in one direction, and only when the trigger circuit (gate) is powered on. The device shuts off when it is subjected to an opposite polarity between the anode and the cathode.
17. A GTO is similar to an SCR, in that it can be turned on and off at will. The GTO is turned on or off, depending on the polarity of the gate signal.
18. A device that basically has two or more power transistors, internally connected in one package. It can be turned on and off by the use of a command signal (base).
19. The difference is in the ability to switch on and off rapidly. The common transistor can switch between 1 kHz and 4 kHz while the IGBT can switch at 16 kHz.
20. Maximum torque may be required between zero and base speed. In addition, many drive manufacturers allow for 150% overload for 1 minute current before the drive automatically shuts down.

21. Machine tools and center driven winder applications.
22. The drive has the ability, through software, to simulate the torque application curve for a centrifugal fan. The drive develops a V/Hz curve, allowing the motor to develop the torque that matches the customer's torque curves. The drive can also allow the motor to develop the braking horsepower used by the application for only fractions of a time
23. Torque is a turning motion, twisting of a device. It is also defined as Force X Distance.
24. Horsepower is the rate at which work gets done.
25. Inertia is the measurement of an object's resistance to change. Measurements are taken or calculated in WK^2 or WR^2.
26. 102 rpm, with 30 lb-ft of torque.

Chapter 3

1. Armature: rotating part of the motor, *contains windings and magnetic flux that repels the flux developed in the field winding. Field winding: stationary part of the motor that develops magnetic flux that interacts and repels the armature flux. The interaction of both magnetic fields produces rotation.*
2. The brushes are carbon devices that transfer voltage from the armature supply to the actual armature circuit inside the motor.
3. To allow for smooth rotational action when operating at low speeds.
4. The commutator acts as an electric switch to cause the armature flux polarity to be in opposition to the field winding flux.
5. Commutation windings are constructed in the armature circuit to straighten out the magnetic flux generated through the armature unit. Increased motor torque is the result.
6. Compensation windings are additional poles installed to the magnetic poles of the field winding (stator). They tend to smooth the flux developed across the pole.
7. Speed is the direct result of the magnitude of the armature voltage applied. A constant field flux must be present for the magnetic interaction to take place.
8. Torque is a direct result of the interaction of the field winding flux and the armature current (flux). When more load is applied to the DC motor, more current is drawn in the armature circuit and more torque is developed.
9. A DPFG motor has no means of external cooling. It does have vents that allow outside air into the motor housing, but reduce the input of airborne materials. A TEFC motor contains an integral fan that circulates the air around the motor housing. It does not allow the entry of air or particles into the unit.
10. Ambient temperature (maximum ambient), insulation class (available temperature rise above the ambient), duty cycle (continuous or intermittent), armature voltage and current (rated voltage and current to be con-

nected to the armature), field voltage and current (rated voltage and current to be connected to the field), enclosure type (indicated degree of protection against incoming particles or fluids), base speed/maximum speed (indicated speed at rated field and armature voltage and current, and rated load).

11. A series wound DC motor includes a series field winding within the armature circuit. One supply voltage is required. A shunt wound DC motor has two separate circuits—one for the armature and one for the field winding.
12. A permanent magnet motor does not have windings in the armature circuit. Permanent magnets replace the armature windings.
13. A DC servomotor is longer and narrower than a standard DC motor. The narrow design and low inertia make the servomotor ideal for quick acceleration and direction changes. The narrow size also allows for higher speed operation, compared with a standard DC motor.
14. The rotor is the part that rotates and develops a magnetic field by induction from the stator. The stator is the stationary part (connected to the frame) that develops a rotating magnetic field. This field causes the rotor to try to catch up to the rotating magnetic field of the stator, thereby producing rotation.
15. Speed is determined by either the frequency applied (Hz) or by the number of pole pairs constructed in the motor. As applied frequency increases, so does the motor speed. The number of pole pairs has an inverse affect on speed.
16. Horsepower is determined by the design of the motor, and also by the product of motor torque and speed, divided by a constant.
17. Base speed is the nameplate speed in rpm, when the motor is operating at rated voltage, rated frequency (Hz), and rated load applied.
18. The V/Hz ratio is the proportion of rated voltage to frequency. Every motor requires this proportion in order to develop rated torque (e.g., 7.67 V/Hz for a 460-V line-operated motor).
19. NEMA design D, per the classification curves.
20. NEMA design E, per the rated current/synchronous speed graph.
21. The first two digits, divided by 4, determine the shaft centerline height.
22. NEMA typically conservatively rates motors and includes horsepower overload capability through an S.F. number. IEC designates more frame sizes than NEMA and rates motors exactly to its capability. IEC also lists more enclosure classifications.
23. A standard AC induction motor uses an induced magnetic field in the rotor, caused by the stator, to produce rotation. A synchronous motor has two separate circuits—rotor and stator. A rotor power supply is used to create magnetic flux. The stator field is energized by another power supply (three-phase) that creates a rotating magnetic field. The rotor exactly matches the rotating magnetic field of the stator, and the speed synchronizes.

24. AC vector motors are used in conjunction with a flux vector drive. The drive causes the motor to create exact amounts of torque, depending on the application requirements. The motor typically has a shaft-mounted feedback device to allow the drive to accurately assess where the rotor is physically located. Vector motors develop a specific amount of torque, given a precise voltage and frequency from the vector drive.

25. Stepper motors operate on a similar principle to that of synchronous motors. The permanent magnet rotor rotates in lock-step with the two-phase stator field. A stepper "controller" is required to input the proper amount of voltage to the stator, which in turn creates the appropriate steps of rotor rotation.

Chapter 4

1. Armature supply and field exciter unit.

2. SCRs can be turned on with a small milliamp pulse, but must be forced off several amps. IGBTs operate on the same principle, with milliamps required to gate them on and off.

3. Line notching is corrected through use of a line reactor, connected ahead of the *drive.*

4. The summing circuit takes the speed feedback signal and matches it against the speed reference to obtain an error signal used for drive speed control. The current controller controls the firing angle of the SCRs and signals the firing unit how long and when to gate the SCRs on. Current measuring/scaling takes a sample of the current feedback signal and sends it to the summing junction error processing and correction of current output.

5. Single-quadrant systems allow for motoring in the forward direction only. Two-quadrant systems allow forward and reverse direction, with reverse torque available for braking; four-quadrant systems allow for forward and reverse direction operation, plus the capability of forward and reverse torque available for braking in either direction.

6. Inertia built up in the motor is transferred back to the drive by means of regenerative voltage. The voltage fed back to the drive is sent to a power resistor for dissipation as heat. A DB contactor is used to connect the motor voltage to the resistor. At the same time, the output contactor of the drive is opened so no voltage can be fed back into the drive output section.

7. RFI is radio frequency interference. This interference is caused by the control circuits, contactors, and oscillators used to control the drive. The best corrective action is to use shielded control cable, as well as shielded input and output power cable in extreme cases. The use of a shielded transformer will also reduce the conducted noise that could be transmitted back to the power line.

8. A macro is a predetermined list of parameter values. These values are designed to allow the user to match the drive parameters to the application. Macros such as three-wire, hand–auto, and PID make drive set-up

quicker, since the default values closely approximate the needed programming.

9. VVI and CSI drives use a variable voltage DC bus circuit. The bus voltage is accomplished through an SCR bridge rectifier in the converter section of the drive. Displacement PF of the units drops as the speed drops. PWM drives use a fixed diode bridge rectifier in the converter section. This causes the DC bus to be a fixed voltage. The DC bus feeds the inverter section, where the variable output voltage and frequency is generated. PWM drives operate at a high displacement PF and could be considered power factor correction devices.

10. Carrier frequency is the speed at which the output IGBTs switch on and off. The higher the carrier frequency, the smoother the output waveform will be, and the closer it approximates that of sine wave power.

11. Cogging is the pulsations of the motor shaft at very low speeds. It is caused by a VVI or CSI drive output that sends out pulses in steps. The motor translates these steps into specific magnetic poles. The rotor flux searches for the next available stator pole, which causes the shaft to jump whenever it finds the next position.

12. Injection braking is the process of inducing a DC voltage into the AC stator winding. The amount of voltage will determine the amount of pole flux that will be set-up in the stator. The rotor is attracted to the definite polarity and stopping torque is the result.

13. Scalar is the term given to standard operation of a PWM voltage controlled drive. With this drive mode, the motor must have several percent slip to rotate. The drive simply supplies the volts and hertz output, and the motor responds with rotation, per the designed slip characteristic. Vector is the term given to a specialized drive that causes full motor torque at zero speed. Flux vector is another term used to describe the control of flux, which is also the control of torque.

14. Standard flux vector drives require feedback from the motor shaft to supply information to the controlling elements in the drive. The drive must know the position of the rotor at all times. The drive generates its control changes, based on the feedback from the shaft. Sensorless flux vector drives receive their name from the fact that no feedback device is used. All the motor data (flux constants, hysteresis curves, temperature coefficients) is stored in a motor model in the drive. The drive responds to small amounts of information fed back by the DC bus, output current, and the actual IGBT switch positions.

15. Voltage reflection is the phenomenon of drive output voltages combining with voltage bouncing back from the motor. These combined peak voltages can cause damage to the stator windings if they are not rated to handle the voltage stress. Precautions would include using an inverter duty motor, adding drive output reactors and/or dv/dt filters. Inductors will reduce the high-voltage spikes that can occur, and keep the values within the range of the motor lacquer insulation.

16. Harmonics are described as distortion; they provide no usable work, yet are fed back to the AC line. This distortion is superimposed on the fundamental waveform of 60 Hz. For a standard six-pulse drive, the 5th, 7th,

11th, and 13th harmonic will be generated and will be the most destructive in value. Line reactors and isolation transformers help in the mitigation of voltage harmonics. Trap filters and 12-pulse drive units will reduce the harmonic content to a significant level.

17. Control wiring needs to be shielded, with the shield cut back and taped at the signal source end. In addition, control wiring must be kept away from power wiring or at a minimum of 12 inches away. Input and output power wiring also need to be separated. A continuous ground wire throughout the entire system is a requirement and will reduce the possibility of conducted noise.

18. PID stands for "proportional integral derivative." PID is the ability to automatically control temperature, pressure, level, humidity, or any other medium that can be supplied as an electrical feedback signal. The drive has the ability to make corrections in speed, due to the error given by the summing junction. This is considered a closed loop system. It operates at a very high performance rate, with small feedback errors translating to thousands of an inch rotation of the shaft.

Chapter 5

1. Open-loop control means the motor is operated directly from the drive unit. In closed-loop control, the motor is connected to the drive, and a feedback device is connected to the motor shaft. The feedback device sends a 0–10 VDC or 4–20 mA signal back to the drive as a representation of actual motor shaft speed.

2. A pulse tach is basically a digital encoder. It uses a light source that shines a light beam through a slotted disk. A photo-detector receives the light beam in the form of pulses. The longer the light beam creates pulses, the slower the disk is rotating (the disk is connected directly to the motor shaft).

3. An AC tach produces an analog output per the revolutions of a rotating device within a magnetic field. AC tachs are devices that indicate strictly speed. No directional indication is available. DC tachs produce a DC voltage output in terms of volts per 1000 RPM. They are generally more accurate than AC tachs and also have the ability of directional indication.

4. Resolution is indicated in PPR (pulses per revolution). An encoder that generates 1024 PPR indicates 1/1024 of a revolution or the equivalent of 0.35 degrees of rotation.

5. The armature voltage feedback (EMF) is a representation of the output voltage, which is a direct indication of speed. The current feedback is a representation of current output from the drive. The IR compensation feedback is used to increase the speed reference circuit to increase speed due to loading of the motor. All three signals are brought back to the summing circuit. If the current feedback signal indicates the drive is exceeding the current capability, the drive will automatically reduce the speed reference. The speed reference will remain at a lower value until the current drops to an acceptable level.

6. The pressure transducer supplies a direct reading signal back to the drive. The signal would be 0–10 VDC or 4–20 mA. The feedback signal is fed back to the regular circuit (which contains a summing circuit). The regulator compares the feedback with the pressure set point and generates an error signal. That error signal is used as a reference to the drive power section, which increases or decreases the voltage and frequency output to the motor.

7. Static performance (static speed regulation) is a change in steady-state speed that is caused by a change in load. Dynamic performance describes the operation during the transition from one operating point to another.

8. Bandwidth is used to describe a drive's ability to accurately follow a changing reference signal. Bandwidth units of measure are given in radians per second.

9. The system is typically adjusted so that motor oscillations are at a minimum or low value after a change in speed or load. Oscillations (instability) may occur after a change, but they rapidly decrease to a low value in a properly tuned system. The ideal adjustment result would be to have a slightly under damped or critically damped system.

10. Both devices use the principle of variable resistance. A temperature sensor uses a material that changes resistance per the ambient temperature. A humidity sensor uses a material that changes length per the amount of humidity in the atmosphere. A hair hygrometer is a device that uses the changing length of human hair to operate a pivot connected to a variable resistor. In both cases, the output is a variable resistance, which if fed to a power supply, generates a variable voltage, which can be fed to the drive (as a reference or feedback signal).

Chapter 6

1. Pressure, humidity, temperature transducers, potentiometers, a variety of electro-mechanical devices that change voltage output given the input signal.

2. Tension control is required or the product quality will suffer. Too little tension on the web will cause bunching and poor quality of the product. Too much tension could stretch the material, causing a thinner product, or in the worst case, cause the web to break.

3. A dancer is a device that changes resistance per the amount of force being applied. This device is typically used to monitor and regulate the amount of tension placed on web-fed material.

4. Jumpers or DIP switches match the analog input signal with the drive input setting. Typical input signals are 4(0) to 20 mA and 0 to 10 VDC.

5. Sinking logic is where the control voltage is tied directly to circuit common. A command is done when a contact closure is between the terminal and ground. Sourcing logic is where the control voltage is directly applied to the appropriate terminal. All circuit commons and ground are tied together.

6. Serial communications is the transmission in sequence of bits of data to or from a controller device. Communications speeds range from 4800 to 19,200 baud. Drives are wired in parallel (daisy chained) to the control device. The controller could be a computer or any device that talks the same language as the drive. The drive may need a language "interpreter" if the language is not pre-loaded in the drive.

7. Termination resistors reduce the introduction of electrical noise into a communication system. They are placed (terminated) on the first and last drive of a communication network. The in-between drives are left non-terminated. These resistors also "close" the communication circuit.

8. Fiber optics are extremely immune to electrical noise. Since they use light as the transmission medium, little to no low-frequency radiation can affect the quality of the transmission (i.e., 60 Hz).

9. DC motors offer very high torque at low speeds. Printing and ski lifts are demanding applications. The system may need to move a fully rated load from zero speed, up to set point. Standard AC PWM, voltage-regulated drives cause the motor to slip to develop torque. However, the newer flux vector, or direct torque-control drives, have very similar operation, compared with a DC drive system.

10. Common DC bus arrangements are used when the likelihood exists for an overhauling load. The extra energy generated by the motor is fed back to the common bus and then transferred to another inverter unit connected to the bus. This increases the overall efficiency of the system.

11. The VFD is used to vary the speed per the feedback from the pressure transducer in the duct (if PID control is used). The outlet dampers are fixed in the open position, with the drive varying the speed of the fan per the feedback received from the transducer. Lower fan speed and pressure in the duct is the result. The fan only supplies the airflow required to meet the application needs.

12. Most significant factors are motor, its options and accessories, transformer and other power equipment, PF and harmonic correction, wire, cable, and conduit costs, installation and commissioning expenses, and overall operating expenses.

Chapter 7

1. Keep it clean, keep it dry, and keep the connections tight.

2. Dust attracts moisture. Moisture can cause the microelectronic circuits to misfire or develop a short. In addition, moisture assists in the development of corrosion. Corrosion on circuit board traces will eventually cause the electrical contacts to disintegrate.

3. Special non-ESD generating air should be used. Cans of ionized air are available for this purpose. Static electricity (ESD—electrostatic discharge) is the silent killer of small microcircuits that cannot handle several hundred volts of static charge.

4. Retightening (re-torquing) of screws and nuts causes a loss of clamping power—in some cases, as much as 50%. A tendency exists to over-tighten

the device, which causes a reduction of compression strength. Replace devices that work loose, rather than keep retightening them.

5. Check capacitors periodically for leaks and bulges. Capacitors should be completely dry and not be deformed in any way. DC bus capacitor measurements should also be periodically done. AC ripple voltage of more than 4 VAC would indicate a possible capacitor malfunction. Spare drives should be powered up every 6 months or so. This keeps the capacitors at their maximum charging capability.

6. Isolate the drive from the external control signals. If the drive satisfactorily operates the motor when in keypad mode, then the drive is not the problem and something external to the drive is causing the problem. If the drive does not operate the motor satisfactorily, then check all inputs to the drive. The drive must have two conditions to operate: start command and speed reference.

7. The operator would look at the I/O status location for the conditions of the digital inputs, analog inputs, etc. A section called operating data would also be helpful in determining drive "healthiness" as well as the last several faults that occurred.

Chapter 9

1. Line notching is corrected through use of a line rea*ctor connected ahead of the drive.*

2. RFI is radio frequency interference. This interference is caused by the control circuits, contactors, and oscillators used to control the drive. The best corrective action is to use shielded control cable, as well as shielded input and output power cable in extreme cases. The use of a shielded transformer will also reduce the conducted noise that could be transmitted back to the power line.

3. Harmonics are described as distortion—they provide no usable work, yet are fed back to the AC line. This distortion is superimposed on the fundamental waveform of 60 Hz. For a standard six-pulse drive, the 5th, 7th, 11th, and 13th harmonic will be generated, and will be the most destructive in value. Line reactors and isolation transformers help in the mitigation of voltage harmonics. Trap filters and 12-pulse drive units will reduce the harmonic content to a significant level.

4. Control wiring needs to be shielded, with the shield cut back and taped at the signal source end. In addition, control wiring must be kept away from power wiring or at a minimum of 12 inches away. Input and output power wiring also need to be separated. A continuous ground wire throughout the entire system is a requirement and will reduce the possibility of conducted noise.

5. PID stands for proportional integral derivative. PID is the ability to automatically control temperature, pressure level, humidity, or any other medium that can be supplied as a feedback signal. The drive has the ability to make corrections in speed because of the error given by the summing junction. This is considered a closed-loop system. It operates at a

very-high-performance rate, with small feedback errors translating to thousandths of an inch rotation of the shaft.

6. Motor load, the horsepower rating, and the speed of operation.

7. The armature supply and the field supply.

8. The commutator acts as an electric switch to cause the armature flux polarity to be in opposition to the field winding flux.

9. The V/Hz ratio is the proportion of rated voltage to frequency. Every motor requires this proportion in order to develop rated torque (ex. 7.67 V/Hz for a 460-V line operated motor).

10. To allow for smooth rotational action when operating at low speeds.

11. The operator would look at the I/O status location for the conditions of the digital inputs, analog inputs, etc. A section called "operating data" would also be helpful in determining drive healthiness as well the last several faults that occurred.

12. Voltage

13. A pulse tach is basically a digital encoder. It uses a light source that shines a light beam through a slotted disk. A photo-detector receives the light beam in the form of pulses. The longer the light beam creates pulses, the slower the disk is rotating (the disk is connected directly to the motor shaft).

14. Static performance (static speed regulation) is a change in steady-state speed, which is caused by a change in load. Dynamic performance describes the operation during the transition from one operating point to another.

15. A series wound DC motor includes a series field winding within the armature circuit. One supply voltage is required. A shunt wound DC motor has two separate circuits—one for the armature and one for the field winding.

16. Tension control is required or the product quality will suffer. Too little tension on the web will cause bunching and poor quality of the product. Too much tension could stretch the material, causing a thinner product, or in the worst case, cause the web to break.

17. Summing circuit—takes the speed feedback signal and matches it against the speed reference to obtain an error signal, used for drive speed control.
Current controller—controls the firing angle of the SCRs and signals the firing unit how long and when to gate the SCRs on.
Current measuring/scaling—takes a sample of the current feedback signal and sends it to the summing junction error processing and correction of current output.

18. NEMA design D, per the classification curves.

19. Armature—rotating part of the motor, it contains windings and magnetic flux that repels the flux developed in the field winding.
Field winding—stationary part of the motor that develops magnetic flux that interacts and repels the armature flux. The interaction of both magnetic fields produces rotation.

20. Base speed is the nameplate speed in RPM, when the motor is operating at rated voltage, rated frequency (Hz), and rated load applied.

21. A DPFG motor has no means of external cooling. It does have vents that allow outside air into the motor housing but reduce the input of airborne materials. A TEFC motor contains an integral fan that circulates the air around the motor housing. It does not allow the entry of air or particles into the unit.

22. A standard AC induction motor uses an induced magnetic field in the rotor, caused by the stator, to produce rotation. A synchronous motor has two separate circuits—rotor and stator. A rotor power supply is used to create magnetic flux. The stator field is energized another power supply (three-phase) that creates a rotating magnetic field. The rotor exactly matches the rotating magnetic field of the stator and the speed synchronizes.

23. Speed is determined by either the frequency applied (Hz) or by the number of pole pairs constructed in the motor. As applied frequency increases, so does the motor speed. The number of pole pairs has an inverse affect on speed.

24. Compensation windings are additional poles installed to the magnetic poles of the field winding (stator). They tend to smooth the flux developed across the pole.

25. A dancer is a device that changes resistance per the amount of force being applied. This device is typically used to monitor and regulate the amount of tension placed on web-fed material.

26. Common DC bus arrangements are used when the likelihood exists for an overhauling load. The extra energy generated by the motor is fed back to the common bus and then transferred to another inverter unit connected to the bus. This increases the overall efficiency of the system.

27. Serial communications is the transmission, in sequence of bits of data to or from a controller device. Communications speeds range from 4800 to 19,200 baud. Drives are wired in parallel (daisy chained) to the control device. The controller could be a computer or any device that talks the same language as the drive. The drive may need a language "interpreter" if the language is not pre-loaded in the drive.

28. The VFD is used to vary the speed per the feedback from the pressure transducer in the duct (if PID control is used). The outlet dampers are fixed in the open position, with the drive varying the speed of the fan per the feedback received from the transducer. Lower fan speed and pressure in the duct is the result. The fan only supplies the airflow required to meet the application needs.

29. Jumpers or DIP switches match the analog input signal with the drive input setting. Typical input signals are 4(0) to 20 mA and 0 to 10 VDC.

30. Pressure, humidity, temperature transducers, potentiometers, a variety of electro-mechanical devices that change voltage output given the input signal.

31. 102 RPM, with 30 lb-ft of torque.

32. An SCR conducts current in one direction—and only when the trigger circuit (gate) is powered on. The device shuts off when it is subjected to an opposite polarity between the anode and the cathode.

33. A device that basically has two or more power transistors, internally connected in one package. It can be turned on and off by the use of a command signal (base).

34. The ability to produce a magnetic field through the use of a voltage and a coil.

35. Power factor, given in %, is the measurement of the phase difference between the utility generated voltage and current waveform.

36. In the DC bus circuit of an AC drive (filters out unwanted AC ripple) so that the voltage delivered to the next stage will be as clean. Also, inductors placed ahead of the drive tent to reduce the amount of voltage harmonics back to the AC line.

37. Keep it clean, keep it dry, and keep the connections tight.

38. Dust attracts moisture. Moisture can cause the microelectronic circuits to misfire or develop a short. In addition, moisture assists in the development of corrosion. Corrosion on circuit board traces will eventually cause the electrical contacts to disintegrate.

39. Isolate the drive from the external control signals. If the drive satisfactorily operates the motor, when in keypad mode, then the drive is not the problem. Something external to the drive is causing the problem. If the drive does not operate the motor satisfactorily, then check all inputs to the drive. The drive must have two conditions to operate—start command and speed reference.

40. A programmable logic controller (PLC) or other computer device.

41. Inertia built up in the motor is transferred back to the drive by means of regenerative voltage. The voltage fed back to the drive is sent to a power resistor for dissipation as heat. A DB contactor is used to connect the motor voltage to the resistor. At the same time, the output contactor of the drive is opened so no voltage can be fed back into the drive output section.

42. Scalar is the term given to standard operation of a PWM voltage controlled drive. With this drive mode, the motor must have several percent slip in order to rotate. The drive simply supplies the volts and hertz output, and the motor responds with rotation, per the designed slip characteristic. Vector is the term given to a specialized drive that causes full motor torque at zero speed. Flux vector is another term used to describe the control of flux, which is also the control of torque.

43. Voltage reflection is the phenomenon of drive output voltages combining with voltage bouncing back from the motor. These combined peak voltages can cause damage to the stator windings, if they are not rated to handle the voltage stress. Precautions would include using an inverter duty motor, adding drive output reactors and/or dv/dt filters. Inductors will reduce the high-voltage spikes that can occur and keep the values within the range of the motor lacquer insulation.

44. Single-quadrant systems allow for motoring in the forward direction only. Two-quadrant systems allow forward and reverse direction, with reverse torque available for braking, Four-quadrant systems allow for forward and reverse direction operation, plus the capability of forward and reverse torque available for braking in either direction.

45. Both devices use the principle of variable resistance. A temperature sensor uses a material that changes resistance per the ambient temperature. A humidity sensor uses a material that changes length per the amount of humidity in the atmosphere. A hair hygrometer is a device that uses the changing length of human hair to operate a pivot connected to a variable resistor. In both cases, the output is a variable resistance, which if fed to a power supply, will generate a variable voltage, which can be fed to the drive (as a reference or feedback signal).

46. PPR means pulses per revolution. This number is a representation of the resolution of the unit. The resolution is the smallest amount of device rotation able to be detected by the encoder. For example, a 1024 tach indicates a shaft movement of 1/1024 of a revolution (i.e., 0.35° of shaft rotation).

47. The armature voltage feedback (EMF) is a representation of the output voltage, which is a direct indication of speed. The current feedback is a representation of current output from the drive. The IR compensation feedback is used to increase the speed reference circuit to increase speed due to loading of the motor. All three signals are brought back to the summing circuit. If the current feedback signal indicates the drive is exceeding the current capability, the drive will automatically reduce the speed reference. The speed reference will remain at a lower value until the current drops to an acceptable level.

48. AC, DC

49. Torque is a turning motion, twisting of a device. It is also defined as force × distance.

50. Special non-ESD-generating air should be used. Cans of ionized air are available for this purpose. Static electricity (ESD—electrostatic discharge) is the silent killer of small microcircuits that cannot handle several hundred volts of static charge.

Appendix B: Formulas and Conversions

General Information

The following information is a summary of typical formulas and conversion factors used in the rotating machinery industry. This information can be used as a basis for sizing drives and evaluating application types and factors.

However, these formulas are to be used for estimating purposes only. They do not include allowance for machine friction, windage, or other machine factors. When sizing a drive, always consider all machine factors (i.e. electrical, mechanical, and environmental) and motor factors (e.g., full load amperes and speed range).

Horsepower Formulas

General Formula

$$HP = \frac{Torque \times Speed}{5252}$$

where:

Torque = lb-ft

Speed = rpm

5252 = a proportional constant

Conveyors

$$HP(Vertical) = \frac{Force \times Velocity}{33{,}000}$$

where:

Force = force or weight (lb)
Velocity = fpm

$$HP(Horizontal) = \frac{Force \times Velocity \times Coef\ of\ Friction}{33{,}000}$$

where:

Force = force or weight (lb)
Velocity = fpm

Fans and Blowers

$$BHP = \frac{CFM \times Pressure}{33{,}000 \times Eff\ of\ Fan}$$

where:

BHP =
CFM = cubic feet per minute
EffofFan = efficiency of fan (%/100)
Pressure = lb/ft^2

$$BHP = \frac{CFM \times Pressure}{229 \times Eff\ of\ Fan}$$

where:

BHP =
CFM = cubic feet per minute
EffofFan = efficiency of fan (%/100)
Pressure = lb/in^2

$$HP = \frac{CFM \times PSI}{6356 \times Eff\ of\ Fan}$$

where:

CFM = cubic feet per minute
EffofFan = efficiency of fan (%/100)
PSI = pressure in inches of water

Pumps

$$BHP = \frac{GPM \times Head \times Specific\ Gravity}{3960 \times Eff\ of\ Pump}$$

where:

BHP =

GPM = gallons per minute
Head = measurement of pressure in ft
EffofPump = efficiency of pump (%/100)
SpecificGravity = 1.0 (water)
Efficiency of pump (positive displacement) may vary between 50 and 80% depending on size
Efficiency of pump (centrifugal) = 500 to 100 GPM = 70 to 75%
1000 to 1500 GPM = 75 to 80%
Over 1500 GPM = 80 to 85%

$$BHP = \frac{GPM \times PSI \times Specific\ Gravity}{1713 \times Eff\ of\ Pump}$$

Affinity laws for centrifugal applications:

$$\frac{Flow_1}{Flow_2} = \frac{RPM_1}{RPM_2}$$

$$\frac{Pres_1}{Pres_2} = \frac{(RPM_1)^2}{(RPM_2)^2}$$

$$\frac{BHP_1}{BHP_2} = \frac{(RPM_1)^2}{(RPM_2)^2}$$

Torque Formulas

General Formulas

$$T = \frac{HP \times 5252}{Speed}$$

where:

T = torque in lb-ft
HP = horsepower
Speed = speed in rpm

$$Torque = Force \times Radius$$

where:

Torque = torque in lb-ft
Force = force in lb
Radius = radius in ft

$$Torque = \frac{WK^2 \times \Delta RPM}{308 \times t}$$

where:

Torque = torque in lb-ft
WK^2 = inertia reflected to the motor shaft (lb-ft^2)
Δrpm = change in speed (rpm)
t = time to accelerate (seconds)

AC Motor Formulas

$$Speed = \frac{120 \times Frequency}{Number\ of\ Poles}$$

where:

Speed = synchronous speed in rpm
Frequency = applied frequency in Hz
NumberofPoles = number of poles per phase

$$Slip = \frac{(Sync\ Speed - \ FL\ Speed) \times 100}{Sync\ Speed}$$

where:

Slip = slip in %
SyncSpeed = synchronous speed in rpm
FLSpeed = full load speed in rpm

Electrical Formulas

Power (DC Circuits)

$$HP = \frac{I \times E}{746}$$

where:

I = intensity of current (amperes)
E = EMF or voltage (volts)

Power (AC Circuits)

$$kVA = \frac{I \times E}{1000}$$

where:

kVA = kilovolt amperes (1 phase)
I = intensity of current (amperes)
E = EMF or voltage (volts)

$$kVA = \frac{I \times E \times 1.73}{1000}$$

where:

kVA = kilovolt amperes (3 phase)
I = intensity of current (amperes)
E = EMF or voltage (volts)

$$kW = \frac{I \times E \times PF}{1000}$$

where:

kW = kilowatts (1 phase)
I = intensity of current (amperes)
E = EMF or voltage (volts)
PF = power factor

$$kW = \frac{I \times E \times PF \times 1.73}{1000}$$

where:

kW = kilowatts (3 phase)
I = intensity of current (amperes)
E = EMF or voltage (volts)
PF = power factor

$$PF = \frac{W}{E \times I} = \frac{kW}{kVA}$$

$$PF = \frac{Input\ Watts}{V \times A \times 1.732}$$

where:

PF = power factor
W = watts
I = intensity of current (amperes)
E = EMF or voltage (volts)
kW = kilowatts
kVA = kilovolt amperes

Motor Amperes (calculating)

$$MotorAmperes = \frac{HP \times 746}{E \times 1.73 \times EFF \times PF}$$

$$MotorAmperes = \frac{kVA \times 1000}{1.73 \times E}$$

$$MotorAmperes = \frac{kW \times 1000}{1.73 \times E \times PF}$$

where:

HP = horsepower
E = EMF or voltage (volts)
EFF = efficiency of the motor (in %/100)
kVA = kilovolt amperes
kW = kilowatts
PF = power factor

Constants

Weight

16 oz =	1 lb
2.204 lb =	1 kg
2.309 ft of water at 62°F =	1 PSI
28.35 gm =	1 oz
62.35 lbs =	Weight of 1 cu. ft of water at 62°F
1 gal of water at 62°F =	8.326 lb

Power

1 kW =	1.34 HP
1 HP =	2.54 BTU/hour
1 HP =	33,000 ft-lb per minute
1 HP =	746 W

Pressure

14.22 PSI =	1 kg per sq. cm (1 metric atmosphere)
1 PSI =	2.035 inches of mercury at 32°F
1 PSI =	2.041 inches of mercury at 62°F
1 PSI =	27.71 inches of water at 62°F
Atmospheric pressure =	29.92 inches of mercury at 32°F
Atmospheric pressure =	30 inches of mercury at 62°F (approx.)

Length

1 inch =	2.54 centimeters (cm)
1 yard =	3 feet
1 yard =	1.094 meters

1 meter (m) = 3.28 feet
1 meter (m) = 39.37 inches

Temperature

$$°C = \frac{(°F - 32)}{1.8}$$

$$°F = (°C \times 1.8) + 32$$

Locate known temperature in either degrees Celsius (°C) or degrees Fahrenheit (°F) in boldface **°F/°C** column. For conversion, read desired temperature in respective column.

Example: To convert 110°C to Fahrenheit, find **110** in the °F/°C column. Then look to the right for the desired conversion value, 230°F. To convert 75°F to Celsius, find **75** in the °F/°C column. Then look to the left for the desired conversion value, 23.9°F.

°C	°F/°C	°F	°C	°F/°C	°F	°C	°F/°C	°F
-45.6	-50	-58	15.6	60	140	76.7	170	338
-42.8	-45	-49	18.3	65	149	79.4	175	347
-40.0	-40	-40	21.1	70	158	82.2	180	356
-37.2	-35	-31	23.9	75	167	85.0	185	365
-34.4	-30	-22	26.7	80	176	87.8	190	375
-31.7	-25	-13	29.4	85	185	90.6	195	383
-28.9	-20	-4	32.2	90	194	93.3	200	392
-26.1	-15	5	35.0	95	203	96.1	205	401
-23.3	-10	14	37.8	100	212	98.9	210	410
-20.6	-5	23	40.6	105	221	101.7	215	419
-17.8	0	32	43.3	110	230	104.4	220	428
-15.0	5	41	46.1	115	239	107.2	225	437
-12.2	10	50	48.9	120	248	110.0	230	446
-9.4	15	59	51.7	125	257	112.8	235	455
-6.7	20	68	54.4	130	266	115.6	240	464
-3.9	25	77	57.2	135	275	118.3	245	473
-1.1	30	86	60.0	140	284	121.1	250	482
1.7	35	95	62.8	145	293	123.9	255	491
4.4	40	104	65.6	150	302	126.7	260	500
7.2	45	113	68.3	155	311	129.4	265	509
10.0	50	122	71.1	160	320	132.2	270	518
12.8	55	131	73.9	165	329	135.0	275	527

Torque

1 Newton-Meters (N-m) =	0.737 lb-ft
1 lb-ft =	1.356 Newton-Meters (N-m)
1 lb-in =	0.083 lb-ft
1 lb-ft =	12.0 lb-in

Note:
A 2-pole motor (3600 rpm) develops 1.5 lb-ft of torque per HP
A 4-pole motor (1800 rpm) develops 3.0 lb-ft of torque per HP
A 6-pole motor (1200 rpm) develops 4.5 lb-ft of torque per HP
An 8-pole motor (900 rpm) develops 6.0 lb-ft of torque per HP

Volume

1 cm^3 (mL)=	0.00001 m^3
1 fl-oz =	29.57 cm^3
1 L =	0.001 m^3
1 yd^3 =	0.765 m^3
1 ft^3 of water at 39.2°F =	28.32 kg or liters
1 cfm =	0.000472 m^3/s

Rotation & Rates

1 rpm =	6.00 degrees/s
1 degree/s =	0.167 rpm
1 in/s =	0.0254 m/s
1 km/hr =	0.278 m/s
1 mph =	0.447 m/s
1 FPM =	0.00508 m/s
1 FPS =	0.305 m/s
1 gal/min =	63.09 cm^3/s
1 yd^3/min =	0.0127 m^3/s

Inertia

1 oz-in^2 =	0.000434 lb-ft^2
1 lb-in^2 =	0.00694 lb-ft^2
1 oz-in-sec^2 =	0.167 lb-ft^2
1 in-lb-sec^2 =	2.68 lb-ft^2
1 N-m^2 =	2.42 lb-ft^2

Conversion Factors

MULTIPLY		BY	=	TO OBTAIN
LENGTH				
Centimeters	×	0.3937	=	Inches
Fathoms	×	6.0	=	Feet
Feet	×	12	=	Inches

Feet	×	0.3048	=	Meters
Inches	×	2.54	=	Centimeters
Kilometers	×	0.6214	=	Miles
Meters	×	3.281	=	Feet
Meters	×	39.37	=	Inches
Meters	×	1.094	=	Yards
Miles	×	5280.0	=	Feet
Miles	×	1.609	=	Kilometers
Yards	×	0.9144	=	Meters
AREA				
Acres	×	43560.0	=	Square feet
Acres	×	4840.0	=	Square yards
Circular mils	×	0.7854	=	Square mils
Square centimeters	×	0.155	=	Square inches
Square feet	×	144.0	=	Square inches
Square feet	×	0.0929	=	Square meters
Square inches	×	6.452	=	Square centimeters
Square meters	×	1.196	=	Square yards
Square miles	×	640.0	=	Acres
Square yards	×	0.8361	=	Square meters
VOLUME				
Cubic feet	×	0.0283	=	Cubic meters
Cubic feet	×	7.481	=	Gallons
Cubic inches	×	0.5541	=	Ounces (fluid)
Cubic meters	×	35.31	=	Cubic feet
Cubic meters	×	1.308	=	Cubic yards
Cubic yards	×	0.7646	=	Cubic meters
Gallons	×	3.785	=	Liters
Gallons	×	0.1337	=	Cubic feet
Liters	×	0.2642	=	Gallons
Liters	×	1.057	=	Quarts (liquid)
Ounces (fluid)	×	1.805	=	Cubic inches
Quarts (liquid)	×	0.9463	=	Liters
FORCE AND WEIGHT				
Grams	×	0.0353	=	Ounces
Kilograms	×	2.205	=	Pounds
Newtons	×	0.2248	=	Pounds (force)
Ounces	×	28.35	=	Grams
Pounds	×	453.6	=	Grams
Pounds (force)	×	4.448	=	Newtons
Tons (short)	×	907.2	=	Kilograms
Tons (short)	×	2000.0	=	Pounds

TORQUE				
Gram-centimeters	×	0.0139	=	Ounce-inches
Newton-meters	×	0.7376	=	Pound-feet
Newton-meters	×	8.851	=	Pound-inches
Ounce-inches	×	72.0	=	Gram-centimeters
Pound-feet	×	1.3558	=	Newton-meters
Pound-inches	×	0.113	=	Newton-meters
ENERGY OR WORK				
BTU	×	778.2	=	Foot-pounds
POWER				
BTU per hour	×	0.293	=	Watts
Horsepower	×	33000	=	Foot-pounds per min
Horsepower	×	550	=	Foot-pounds per sec
Horsepower	×	746	=	Watts
Kilowatts	×	1.341	=	Horsepower
PLANE ANGLE				
Degrees	×	0.0175	=	Radians
Minutes	×	0.01667	=	Degrees
Minutes	×	2.9×10^{-4}	=	Radians
Quadrants	×	90.0	=	Degrees
Quadrants	×	1.5708	=	Radians
Radians	×	57.3	=	Degrees

Appendix C: Drive Enclosure Types

The following information is an overview of NEMA enclosures available for drives. For detailed descriptions consult the *National Electrical Manufacturers Association (NEMA) Standards Publication No. 250*. Refer to the sales manual for specific ABB enclosures available as standard or as an option.

Enclosures normally do not protect devices against internal conditions such as condensation, corrosion, or contamination. The user is responsible for protecting equipment from these conditions.

Enclosures normally do not protect internal devices against conditions such as condensation, icing, corrosion, or contamination. These conditions may occur inside the enclosure or may enter by way of the conduit or unsealed openings. Ultimately, protection is in the hands of the user who must take adequate precautions to protect the equipment inside the enclosure.

NEMA Type 1 (Surface Mounting) (IP 21)

These enclosures provide a degree of protection against contact with the enclosed equipment; they are intended for indoor use and in typical service conditions. The enclosure is sheet steel, treated to resist corrosion.

NEMA Type 1 (Flush Mounting)

These enclosures are for installation in machine frames and plaster walls; they are for similar applications and are designed to meet the same tests as NEMA Type 1 surface mounting.

NEMA Type 3

These enclosures are intended for outdoor use primarily to provide a degree of protection against windblown dust, rain, sleet, and external ice formation. They are designed to meet rain,[1] external icing,[2] dust, and rust-resistance design tests. They are not intended to provide protection against conditions such as internal condensation or internal icing.

NEMA Type 3R

These enclosures are intended for outdoor use primarily to provide a degree of protection against falling rain, sleet, and external ice formation. They are designed to meet rod entry, external icing,[2] rain,[3] and rust-resistance design tests. They are not intended to provide protection against conditions such as dust, internal condensation, or internal icing.

NEMA Type 4 (IP 55)

These enclosures provide protection against windblown dust and rain, splashing water, and hose-directed water. They can be used in both indoor and outdoor installations. They are designed to meet hosedown, dust, external icing, [1] and rust-resistance design tests. These enclosures do not provide protection against conditions such as internal condensation or internal icing. Enclosures are made up of heavy-gauge stainless steel, cast aluminum, or heavy-gauge sheet steel, depending on the type and size of unit. Cover has a synthetic rubber gasket.

NEMA Type 4X (IP 45)

These enclosures are intended for indoor or outdoor use, primarily to provide a degree of protection against corrosion, windblown dust and rain, splashing water and hose-directed water. Ice formation on the enclosure should cause no damage.

NEMA Type 6

These enclosures are intended for use indoors or outdoors where occasional submersion is encountered.

NEMA Type 6P

These enclosures are intended for indoor or outdoor use primarily to provide a degree of protection against the entry of water during prolonged submersion at a limited depth. They are designed to meet air pressure, external icing,[2] and corrosion-resistance design tests. They are not intended to provide protection against conditions such as internal condensation or internal icing.

---

1. Evaluation criteria: Undamaged after ice that built up during specified test has melted. (Note: **NOT** required to be operable while ice-laden.)
2. Evaluation criteria: No water shall rise as high as the lowest electrical part after the specified test.
3. Evaluation criteria: No water shall rise as high as the lowest electrical part after the specified test.

NEMA Type 7

(For hazardous gas locations with bolted enclosure) These enclosures are for indoor use in locations classified as Class 1, Groups C or D, defined in the National Electrical Code. Enclosures of this type are designed to be capable of withstanding the pressures resulting from an internal explosion of specified gases, and contain such an explosion sufficiently that an explosive gas-air mixture existing in the atmosphere surrounding the enclosure will not be ignited. Enclosed heat-generating devices are designed not to cause external surfaces to reach temperatures capable of igniting explosive gas-air mixtures in the surrounding atmosphere. Enclosures are designed to meet explosion, hydrostatic, and temperature design tests. The exterior finish of this enclosure is a special corrosion-resistant enamel.

NEMA Type 9

(For hazardous dust locations) These enclosures are intended for indoor use in locations classified as Class II, Groups E, F, or G, as defined in the National Electrical Code. Type 9 enclosures are designed to be capable of preventing the entrance of dust. Enclosed heat-generating devices are designed not to cause external surfaces to reach temperatures capable of igniting or discoloring dust on the enclosure or igniting dust-air mixtures in the surrounding atmosphere. Enclosures are designed to meet dust penetration and temperature design tests and aging of gaskets. The outside finish is of a special corrosion-resistant enamel.

NEMA Type 12 (IP 54)

Type 12 enclosures are intended for indoor use primarily to provide a degree of protection against dust, falling dirt, and dripping noncorrosive liquids. They are designed to meet drip,[4] dust, and rust-resistance tests. They are not intended to provide protection against conditions such as internal condensation.

NEMA Type 13

These enclosures are intended for indoor use primarily to provide a degree of protection against dust, spraying of water, oil, and noncorrosive coolant. They are designed to meet oil exclusion and rust-resistance design tests. They are not intended to provide protection against conditions such as internal condensation.

4. Evaluation criteria: No water shall rise as high as the lowest electrical part after the specified test.

Appendix D: Terms and Definitions

AC Contactor

Designed for the specific purpose of establish or interrupting an AC power circuit._A contactor is a high power, electromagnetic switch. It is constructed of a low voltage "control circuit" (for example, 24VDC) and a "power circuit," where the high voltage is being controlled (for example – 460VAC, 3-Phase). A contactor is essentially a high power relay._

AC Drive

An electronic device that converts a fixed frequency and voltage source to an adjustable frequency and AC voltage source. It controls the speed, torque, horsepower, and direction of an AC motor.

A/D Converter

A device that converts an analog signal (continuous values of voltage or current, e.g., sinewave) to a digital number.

Adjustable Speed

Varying the speed of a motor, either manually or automatically. The desired operating speed (set speed) is relatively constant regardless of load.

Adjustable Speed Drive (Electrical)

An adjustable-speed drive consists of the motor, drive controller, and operator's controls (either manual or automatic).

Analog Input (AI)

An analog input is an input for the user-supplied DC signal. The signal may be a speed reference or a process feedback. This signal can be from manual speed pot DC voltage (0 to 10 VDC) DC current (0 to 20 mADC). For many drives, the abbreviation is AI.

Analog Input Module
An I/O module that converts an analog signal from an analog measuring device that may be processed by the processor.

Analog Output Module
An I/O module that converts a digital signal from the processor into an analog output signal for use by a user analog device.

Analog-to-Digital Converter (A/D)
A hardware device that senses an analog signal and converts it to a representation in digital form.

ASCII
Acronym for American Standards Code for Information Interchange. Basically, it is a 7-bit code with an optional parity bit used to represent alpha numeric, punctuation marks, and control code characters.

Bandwidth
The frequency range of a system input over which the system will respond satisfactorily to a command.

Base Speed
The point where the motor will develop rated horsepower (HP) at rated load and voltage. With DC drives it is commonly the point where full armature voltage is applied with full rated field excitation. With AC systems, it is commonly the point where 60 Hz and rated voltage is applied to the induction motor.

Baud
A unit of signaling speed equal to the number of discrete conditions or signal events per second.

BCD (Binary Coded Decimal)
A numbering system that is used to express individual decimal digits (i.e., 0 through 9) in a four-bit binary rotation.

Bearing (Ball)
A ball-shaped component that is used to reduce friction and wear while supporting rotating elements. For a motor, this type of bearing provides a relatively rigid support for the output shaft.

Bearing (Roller)
A special bearing system with cylindrical rollers capable of handling belted load applications that are too large for standard ball bearings.

Binary Digit (Bit)

In the binary system, a bit can represent either 0 or 1; to a computer a bit will indicate an off or on signal. Bits are the units of information that, when combined in certain configurations, will signal to the computer what it is to do. Bits are organized into larger units called words for access by computer instructions. Computers are often categorized by word size in bits, that is, the maximum word size that can be processed as a unit during an instruction cycle (e.g., 16-bit or 32-bit computers). The number of bits in a word is an indication of the processing power of the system, especially for calculations or for high-precision data.

Bit Rate

The speed at which bits are transmitted, usually expressed in bits per second (sometimes referred to as *baud rate*).

Block

A group of electronic words transmitted as a one unit.

Braking

Provides a means of stopping an AC or DC motor and can be accomplished in several ways:

Braking (Dynamic AC Drives). AC motors do not have separate field excitation. Dynamic braking is accomplished by continuing to excite the motor from the drive. This causes a regenerative current to the drive's DC bus In Drive terminology, DC Bus is an actual circuit -- - should be capital B? (Check for consistency throughout the book) to dissipate the power returned. The brake resistor is usually switched by a transistor or other power switch controlled by the drive.

Braking (Dynamic DC Drives). The motor slows by applying a resistive load across the armature leads after disconnection from the DC supply. This must be done while the motor field is energized. The motor then acts as a generator until the energy of the rotating armature is dissipated. This is not a holding brake.

Braking (Regenerative). This is essentially *electronic braking*. The generated power is returned to the line through the power converter. It may also be dissipated as losses in the converter (within its limitations).

Braking (Mechanical). This is a positive-action friction device. In a normal configuration the brake is set when power is removed. This can be used as a holding brake. (**Note:** A *separately-mounted brake* is one that is located on some part of the mechanical drive train other than the motor.)

Breakaway Torque

The torque required to start a machine from a stopped position. It is always greater than the torque needed to maintain motion.

Bridge Rectifier

A full-wave rectifier that conducts current in only one direction of the input current. AC applied to the input results in approximate DC at the output. A *diode bridge* rectifier is a non-controlled full-wave rectifier that produces a constant DC voltage. An SCR bridge rectifier is a full-wave rectifier with an output that can be controlled by switching on the gate-control element.

Burn-In

The process of operating a unit (e.g., drive) at elevated temperatures. This operation, performed before the unit's use in an application, tends to stabilize the unit's characteristics and detects early failures.

Byte

This is equal to eight consecutive bits.

"C" Face (Motor Mounting)

This type of motor mounting is used to close-couple pumps and similar applications where the mounting holes in the face are threaded to receive bolts from the pump. Normally the "C" face is used where a pump or similar item is to be overhung on the motor. This type of mounting is a NEMA standard design and available with or without feet.

CEMF

Counter electromotive force is the product of a motor armature rotating in a magnetic field. This generating action takes place whenever a motor is rotating. Under stable motoring conditions, the generated voltage (CEMF) is equal to the voltage supplied to the motor minus small losses. The polarity of the CEMF is opposite to that of the power being supplied to the armature.

Cable Termination Filters

Filters installed at the motor, designed to match the terminating impedance at the motor to the characteristic impedance of the power cable between the drive and motors.

CE Marking

CE marking is a label attached by the manufacturer to a product certifying that the product complies with certain European directives (e.g., EMC) and safety standards.

Closed Loop

A regulator circuit in which the actual value of the controlled variable (e.g., speed) is sensed. A signal proportional to this value (feedback signal) is compared with a signal proportional to the desired value (reference signal). The difference between these signals (error signal) causes the actual value to change in the direction that will reduce the difference in signals to zero.

Cogging

A motor condition where the shaft does not rotate smoothly but "steps" or "jerks" from one position to another. Cogging is most evident at low motor speeds and can cause objectionable vibrations in the driven machine.

Common DC Bus

A drive system where several inverters are connected to a common DC bus. The advantages are space reduction, reduced cabling costs (only one incoming section is used), and in some instances, energy saving. For example, in a sugar mill, a battery of centrifuges can be driven by a common DC bus Bus system such that energy generated from a decelerating machine may be utilized, via the DC bus, by an accelerating machine.

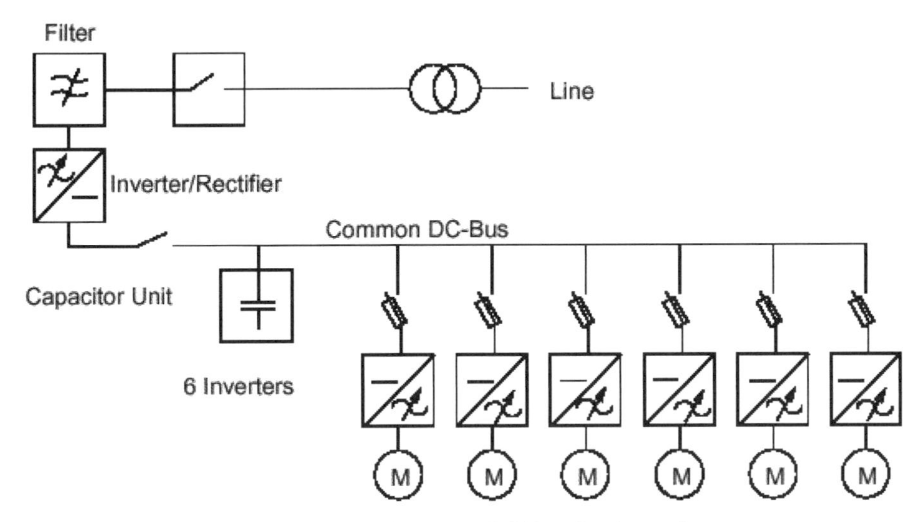

AC Drive Common DC Bus Configuration

Commutation (Inverter)

This is a process where forward current is interrupted or transferred from one switching device to the other. In most AC circuits, turn-on-control is adequate and turn-off occurs naturally when the AC cycle causes the polarity across a given device to reverse.

Complementary Metal-Oxide Semiconductor (CMOS)

An integrated circuit logic family characterized by very low power dissipation and moderate circuit density per chip, at moderate speed of operation.

Comparator

A device that compares one signal to another, usually the process signal compared with the set point or command signal.

Concentric Windings

Motor windings that are wound so that each turn of the coil is next to the previous turn, and the coil is built up in successive layers. This ensures that each turn of the coil is in contact with immediately preceding and successive turns.

Constant Horsepower Load

A load characterized by torque relative to the inverse of speed, abbreviated *CHP*. This type of load occurs above base speed. Horsepower stays constant because torque decreases as speed increases. The load requires low torque at high speeds. Some typical applications would be drilling, shaping, milling, and turning metal. In AC applications, the CHP range is sometimes referred to as the *constant voltage range*.

Constant Horsepower Range

A motor-operation range where motor speed is controlled by field weakening. In this range, motor torque decreases as speed increases. Since horsepower is speed times torque (divided by a constant), the value of horsepower developed by the motor in this range is constant.

Constant Torque Load

A load characterized by torque proportional to a constant at any speed. Torque stays constant because horsepower increases as speed increases up to base speed. The load requires the same amount of torque from zero to base speed. Some typical applications would be hoists, conveyors, and printing presses.

Constant Torque Range

A speed range in which the motor is capable of delivering a constant torque, subject to cooling limitations of the motor.

Constant Voltage Range

This term is related to AC drives. It is the range of motor operation where the drive's output voltage is held constant as output frequency is varied. This speed range produces motor performance similar to a DC drive's constant horsepower range.

Constant Volts per Hertz (v/Hz)

The relationship that exists in AC drives where the output voltage is varied in direct proportion to frequency. This type of operation is required to allow the motor to produce constant-rated torque as speed is varied.

Continuous Duty

A motor that can continue to operate within the insulation-temperature limits after it has reached normal operating temperature.

Control Logic Section

Low voltage and current circuits that tell the power conversion sub-section devices when to switch on or off.

Converter

The process of changing AC to DC. This is accomplished through use of a diode rectifier or thyristor rectifier circuit. The term converter may also refer to the process of changing AC to DC to AC (e.g., in an adjustable-frequency drive). A *frequency converter*, such as that found in an adjustable frequency drive, consists of a *rectifier*, a *DC intermediate circuit* (*DC bus*), an *inverter*, and a *control unit*.

A variable-frequency drive uses a three-phase diode bridge to convert the applied AC line voltage to rectified DC. The DC bus Bus consists of the DC potential source (internal rectifier bridge or external source), DC link inductor (connecting the DC bus Bus capacitors to the DC potential source), and DC bus Bus capacitors that, together with the DC link inductor, provide filtration of the DC source potential and provide some buffering between the DC source and the power inverter section. The DC bus Bus voltage is 1.35 × supply voltage (V in).

Critical Frequency

The frequency at which continuous operation will cause mechanical vibration of the machine being controlled.

Current Limiting

An electronic method of limiting the maximum current available to the motor. This is adjustable so that the motor's maximum current can be controlled. It can also be preset as a protective device to protect both the motor and control from extended overloads.

Current Regulation

This is the drive's ability to control the amount of current output. If the motor current exceeds the current limit setting, the drive output will stop. The output frequency will decrease until the motor current is reduced below the current limit level. The drive will then accelerate at the rate determined by the acceleration time.

Cycle

One complete cycle is the variation of an AC signal from zero to a maximum and back to zero in a positive direction and then in a negative direction.

"D" Flange (Motor Mounting)

This type of motor mounting is used when the motor is to be built as a part of the machine. The mounting holes of the flange are not threaded. The bolts protrude through the flange from the motor side. Normally "D" flange motors are supplied without feet since the motor is mounted directly to the driven machine.

D/A Converter

A device that converts a digital number into an analog voltage or current level (continuous values of voltage or current, e.g., sinewave).

Damping

The reduction in amplitude of an oscillation in the system.

DC Braking

This is sometimes referred to as *DC injection braking*. This process provides quicker stopping times compared with a standard ramp-to-stop. The drive applies a DC voltage to the stator windings, quickly dissipating any energy within the drive system.

DC Bus

Circuitry that filters the DC voltage entering the power output subsection from the rectifier.

DC Contactor

A contactor specifically designed to establish or interrupt a direct-current power circuit.

DC Line Reactor

Sometimes called a *DC link inductor*, this component adds impedance to the DC bus. Because of this, the inductor slows the rate of rise of current spikes, smoothing the effects of DC ripple on the bus Bus voltage output. The results are improvement in the displacement power factor and lower harmonic distortion sent back to the AC line.

Dead Band

The range of values through which a system input can be changed without causing a corresponding change in system output.

Default

A default is a preprogrammed value for a parameter. During start-up of an AC drive, all application macro parameter values appearing on the keypad display are default settings. These default settings may be changed during the process of customizing your drive for your particular application.

Definite-Purpose Motor

A definite-purpose motor is any motor design, listed, and offered in standard ratings with standard operating characteristics from a mechanical construction for use under service conditions other than usual, or for use on a particular type of application.

Definite-Purpose Inverter-Fed Motor

Motors that are specifically designed for use with adjustable-frequency drives, also called *inverter duty motors.* NEMA MG1-1993, Part 31 defines performance requirements for definite-purpose inverter-fed motors.

Deviation

Difference between an instantaneous value of a controlled variable and the desired value of the controlled variable corresponding to the set point. Also called error.

di/dt

The rate of change in current versus the rate of change in time. Line reactors and isolation transformers can be used to provide the impedance necessary to reduce the effects of unlimited current on phase-controlled rectifiers (SCRs).

Digital Communications

Transfer of information by means of a sequence of signals called bits (for binary digits), each of which can have one of two different values. The signals may, for example, take the form of two different voltage levels on a wire or the presence or absence of light in a fiber-optic light guide. It can be made arbitrarily insensitive to external disturbances by means of error-control procedures.

Digital Input (DI)

The digital inputs (DI) receive bi-stable (two-state on-off) control signals from the outside world. An example would be a two-position start-stop selector switch. Digital inputs are on some AC drive keypad displays.

Digital Signal Processor (DSP)

A digital signal processor is a fast-acting component for mathematical calculations. It operates at 40 MHz and is able to multiply two numbers (8,000,000) in the time it takes for light to travel 20 m.

Diode

A device that allows current to flow in one direction but does not allow current t flow in the reverse direction.

Direct Torque Control (DTC™)

Direct torque control is a term used for vector control without feedback, similar to a sensor-less flux vector AC drive. It is an optimized AC drive control principle where inverter switching directly controls the motor variables (e.g., flux and torque). The measured motor current and voltage are inputs to an adaptive motor model, which produces an exact value of flux and torque every 25 μs. Motor torque and flux two-level comparators compare the actual values produced by torque and flux reference controllers. Depending on the outputs from the two-level controllers, the optimum pulse selector directly determines the optimum inverter switch positions. The inverter switch positions again determine the motor voltage and current, which in turn influence the motor torque and flux, and the control loop is closed.

Drift
Deviation from the initial set speed with no load change over a specific time period. Normally the drive must be operated for a specific warm-up time at a specified ambient temperature before drift specifications apply. Drift is normally caused by random changes in operating characteristics of various control components.

Drive Controller
An electronic device that can control the speed, torque, horsepower, and direction of an AC or DC motor. This device is also called a variable-speed drive.

Drive End of a Motor
The end (D.E.) that carries the coupling or driving pulley.

Driver
A circuit that adjusts the reference signal to the correct level. It could also be considered the circuit that controls the "firing" of an IGBT. Driver circuits turn the power device on and off. With an IGBT, less current is required to turn the device off compared with an SCR.

Duty Cycle
The relationship between the operating and rest times or repeatable operation at the different loads.

dv/dt
The term dv/dt comes from differential calculus and means the derivative of v (voltage) with respect to t (time). It is the instantaneous rate of change in voltage with respect to time. To conform to the mathematical definition, the dv/dt of a voltage pulse should be defined as a function that describes the rate of change in voltage at any time during the duration of the pulse. In most discussions of motor insulation voltage stress, the term dv/dt is applied to the average rate of voltage change as voltage rises from 10% to 90% of the peak voltage or:

$$\frac{dv}{dt} = \frac{\text{peak voltage} \times 0.8}{\text{rise time}}$$

The rate of change in voltage versus a rate of change in time. Specially designed resistor-capacitor networks can help protect the SCRs from excessive dv/dt, which can result from line voltage spikes, line disturbances, and circuit configurations with extreme forward conducting or reverse-blocking requirements.

Dwell

The time spent in one state before moving to the next. In motion-control applications for example, a dwell time may be programmed to allow time for a tool change or part clamping operation.

Dynamic Braking

See Braking

Eddy Current

Currents induced in motor components from the movement of magnetic fields. Eddy currents produce heat and are minimized by lamination of the motor poles and armature. In transformers, it is the current that circulates in the metallic core material. This current is a result of electromotive forces induced by a variation of magnetic flux. Magnetic flux is a condition produced by the movement of voltage induced in an electrical conductor.

EEPROM

EEPROM is an acronym for *electrically-erasable programmable read-only memory*. The EEPROM is the non-volatile memory that stores all parameters, even when power is removed. (Sometimes referred to as E^2PROM™).

Efficiency

Ratio of mechanical output to electrical input indicated by a percentage. In motors, it is the effectiveness with which a motor converts electrical energy into mechanical energy.

Electromagnetic Compatibility (EMC)

Electromagnetic Compatibility is the ability of a device or system to function satisfactorily in its electromagnetic environment without introducing intolerable electromagnetic disturbances to anything in the same environment. To achieve EMC, the immunity of all equipment in the environment must be higher than the emissions from any source in the environment.

Electromotive Force (EMF)

Electromotive force is a way of expressing voltage or potential difference.

Electromagnetic Interference (EMI)

This is an abbreviation for electro-magnetic interference. This characteristic occurs during the switching of electronic power supplies and is similar to a radio wave. If the EMI signal is strong enough, it will cause unwanted reference signals or "noise" in other electronic equipment, such as drives.

Electrostatic Discharge

See ESD

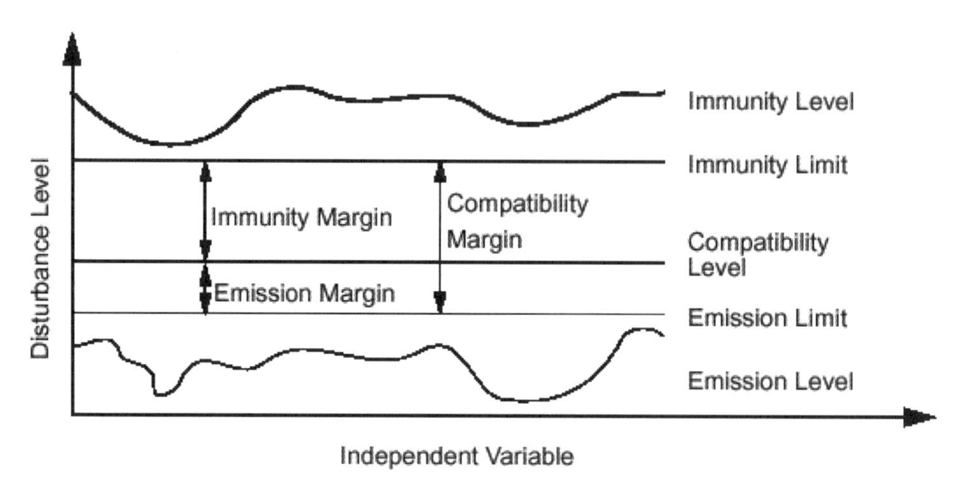

Representation of EMC Immunity and Emissions Limits

EPROM

EPROM is an acronym for *erasable programmable read only memory.* The EPROM is a circuit that can be erased with ultraviolet light, then reprogrammed with electrical pulses. It is essentially where the drive software exists—the section that controls semiconductor firing signals, etc.

Enable

To allow an action or acceptance of data by applying an appropriate signal to the appropriate input (e.g., to allow the drive to start).

Enclosure

The housing in which the control is mounted. Enclosures are available in designs for various environmental conditions.

Encoder

A device that produces a serial or parallel digital indication of mechanical angle or displacement. Essentially, an encoder provides high-resolution feedback data related to shaft position and is used with other circuitry to indicate velocity and direction. The encoder produces discrete electrical pulses during each increment of shaft rotation.

There are two types of encoders available: *absolute* and *incremental*. The *absolute encoder* provides multiple-channel coding of shaft position, with the output in a unique binary code. This type of encoder costs more than an incremental one because of the complexity of the circuit.

The *incremental encoder* consists of magnetic or optically-coupled electronic devices inside a case. These devices give out a number of pulses that correspond to speed and direction. This type of encoder has a disadvantage when used in positioning. When power is lost, this device also loses its starting point.

Error
Difference between the set-point signal and the feedback signal. An error is necessary before a correction can be made in a controlled system.

ESD
ESD is an acronym for *electrostatic discharge*. Electrostatic-discharge cautions indicate situations in which static electricity can damage circuit boards without any visible signs of damage. Precautions listed in an AC drive installation start-up manual must be followed when installing or removing circuit boards. As little as 50 V of static charge can damage a gate-emitter junction or a microcircuit in a "chip." Humans don't feel a discharge unless it is over 3000 V of static charge. Therefore, it is imperative that ESD grounding devices are worn when working on drive circuitry with the power off. By the time a human would feel ESD, the circuitry on the board could be damaged and not repairable.

FCC (CFR47)
Limits from the Code of Federal Regulations. Defines the limits of radiated energy (expressed as RFI—radio frequency interference) from computing devices. These limits indicate protection from interference when receiver located at least 10 m from the RFI source.

Feedback
This part of a system provides an actual operation signal for comparison with the set point to establish an error signal used by the regulator circuit.

Feedback Loop
The feedback loop provides the self-corrective signal necessary to tell the drive to adjust output to the motor. The motor performs the required adjustment in speed or direction. The feedback loop is critical to the automatic accurate operation of the system. Because the feedback loop is directly connected to the motor or machine, it provides an exact representation of speed.

Fieldbus
The word field indicates that we are dealing with the field level, the lowest layer of automation hierarchy, where the field devices like sensors and actuators are used. The word bus tells us that these communication devices are connected to a common connecting point instead of point-to-point connections.

Field Range
The range of motor speed from base speed to the maximum rated speed. With AC drives this is also referred to as the *above base speed* range or *constant horsepower* range. With DC drives, this indicates the area where *above base speed* operation is a result of weakening the shunt field flux.

Field Weakening Point

On AC drive systems, this is the point at which the output voltage no longer increases even though the output frequency is increased. Operation above this point results in reduced motor torque capability while the output kVA remains constant.

Filter

A device that passes a signal or a range of signals and eliminates all others.

Flash Prom

This is a memory chip imbedded on a circuit board similar to an E^2PROM™. This memory can contain drive parameters and values and can be upgraded to a new software version through fiber-optic communications.

Flux Vector

Flux-vector drives use a method of controlling torque similar to that of DC drive systems, including a wide speed-control range with quick response. Flux-vector drives have the same power section as all PWM drives, but use a sophisticated *closed-loop control* from the motor to the drive's microprocessor. The motor's rotor position and speed is monitored in real time via a resolver or digital encoder to determine and control the motor's actual speed, torque, and power produced.

Firmware

This is a series of instructions in an EPROM. The instructions are used for internal processor functions only and are transparent to the drive operator.

Floating Ground

An electrical common point that is not at earth-ground potential or the same ground potential as circuitry it is associated with. A voltage difference can exist between the floating ground and earth ground.

Flying Start

The inverter (AC drive) searches for the frequency that corresponds to the motor speed and synchronizes with it smoothly. Some modern inverters will even find a motor rotating in the opposite direction.

Form Factor

A figure of merit that indicates how much rectified current deviates from pure (non-pulsating) DC. A large departure from unity form factor (pure DC) increases the heating effect of the motor. It is expressed as I_{RMS}/I_{AV} (motor-heating current/torque-producing current).

Four-Quadrant Operation

The four combinations of forward and reverse rotation and forward and reverse torque of which a regenerative drive is capable. The four combinations are (1) forward rotation/forward torque (motoring), (2) forward rotation/reverse torque (regeneration), (3) reverse rotation/reverse torque (motoring), and (4) reverse rotation/forward torque (regeneration).

Frame Size

The physical size of a motor, usually consisting of NEMA-defined "D" and "F" dimensions at a minimum. The "D" dimension is the distance in quarter inches from the center of the motor shaft to the bottom of the mounting feet. The "F" dimension relates to the distance between the centers of the mounting feet holes.

Frequency

The number of cycles generated each second. The unit of measurement is hertz (Hz). (1 hertz = 1 cycle per second)

Frequency Converter (AC Drive)

Equipment to convert single- or three-phase alternating voltage into alternating voltage with another frequency or phase number. The frequency converter typically consists of a rectifier and an inverter. Main types are direct converter and indirect converter.

Frequency Resolution (Analog)

This is the minimum step in motor frequency the drive can deliver in relation to the analog input. The smaller the step, the finer the control. This becomes important for fine speed control in conveying systems. Frequency can also be set with the panel, but as the process is usually controlled by the analog input, panel frequency setting is not as important.

Full-Load Torque

The torque necessary to produce rated horsepower at full-load speed.

Gate

The control element of an SCR (silicon-controlled rectifier). When a small positive voltage is applied to the gate momentarily, the SCR will conduct current (when the anode is positive with respect to the cathode of the SCR). Current conduction will continue even after the gate signal is removed.

Gateway

An electronic device that is used to translate one form of data to another form of data. It could also be considered an electronic "interpreter." It interprets the protocol of a device such as a PLC.

General-Purpose Motor

This motor has a continuous Class "B" rating and design, listed and offered in standard ratings with standard operating characteristics and mechanical construction for use under usual service conditions without restriction to a particular application or type of application. These types of motors are not recommended for use with variable-frequency drives.

Group

In many AC and DC drives, a "group" is a category of parameters. Groups identify parameters by their functionality.

GTO

Gate turn-off or gate turn-on power semiconductor device.

Hall Effect Sensor

A transducer that produces a voltage feedback proportional to the magnetic field generated in a conductor. The magnetic field is proportional to the current flow in the conductor and is used in drives in the current limit circuit. The benefit of this type of sensor is the ability to very accurately measure AC current at low-frequency output.

Harmonic

The component frequency that is an integral of the fundamental frequency (i.e., 60 Hz). For example, the 3rd harmonic is 60 × 3 or 180 Hz.

Harmonic Distortion

A condition that exists in a power-distribution system due to the switching of equipment power supplies (computers, etc.) This "distorting" of the AC sine wave occurs wherever an electronic device (computer, drive, etc.) draws current in short pulses. Drives, for example, draw current only during a controlled part of the incoming voltage waveform. This process improves the efficiency, but causes harmonic distortion (currents) which could cause overheating in transformer neutrals. The harmonic currents would show up as an AC waveform that no longer looks like a pure sine wave. The voltage and current waveforms are no longer related. They are therefore called *nonlinear.*

Head

A measurement of pressure, usually in feet of water. A 20-foot head is the pressure equivalent to the pressure found at the base of a column of water 20 feet high.

Horsepower

A measure of the amount of work that a motor can perform in a given period of time (see Appendix B, "Formulas and Conversions").

Hunting
Fluctuations in motor speed that can occur after a step change in speed reference (either acceleration or deceleration) or load.

Hysteresis Loss
Laminated iron materials offer some resistance to becoming magnetized. This resistance results in energy being expended. Hysteresis loss in a magnetic circuit is the energy expended to magnetize and demagnetize the core.

IEEE Standard 519
An Institute of Electrical and Electronics Engineers standard that indicates the guidelines for harmonic control and inductive reactance of static power converters. This guide recommends limits of disturbances to the AC power distribution system which affects other equipment and communications.

Impedance
The total opposition to AC that occurs in a circuit. This opposition (indicated by Z) is sometimes referred to as an "AC resistance." It is actually the combined product of resistance, inductance, and capacitance. Because of the inductor and capacitor part of the circuit, impedance is very frequency-sensitive.

I_N
This notation abbreviates the current at which the drive trips and on which current settings the trip point is based.

Induction Motor
An AC motor that has the primary winding on one member (usually the stator), which is connected to the power source. A secondary winding on the other member (usually the rotor) carries the induced current. There is no physical electrical connection to the secondary winding.

Inertia
A measure of a body's resistance to changes in velocity, whether the body is at rest or moving at a constant velocity. The velocity can be either linear or rotational. The moment of inertia (WK^2) is the product of the weight (W) of an object and the square of the radius of gyration (K^2). The radius of gyration is a measure of how the mass of the object is distributed axis of rotation. WK^2 is usually express in units of lb-ft^2.

Instability
Characteristics of a system where there is an output but no corresponding input.

Insulated Gate Bipolar Transistor (IGBT)

A current-operated power device that incurs lower losses than standard bipolar transistors. This results in increased switching frequencies and requirements for smaller heat sinks. Smaller gate currents can control large motor currents. Higher switching frequencies reduce the amount of audible motor noise and allow for smoother motor control (compared with low switching rates of 1 kHz and below). These devices allow a drive to operate at near "triples" control. They also allow the motor to develop high starting torque with 100% load capability.

Integral Horsepower Motor

A motor built in a frame having a continuous rating of 1 HP or more.

Intelligent Power Module (IPM)

This module includes the drive and protection circuits in a compact unit that is attached to the heat sink. IPMs offer increased reliability and lower losses because the IGBTs within the module have lower power losses.

Intermittent Duty Motor

A motor that never reaches maximum temperature, but is permitted to cool down between operations.

Inverter

A term commonly used for an AC variable-frequency drive. An inverter is also a term used to describe a particular section of an AC drive. The section uses the DC voltage from a previous circuit stage (DC busBus) to produce an AC current or voltage having the desired frequency.

Inverter Duty Motor

This type of motor is designed to be operated on variable-frequency drives. An inverter duty motor design includes phase insulation paper between the first few turns of stator windings. In addition, the stator windings are *form wound* (windings are laid exactly parallel next to each other). This increases inductance in each length of winding. An inverter duty motor also has winding insulation of a high-voltage class (e.g., 1600 V).

Inverter Spike-Resistant (ISR™) Wire

A trademark of the Phelps-Dodge company applied to a new magnet wire insulation that provides an increased level of protection from voltage peaks. This type of wire is found in some motors powered by adjustable-frequency drives.

IP-Classes

Protection of equipment against ingress of water or solid bodies such as dust. IP stands for ingress protection. Examples: IP00 indicates no water protection, no guards; IP54 indicates protection against damaging dust accumulation and against splashing water from any direction.

I_R

This notation abbreviates the constant torque rated output current, in amperes, of an AC drive.

IR Compensation

This term is used in DC drive systems and relates to the voltage drop across the armature ($E = I \times R$). It is a way to compensate for the loss in speed because of additional load on the motor. This compensation provides a way to improve the speed-regulation characteristics of the motor, especially at low speeds. Drives that use a tachometer-generator for speed feedback generally do not require an IR compensation circuit because the tachometer will inherently compensate for the loss in speed. In AC drives, IR compensation is a parameter that allows the motor to develop extra torque at motor speeds between 0.1 Hz and the set field weakening point. This term is also used in variable-frequency drives, referring to improved speed regulation through additional volts per hertz control.

I_{RSQ}

This notation stands for the rated variable-drive output current, in amperes, of an AC drive.

Isolation Transformer

A transformer that electrically separates the drive from the AC power line. An isolation transformer provides several advantages: It enhances protection of semiconductors from line voltage transients; reduces disturbances from other solid-state control equipment such as drives without isolation transformers, time clock systems, electronic counters, etc.; and allows voltage matching of line power and drive input power (either step-up or step-down transformer).

I^2T (Thermal Protection)

The ability of an AC drive to calculate the motor heating from the operation history.

Jogging

Momentary motor movement by repeated contact closures (e.g., using a single pushbutton).

Joystick Control

Joystick control allows you to use a joystick for external speed and direction drive control through an analog input. Typically, the center joystick position is zero speed and movement of the control causes forward or reverse direction.

Local Area Network (LAN)

A privately owned network communication channel, which is used for connecting communication equipment (e.g., data processing, drives, PLCs, etc.) This system is usually in a limited geographical area.

LED (Light Emitting Diode)
A solid-state device used for signal indication on the manual control and the I/O module.

LED Display
An alphanumeric display consisting of an array of LEDs (light emitting diodes).

Limit Switch
An electrical switch positioned to be actuated when a certain motion limit occurs. The switch then opens a contact that may then be used as a digital input to an AC drive.

Line Reactor
Reduces the amount of electrical noise fed back to the AC power line. It reduces the line notching (absence of power) caused by switching of power conversion devices (phase controlled rectifiers such as SCRs). Line reactors also serve to limit the current surge seen by the DC Bus capacitors. This surge happens when a voltage surge occurs to the input of the drive. When a voltage surge occurs, a large current surge will occur as the bus capacitors charge to the peak voltage of the surge. The higher the surge level, the quicker the capacitor will charge (the surge may be 5 to 10 times higher than normal operating current). When the capacitors reach an overvoltage level, the drive shuts down. Line reactors, connected in series with the drive input, limit the magnitude of the current surge. The capacitor charges at a slower rate, thereby not allowing the capacitor to reach the voltage trip level.

Line Voltage
The input voltage that provides power to the drive. Line voltage is connected to the terminals L_1, L_2, and L_3 (U_1, V_1, and W_1). Also refer to *Supply Voltage* in this glossary.

Linear Acceleration/Deceleration
This drive circuit controls the rate at which the motor is allowed to accelerate to a set speed or decelerate to zero speed. On most drives, this circuit is adjustable and can be set to a particular application.

Linearity
A measure of how closely a characteristic follows a straight line function.

Linear Load
Any type of electrical equipment that does not change the voltage or current waveform. This load does not distort the AC sine wave. Examples of this type of load include standard incandescent lights and AC induction motors.

Living Zero

The living zero function allows an AC drive to detect a loss of reference signal. This function operates in many drives when a "minimum AI1" parameter is set to a value greater than 0.3 V/0.6 mA. You can then supervise the presence of a control signal by setting an "AI < min function" to Warning or Fault. A Warning or Fault message will then display if the analog input falls below the set minimum.

Load Sharing

This is an application where the shafts of several motors are mechanically connected together through the load. If the load is shared unevenly, one or more motors may be overloaded while the others operate lightly loaded. With DC motors, load sharing can be adjusted by adjusting the field currents of the individual motors. With AC motors, there is no comparable means of adjusting the load sharing. Load sharing with AC motors is determined by the mechanical design of the driven equipment, the placement of the motors, and the motor torque-speed curves.

Since the AC motor torque-speed curve dictates that the motor speed must decrease when the torque speed increases, motors will share the load evenly if the mechanical connection among the motors prevents them from operating at different speeds.

Locked-Rotor Current

Current taken from the line with the rotor at standstill (at rated voltage and frequency). This is the starting current when the motor is connected to the load.

Locked-Rotor Torque

Torque that a motor will develop for all positions of the rotor (with rated voltage applied at rated frequency).

Logic Control

Controlling the power switching devices to obtain adjustable frequency. It also controls the firing sequence to maintain phase coordination and the output voltage to produce the required V/Hz ratio. The *driver* subsection adjusts the reference signals to the correct level. The *power output control* subsection automatically adjusts the switching of the power output subsection. Monitoring devices for overcurrent and bus Bus voltage level report to the control logic.

Macro

A macro is a pre-programmed set of defaults for all of the parameters, which are typical for the specified application. You typically select the macro that most closely defines the drive functions necessary for your particular application. After selecting the macro, you can modify or customize the macro to specifically conform to your application.

Mean-Time-Between-Failures (MTBF)

The average time that a device will operate before failure.

Meggar Test

A measurement an insulation system's resistance. This is usually in megohms and tested by passing a high voltage at low current through the motor windings and measuring the resistance of the various insulation systems.

Metal Oxide Varistor (MOV)

A surge protection device that has low resistance to a voltage spike above operating level. The spike is routed back to the AC line.

Motor Model

A motor model is an electronic circuit or software modeling of the internal circuits of the asynchronous motor. Examples of inputs to the model are motor current, DC-bus voltage, and switching positions of the inverter. Examples of outputs are calculated flux and calculated torque. Examples of internal parameters in the model are stator resistance, mutual inductance, and saturation coefficients. These parameters can be tuned during an identification run as part of the drive commissioning.

Multimeter

Measures electric component functions and values such as voltage (volts), resistance (ohms), and current (amperes). Some multimeters also test the condition of diodes.

Multispeed Motor

An induction motor that can obtain two, three, or four fixed speeds by the selection of various stator winding configurations.

NEC (National Electric Code)

Recommendations of the National Fire Protection Association. It is revised every 3 years. City or state regulations may differ from code regulations and take precedence over NEC rules.

NEMA

The National Electrical Manufactures Associates is a nonprofit organization organized and supported by manufacturers of electrical equipment and supplies. Some of the standards NEMA specifies are HP ratings, speeds, frame sizes and dimensions, torque, and enclosures.

Nonlinear Load

Any type of electrical equipment that changes or modifies the voltage or current waveform to one that is somewhat distorted. Prime examples of this type of load include personal computers, magnetic ballasts, electronic ballasts, and variable-speed DC and AC drives. Basically, a nonlinear load is one that uses a "switch mode power supply" (a circuit that changes AC to DC. This supply takes voltage in "surges" not in a linear fashion.)

OEM

Original Equipment Manufacturer or Machine manufacturer.

Offset

Deviation of a controlled variable from a fixed setpoint.

Open Loop

A control system that does not use a feedback element.

ODP or Open Drip-proof

Open drip-proof motors have ventilation openings that allow an exchange of cooling air to flow through the interior of the motor from the surroundings. The air is forced through the motor by fins on the end of the motor's rotor. Since outside air comes into contact with the stator windings, rotor, and air gap, ODP motors are suitable only for installation in clean, dry environments.

Open Machine (Open Motor)

A machine having openings that allow external cooling air over and around the windings of the machine.

Drip-proof Machine is an open-type machine in which the ventilating openings are so constructed that successful operation is not interfered with when drops of liquid or solid particles strike or enter the enclosure at any angle from 0 to 15 degrees downward from vertical.

Splash-proof is an open machine in which the ventilating openings are so constructed that successful operation is not interfered with when drops of liquid or solid particles strike or enter the enclosure at any angle not greater than 100 degrees downward from the vertical.

Semiguarded is an open machine in which part of the ventilating openings in the machine, normally in the top half, are guarded as in the case of a "guarded machine" but the others are left open.

Guarded Machine (NEMA standard) is an open machine in which all openings giving direct access to live metal or rotating parts (except smooth rotating surfaces) are limited in size by the structural parts or by the screens, baffles, grills, expanded metal, or other means to prevent accidental contact with hazardous parts. Openings giving direct access to such live or rotating parts shall not permit the passage of a cylindrical rod 0.75 inch in diameter.

Drip-proof Guarded Machine is a drip-proof machine whose ventilating openings are guarded in accordance with the definition of a guarded machine.

Open Externally Ventilated Machine is one which is ventilated by means of a separate motor driven blower-mounted on the machine enclosure. This machine is sometimes known as a blower-ventilated or a force-ventilated machine.

Open Pipe Ventilated Machine is an open machine except that it allows ventilating air inlet ducts or pipes connected to them. Air may be circulated by means integral with the machine or by means external to the machine (separately or forced ventilated).

Weather-Protected Machine is an open enclosure divided into two types:

1. *Type 1* enclosures have ventilating passages constructed to minimize the entrance of rain, snow, and airborne particles and prevent passage of a 0.75-inch-diameter cylindrical rod.
2. *Type 2* enclosures provide additional protection through the design of their intake and exhaust ventilating passages. The passages are so arranged that wind and airborne particles blown into the machine can be discharged without entering directly into the electrical parts of the machine. Additional baffling is provided to minimize the possibility of moisture or dirt being carried inside the machine.

Operating/Service Deviation

A means of specifying the speed-regulating performance of a drive controller generally in percentage of base speed.

Operating deviation defines speed change due to load change and typically assumes a change from one steady-state load value to another (not transient) and a 95% maximum load change.

Service deviation defines speed change due to changes in ambient conditions greater than these typical variations:

Condition change

AC line voltage, +10%, –5%

AC line frequency, + 3%, –3%

Ambient temperature, 15°C

Output Reactors

Inductors, also called reactors or chokes, placed in series with the output terminals of an variable-frequency drive. Inverter output reactors are usually located near the VFD.

Overcurrent

This circuit shuts down the drive when a safe current level is exceeded (e.g., 375% instantaneous or 150% nominal RMS for 1 minute).

Overload Capacity

The ability of the drive to withstand currents beyond the system's continuous rating. It is normally specified as a percentage of full load current for a specific time period. Overload capacity is defined by NEMA as 150% of rated full load current for 1 minute for *Standard Industrial* DC Motors.

Overshoot

The amount that a controlled variable exceeds desired value after a change of input.

Overvoltage

This circuit shuts down the drive when a safe voltage level is exceeded.

Parallel Communications

A digital communication method that transmits the bits of a message several at a time (usually 8 to 17 bits at a time), usually only used over distances of a few feet with electrical cables as the transmission medium.

Parallel Interface

A type of digital interface using multiple data lines, each line transmitting one bit of data at a time.

Parallel Operation

The type of electronic information transfer that occurs when all bits, bytes, or words are handled simultaneously.

Parity Bit

An additional bit added to a memory word to make the sum of the number of 1's in a word always even parity or odd parity.

PI (PID) Control

PI is an acronym for "proportional integral" control. PID is an acronym for "proportional integral derivative" control. In this type of motor control, two signals are sent to the drive. One signal acts as a process reference and the other acts as an actual signal (feedback) brought back from the process. The drive compares the two signals and adjusts the output up or down to reduce the difference between the signals (zero error). The "D" function dictates how much error correction should take place per unit of time. This type of control maximizes the efficiency of the process. PI control is very useful in maintaining a process variable such as speed, flow, fluid level, pressure of a system, etc.

PLC

See *Programmable Logic Controller.*

Plugging
Motor braking provided by reversing either line voltage polarity or phase sequence so that the motor develops a counter-torque that exerts a retarding force to brake the motor.

Position Transducer
An electronic device (e.g., encoder or resolver) that measures actual position and converts this measurement into a feedback signal convenient for transmission. This signal may then be used as an input to a programmable controller that controls the positioning system.

Power
Work done per unit of time. Measured in horsepower or watts: 1 HP = 33,000 ft-lb/min. = 746 W.

Power Conversion Section
Electronic power devices that convert a fixed AC voltage into DC voltage (i.e., AC drive converter).

Power Factor (Displacement)
A measurement of the time phase difference between the fundamental voltage and fundamental current in an AC circuit. It represents the cosine of the angle of the phase difference.

Power Factor (Distortion)
A measurement of the ratio of the real power (kW) to the apparent power (kVA). Distortion power factor takes into account harmonic voltage and current distortion as well as voltage to current displacement.

Power Loss Ride-Through
The ability of a VFD to continue to operate for a period of time without input power. Typical power loss ride-through is 2 to 5 cycles (each cycle is 16 ms). For some drives, a more extensive circuit is used. If the supply to a VFD is lost, the drive may continue to run without external power supply utilizing the kinetic energy of the rotating motor and driven equipment. The power loss ride-through time depends on the relationship between the load and the inertia of the rotating masses.

Power Output
The section of the drive that delivers adjustable voltage/frequency to the motor (AC drives). The output terminals are typically referred to as U_2, V_2, and W_2.

Power Output Control
The circuit that automatically adjusts the switching of the power output subsection.

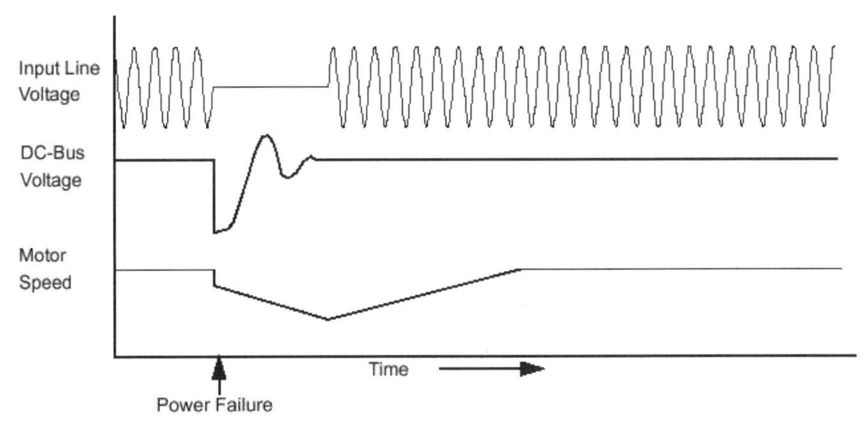

Characteristics of Power Loss Ride-Through

Precharge

A circuit within the drive that supplies a limited amount of current to the DC bus capacitors. This allows the capacitors to gain an small initial charge prior to receiving a full charge during a "drive enable" function. This process reduces the amount of inrush current to the bus Bus capacitors.

Preset Speed

Preset speed refers to one or more fixed speeds at which the drive will operate.

Programmable Logic Controller (PLC)

A stored program device intended to replace relay logic used in sequencing, timing, and counting of discrete events. Instead of physical wiring relay, pushbuttons, limit switches, etc., a PLC is programmed to test the state of input lines, to set output lines in accordance with input state, or to branch to another set of tests. The instruction sets of these machines generally exclude all arithmetic and Boolean operators, but do include vital decision instructions such as skip, transfer unconditional, transfer conditional, and even transfer and link.

Protection Devices

The subsection of the drive that works to reduce the electrical hazard within the drive.

Protocol

A set of standards governing the format and timing of data between different types of communicating devices. Essentially, a protocol is a communication language (i.e., Modbus™, Profibus, DeviceNet®, etc.).

P_{RSQ}

This notation abbreviates the rated variable torque output power rating of an AC drive.

Pull-In Torque
The maximum constant torque that a synchronous motor will accelerate into synchronism at rated voltage and frequency.

Pull-Out Torque
The maximum running torque of a synchronous motor.

Pull-Up Torque
The torque required to accelerate the load from standstill to full speed (where breakdown torque occurs), expressed in percentage of running torque. It is the torque required not only to overcome friction, windage, and product loading but also to overcome the inertia of the machine. The torque required by a machine may not be constant after the machine has started to turn. This load type is characteristic of fans, centrifugal pumps, and certain machine tools.

PWM
Abbreviation for *pulse width modulation*. An adjustable frequency AC drive that accomplishes frequency and voltage control at the output section (inverter) of the drive. The drive's output voltage is always a constant amplitude and by "chopping" (pulse width modulating) the average voltage is controlled.

Radio Frequency Interference (RFI)
This is an abbreviation for "radio frequency interference." This is also referred to as an electromagnetic noise that can cause operating problems in other electronic equipment. RFI is caused by switching circuits in electronic equipment. The effects are noticed more with equipment that is not properly grounded or in inductive devices like solenoids that do not have noise suppressors.

Random Winding
A method of winding wire in a motor in which the wire is inserted into the stator slots randomly without controlling the positions of the individual turns. With random winding, it is possible for the first turn of a coil to be in contact with the last turn.

Reactance
Measurement of the opposition of a circuit or component to an alternating current, expressed in ohms.

Rectifier
A device that permits current flow in one direction and blocks the flow of current in the other direction. In today's technology, rectifiers are of the silicon diode type. A 6-pulse AC drive uses six rectifiers, configured into a three-phase bridge configuration, as the power converter section of the drive.

Regeneration

This occurs when a motor acts as a generator. Regeneration also occurs when the CEMF is larger than the drive's applied voltage (DC drives) or when the rotor synchronous frequency is greater than the applied frequency (AC drives).

Regenerative Braking

The motor becomes a generator by taking the mechanical power of the motor and converting it into electrical power. The generated power is dissipated in the power source through a regenerative bridge circuit in the drive. The power may also be dissipated as losses in the power conversion section of the drive (within its limitations). Also see *Braking*.

Regenerative Control

A drive that has capability to control the flow of power to and from the motor.

Regulation

The ability of a control system to hold a set speed. Regulation is given in percentages of either base speed or set speed. Regulation is rated upon two separate sets of conditions:

Load Regulation (speed regulation) is the percentage of speed change with a defined change in load, assuming all other parameters to be constant. Speed regulation values of 2% are possible in drive utilizing armature voltage feedback, while regulation of 0.01% is possible using digital regulator schemes.

Line Regulation is the percentage of speed change with a given line voltage change, assuming all other parameters to be constant.

Resolution

The smallest distinguishable increment into which a quantity can be divided (e.g., position or shaft speed). It is also the degree to which nearly equal values of a quantity can be discriminated. For encoders, it is the number of unique electrically identified positions occurring in 360 degrees of input shaft rotation.

Resolution—10 and 12 Bit

A circuit that has 10-bit resolution means has an accuracy of 1.7 rpm or 0.06 Hz. This number is generated by the fact that a speed range of 0 to 60 Hz is divided in even increments that equal 1024. In other words, $(2)^{10} = 1024$. A circuit that has 12-bit resolution would have an accuracy of 0.4 rpm or 0.015 Hz. $2^{12} = 4096$.

Resolvers

A resolvers (delete "s" in Resolvers) is inherently an analog device, as opposed to a digital encoder. A resolver accepts an AC signal, then modifies the signal relative to the rotor/stator position inside the case. A disadvantage of resolvers is the need to convert sinewave signals to digital pulses. This is required for the newer digital drive technology in existence.

Reversing

Changing direction of the motor shaft. An AC motor is reversed by reversing the connections of one leg on the three-phase power line. A DC motor is reversed by changes the armature polarity. The reversing function can be performed in one of the following ways:

(DC) Contactor Reversing is done by changing the polarity to a DC motor armature with switching contactors. The contactors are operated by momentary pushbuttons, and/or limit switches to stop the motor and change directions. A zero speed (antiplugging) circuit is associated with this system to protect the motor and control.

(AC or DC) Static Reversing is the act of reversing the DC polarity of the DC motor armature or phase rotation of an AC motor with no mechanical switching. This is accomplished electronically with solid-state devices. Solid-state anti-plugging circuitry is generally a part of the design.

AC Static Reversing is the act of reversing the phase rotation of an AC motor with no mechanical switching. This is accomplished electronically with solid-state devices.

Rise Time

The time required for a voltage pulse to rise from 10 to 90% of the peak voltage.

RS-232

An electrical connection standard that is used as an interface between data terminal equipment and communications equipment. One disadvantage of this type is usually a maximum cable length of about 15 feet and communication only between two devices at separate locations (point-to-point communication).

RS-422

An electrical connection standard that is used as an interface between data terminal equipment and communications equipment. Unlike the RS-232 connection, the RS-422 allows data transmission to be received by multiple locations.

RS-485

An electrical connection standard that is used as an interface between data terminal equipment and communications equipment. This type of connection allows faster data transmission rates (100 ms, 9600 baud) as compared with an RS-232 connection. In addition, longer cable lengths may be used (up to 1200 feet) with very little additional amplification required.

RS-485 also allows multiple-point transmission and receiving of data on the same communication link.

RTD Module

This optional monitor circuit accepts temperature inputs from an RTD mounted on a motor. (RTD is an abbreviation for *resistive temperature device.* This device changes resistance with changes in temperature and is an accurate indicator of heat generated within the motor.) A monitor circuit can provide actual temperature monitoring during motor operation as opposed to a thermistor (bi-metallic switch) that opens only when a dangerous condition exists.

Scalar

A type of drive (inverter) control that regulates the frequency to the motor to achieve a set speed without use of a tachometer. This is the simplest form of control and is considered "open loop" (no feedback device).

Scalar Control

Scalar control adjusts the motor speed by varying the output frequency of a drive. The motor speed is then defined by the frequency and loading torque. The speed accuracy can be improved by speed feedback (tach generator) and this system calls for closed-loop scalar control.

Separately Ventilated

Separately ventilated motors have provisions for connecting an air duct that supplies cooling air from an external source. Since the cooling air comes into contact with the stator windings, rotor, and air gap, a clean, dry air source is required.

Serial Communications

A method of digital communication where transmission occurs one electronic bit at a time. This is the most common long-distance communication method such as from PLC in the control room to drive on the assembly floor.

Serial Interface

A method of data transmission that permits transmitting of a single bit at a time through a single line. Used where high-speed input is not necessary. Requires only one wire.

Serial Port

A connection point on a piece of electronic equipment that allows communication to another device. This port has fewer signal lines than a parallel port and passes information as a series of binary "on's" and "off's" (0's and 1's). An I/O configuration of only three lines will allow two-way communication (send and receive). This simple design is suitable for long-distance transfer of information but is at a slower rate compared to parallel communication.

Service Deviation

See *Operating/Service Deviation.*

Service Factor

A number that indicates how much above the nameplate rating a motor can be loaded without causing series degradation (e.g., a motor with 1.15 S-F can produce 15% greater torque than one with 1.0 S-F). When used in applying motors or gear motors, it is a figure of merit that is used to adjust measured loads in an attempt to compensate for conditions that are difficult to measure or define.

Set Speed

The desired operating speed.

Silicon Controlled Rectifier (SCR)

A solid-state switch, sometimes referred to as a thyristor. The SCR has an anode, cathode, and control element called the gate. The device provides controlled rectification since it can be turned on at will. The SCR can rapidly switch large currents at high voltages. They are small in size and low in weight.

Shield

A wire barrier, sometimes a wire mesh braid, that reduces the effect of electrical and/or magnetic fields. If shield braid is used, it completely surrounds the wires inside the outer casing.

Shock Load

The load seen by a clutch, brake, or motor in a system that transmits high peak loads. This type of load is present in crushers, grinders, conveyors, winches, and cranes.

Skew

The slight angular pattern of laminations on a rotor or armature with respect to the shaft axis. This pattern helps to eliminate low-speed cogging in an armature and minimize induced vibration in a rotor, as well as reduce associated noise.

Skewing

Refers to time delay or offset between any two signals in relation to each other.

Slip

The difference between rotating magnetic field speed (synchronous speed) and rotor speed of AC induction motors. Usually expressed as a percentage of synchronous speed.

Slip Compensation

Slip compensation is a technique for reducing the speed drop caused by the application of load in the asynchronous motor. The speed drop can be reduced to about 10% of the nominal slip. If very high-speed control accuracy is required, a speed controller with a tach generator is required.

Special-Purpose Motor

A motor with special operating characteristics or special mechanical construction or both, designed for a particular application and not falling within the definition of a general purpose motor.

Speed Range

Minimum and maximum speed at which a motor must operate under constant or variable torque load conditions. A 10:1 speed range for a motor with a top speed of 1800 rpm means the motor must operate as low as 180 rpm and still remain within regulation specifications. Controllers are capable of wider controllable speed ranges than motors because there is no thermal limitation, only electrical. Controllable speed range of a motor is limited by the ability to deliver 100% torque below base speed without additional cooling.

Speed Regulation

A measurement, in percentage, of how accurately the motor speed can be maintained. It is the percentage of change in speed between full load and no load.

Stability

Ability of a drive to operate a motor at constant speed (under varying load), without "hunting" (alternately speeding up and slowing down). It is related to both the characteristics of the load being driven and electrical time constants in the drive regulator circuits.

Stiffness

The ability of a device to resist deviation due to load change.

Supply Voltage

Normally refers to the input voltage that provides power to the drive. Supply voltage is connected to terminals L_1, L_2, and L_3 (U1, V1, and W1).

Surge Protection

Absorbing and clipping voltage transients on an incoming AC line or control circuit. MOVs (Metal Oxide Varistors) and specially designed R-C networks are usually used to accomplish this.

Switching Frequency

Switching frequency is the internal operating frequency of and inverter. Typical values are from 1 to 16 kHz. Increase of switching frequency reduces the motor noise but also reduces the efficiency of the drive.

Switching Frequency Range

This is the frequency of the PWM waveform for driving the output switches. The motor will make a noise that has its fundamental at twice the switching frequency. Most drives that use IGBT switches can go to a 16-kHz switching frequency. When setting up a drive system, adjust the switching frequency for the lowest value that gives an acceptable noise level. As the switching frequency goes up, the drive efficiency goes down and losses increase. It is best to set the switching frequency as low as possible.

Synchronous Motors

A synchronous motor is a motor that operates at its synchronous speed without any slip. As long as the load does not exceed the limit for synchronous operation, the average operating speed is maintained exactly at the synchronous speed. There are several types of synchronous motors. The types that are sometimes used in VFD applications are permanent magnet motors, wound rotor synchronous motors, and synchronous reluctance motors. Synchronous reluctance motors are also called *synchronous induction motors*. Wound rotor synchronous motors require special VFD controllers that are specifically designed for use only with synchronous motors. Permanent magnet and synchronous reluctance motors are sometimes used with AF controllers that are designed for use with induction motors, but special modifications are usually required.

Synchronous Speed

The speed of an AC induction motor's rotating magnetic field. It is determined by the frequency applied to the stator and the number of magnetic poles present in each phase of the stator windings. Mathematically, it is expressed as sync speed (rpm) = 120 × applied freq. (Hz)/number of poles per phase.

Tachometer Generator (Tach)

There are two main types: AC and DC. The speed accuracy and motor type will dictate which type is required (e.g., PY, AN, C42, C46, etc.). The cost of these devices is related to the accuracy provided. An AC tachometer has lower maintenance and is generally less expensive than a DC tach. The DC tach, however, operates over a higher speed range and has a higher accuracy than an AC tachometer. Also, no rectification is needed of a DC tachometer signal as compared with an AC tachometer. A tach is basically a small generator normally used as a rotational speed sensing device. Tachometers are typically coupled to the shaft of DC or AC motors requiring close speed regulation. The tach feeds a signal to a controller, which then adjusts the output voltage or frequency to the motor.

TEFC (Totally Enclosed Fan Cooled)

TEFC motors are completely enclosed to prevent the entry of air or moisture into the interior of the motor. They are cooled by a small fan that is mounted on the motor shaft at one end of the motor. The fan forces air to flow over the outside surface of the motor. The motor surface may have fins or ribs to increase the outside surface area.

TENV (Totally Enclosed Non-ventilated)

TENV motors are completely enclosed to prevent the entry of air or moisture into the interior of the motor. They are cooled only by the convection flow of air over the outside surface of the motor. The motor surface may have fins or ribs to increase the surface area. TENV motors are available in sizes of about 10 HP and smaller.

TEBC (Totally Enclosed Blower Cooled) or TEAO (Totally Enclosed Air Over)

TEBC and TEAO motors are completely enclosed to prevent the entry of air or moisture into the interior of the motor. They are cooled by a separately powered fan or blower that is mounted on one end of the motor. The fan or blower forces air to flow over the outside surface of the motor. The motor surface may have fins or ribs to increase the surface area.

Termination Resistor

This resistor (located on many AC drive boards) provides an ending point for data transmission when connected to a PLC. The transmission and receiving devices therefore see the network as a complete electrical circuit.

Thread Speed

An adjustable, low fixed speed that provides a convenient method for loading and threading machines. May also be called a preset speed.

Thyristor

A controllable silicon rectifier is a contactorless switching element (also known as an SCR). 100 to 4500 V (0.4 to 1500 A)

Torque

A turning force applied to a shaft, tending to cause rotation. Torque is normally measured in ounce-inches or pound-feet and is equal to the force applied, times the radius through which it acts.

Torque Boost

The automatic increase of starting current for loads with high starting torque. It is possible for a short time to have a starting current higher than the normal current limit for the drive in the frequency range up to 20 Hz. Operates simultaneously with IR-compensation.

Torque Constant

This motor characteristic provides a relationship between input current and output torque. For each ampere of current applied to the rotor, a fixed amount of torque will result. This constant is listed in ft-lbs or in-lbs.

Torque Control

With torque control, the motor torque is always controlled by the torque reference. The motor speed operating point is defined by the intersection of motor torque and load torque curves. Direct torque control or Sensorless flux vector control is used when a very fast or accurate torque control is required.

Torque Loop

Basically, the same as a *Current Loo*p. Because current is in direct relation to torque, the terms are sometimes used interchangeably. Current sensors within the drive monitor the current output. These sensors tell the drive control logic if the current output is within power device limitations.

Total Harmonic Distortion (THD)

A condition that exists when one or more harmonic current or voltage waveforms are added to the fundamental waveform (i.e., 60 Hz). This harmonic alters the fundamental waveform. The value is expressed in a percentage.

Totally Enclosed Machine (Enclosed Motor)

A totally enclosed machine is one so enclosed as to prevent the free exchange of air between the inside and the outside of the case but not sufficiently enclosed to be termed air-tight.

Totally Enclosed Fan-Cooled is a totally enclosed machine equipped for exterior cooling by means of a fan or fans integral with the machine but external to the enclosing parts.

Explosion-Proof Machine is a totally enclosed machine whose enclosure is designed and constructed to withstand an explosion of a specified gas or vapor, which may occur within and to prevent the ignition of the specified gas or vapor surrounding the machine by sparks, flashes, or explosions of the specified gas or vapor that may occur within the machine casing.

Dust-Ignition-Proof Machine is a totally enclosed machine whose enclosure is designed and constructed in a manner that will exclude ignitable amounts of dust or amounts that might affect performance or rating and that will not permit arcs, sparks, or heat otherwise generated or liberated inside of the enclosure of cause ignition of exterior accumulations or atmospheric suspensions of a specific dust on or in the vicinity of the enclosure.

Waterproof Machine is a totally enclosed machine so constructed that it will exclude water applied in the form of a stream from a hose, except that leakage may occur around the shaft, provided the water is prevented from entering the oil reservoir and provision is made for automatically draining the machine. The means for automatic draining may be a check value or a tapped hole at the lowest part of the frame, which will serve for application of a drain pipe.

Totally Enclosed Water-Cooled Machine is a totally enclosed machine that is cooled by circulating water, the water or water conductors coming in direct contact with the machine parts.

Totally Enclosed Water–Air-Cooled Machine is a totally enclosed machine that is cooled by circulating air which, in turn, is cooled by circulating water. It is provided with a water-cooled heat exchanger for cooling the internal air and a fan or fans, integral with the rotor shaft or separate, for circulating the internal air.

Totally Enclosed Air-to-Air Cooled Machine is a totally enclosed machine that is cooled by circulating the internal air through a heat exchanger that is cooled by circulating external air. It is provided with an air-to-air heat exchanger for cooling the internal air and a fan or fans, integral with the rotor shaft or separate, for circulating the internal air and a separate fan for circulating the external air.

Totally Enclosed Fan-Cooled Guarded Machine is a totally enclosed fan-cooled machine in which all openings giving direct access to the fan are limited. They are limited in size, the design of the structural parts, or by screens, grills, expanded metal, etc. These parts prevent accidental contact with the fan. Such openings shall not permit the passage of a cylindrical rod 0.75 inch in diameter and a probe shall not contact the blades, spokes, or other irregular surfaces of the fan.

Totally Enclosed Air-Over Machine is a totally enclosed machine intended for exterior cooling by a ventilating means external to the machine.

T_R

This notation abbreviates the rated output torque of the motor.

Transducer

A device that converts one form of energy (e.g., mechanical to electrical) to another. For example, a tach or encoder converts mechanical rotation or position into electrical signals. These signals are understood by the drive control logic circuits. A pressure transducer (PT) converts air pressure to an analog electric signal.

Transient

A momentary deviation in an electrical or mechanical system (e.g., voltage spikes imposed on the AC supply line).

Transistor

An electronic, three-terminal device that allows amplification of signals and can be used for switching and control. The three terminals are called the *Emitter*, *Base,* and *Collector*.

Variable-Frequency Drive (VFD)

A drive system including the electric machine with its mechanical and electrical control equipment where the speed of the driven equipment is varied electrically. The output of this drive is variable frequency (Hz) which changes the speed of an AC motor. A VFD typically indicates an AC Drive.

Variable-Torque Load

A load where torque varies directly to the square of speed and horsepower varies directly to the cube of speed. The load requires much lower torque at low speeds than at high speeds. Typical applications include centrifugal pumps, fans, and some mixers.

Vector

A quantity that has magnitude, direction, and sense. This quantity is commonly represented by a directed line segment whose length represents the magnitude and whose orientation in space represents the direction.

Vector Control

The technique of controlling a standard AC induction motor by electronically modeling the motor within the logic of the AC drive. The AC drive logic simulates what actually happens in a DC motor. This process allows the AC motor to operate much like a DC motor, with high speed response and without speed oscillations. The result is a fast, controlled torque response, which was previously obtained only by DC systems. In vector control, a feedback device (e.g., digital encoder) sends back a signal to the drive indicating actual rotor/stator position or relationship. The drive then calculates the voltage and current "vectors." This permits the accurate control of speed and motor torque at all speeds, even zero.

V_{IN}

This notation abbreviates the input voltage of the drive. Refer to *Supply Voltage* in this section.

V_N

This notation abbreviates the voltage for which the drive is programmed (e.g., nominal).

Voltage Reflection

A phenomenon in which a voltage wave or pulse is transmitted through the cable to a motor and is reflected or transmitted back to the AC drive.

V/Hz (Volts per Hertz)

This is the fixed relationship between voltage and frequency that exists in a motor. The motor will develop rated torque if this relationship is kept constant (linear). The drive can vary this relationship to minimize audible noise, motor losses, and maximize efficiency. If a "squared" V/Hz pattern is programmed, the voltage of the motor varies as the square of the frequency applied by the drive. This is useful in applications where the load torque is proportional to the square of speed (e.g., centrifugal pumps and fans). These loads are called variable torque loads. An "automatic" V/Hz pattern automatically controls the voltage to the motor, thereby controlling the torque. This is considered an energy saving feature of the drive and is useful in lightly loaded applications.

V_R

In an AC drive, this notation abbreviates the rated input voltage setting, in volts.

VVI

This type of AC drive controls the voltage and frequency to the motor to produce variable-speed operation. A VVI type drive controls the voltage in a section other than the output section where frequency generation takes place. Frequency control is accomplished by an output bridge circuit which switches the variable voltage to the motor at the desired frequency.

Wound Rotor Motors

Wound rotor motors are sometimes used with variable-frequency drives by shorting their slip rings and operating them like regular induction motors.

Bibliography

1993 Guide to PT Products, Penton Publishing, Inc., Cleveland, OH, Power Transmission Design, p. A151–A155, A183, A235–A237, A270–A273, A337–A339., 1993.

ABB Industry Oy, Power Electronics, publication 3AFY 58056685 R0001, March, 1995, "Direct Torque Control – The world's most advanced AC drive technology" pg. 16. Also, original publication, in German: Blaschke, F: Das Prinzip der Feld-orientierung, die Grundlage fur die Transvector-Regelung von Drehfeldmaschinen, Siemens-Z. 45 (1971) pg. 757-760. Also, original in German: Depenbrock, M.; Direckte Selbst-regelung (DSR) fur hochdynamische Drehfeldantriebe mit stromricter-speisung. EtzArchiv BD7 (1985) H.7 pg. 211-218. Also: Pohjalainen P., Tiitinen P., Lalu J.; The Next Generation Motor Control Method - Direct Torque Control, DTC., EPE Chapter Symposium, Lausanne, 1994.

Adjustable Speed Drive Applications Guidebook, Ebasco Services, Inc. and EA-Mueller Inc., Portland, OR, (prepared for Bonneville Power Administration), p. 28–29, 32–33, and 36–37, Jan. 1990.

Basics of Polyphase AC Motors, ST-223-1, Reference Information, Drive Operations, ABB Inc., New Berlin, WI, p. 6–29, Oct. 1998.

Byrd, Roy D., *Electro Mechanisms—Automatic Controls,* Delmar Publishers, Albany, New York, p. 9–16, 1972.

Carrow, Robert S., *Electronic Drives,* Tab Books, New York, p. 96–100, 201–207, and 254–255, 1996.

DC Motors Home Study Course, No. HSC616-124, U.S. Electrical Motors, Division of Emerson Electric Co., St. Louis, MO, p. 12–18 and 20–27, 1993.

DC or AC Drives?, Revision B, ABB Automation Products, Lampertheim Germany, p. 8–9, Jan. 2002.

Electrical Engineering Pocket Handbook, 197JS100M, Electrical Apparatus Service Association, St. Louis, MO, p. 10–13 and 25–26, 1997.

Mitigating the Effect of Long Motor Leads on Motors Powered by PWM ASDs, TA-106576, PQTN Application, EPRI Power Electronics Application Center, Electric Power Research Institute, p. 1-2, May 1996.

Module 1A, Basics—Mechanical Concepts, Training Resources, Allen-Bradley, Co., Rockwell Automation, Cedarburg, WI, p. 1A-18–1A-26, Dec. 1985.

Module 1C, Basics—Fundamentals of Electricity / Electronics, Training Resources, Allen-Bradley, Co., Rockwell Automation, Cedarburg, WI, p. 1C-3–1C-6, 1985.

Module 1D, Basics—Power and Logic Semiconductor Devices, Training Resources, Allen-Bradley, Co., Rockwell Automation, Cedarburg, WI, p. 1D-3 and 1D-11, Dec. 1985.

Olliver, James A., *Adjustable Speed Drives—Application Guide,* JARSCO Engineering Corp., Palo Alto, CA, p. 46–47, (prepared for Electric Power Research Institute, in cooperation with Poole, James N. and Singh, Tejindar P. P.E.) Dec. 1992.

Patrick, Dale R., and Fardo, Stephen W., *Rotating Electrical Machines and Power Systems,* 2nd Ed., The Fairmont Press, Inc., Lilburn, GA, p. 249–250, 287–290, and 296–297, 1977.

Phipps, Clarence A., *Variable Speed Drive Fundamentals,* The Fairmont Press, Inc., Lilburn, GA, p. 22–28, 1994.

Polka, Dave, *How to Maintain a VFD,* P/N Training Notes 02-US-00, ABB Inc., New Berlin, WI, p. 1–3, 2001.

Polka, Dave, *What is a VFD,* P/N Training Notes 01-US-00, ABB Inc., New Berlin, WI, p. 1-3, June 2001.

Preventing Premature Failure of Bearings in Motors Powered by PWM ASDs, PQTN Application, EPRI Power Electronics Application Center, Electric Power Research Institute, p. 1–2, May 1996.

Reference Manual—AC Drives and Motors, ST-10, Drive Operations, ABB, Inc., New Berlin, WI, p. 1–36 and 48–67., Oct. 1998.

Rollain, Philip J., and Kraus, Thomas E., *Exploring Electricity / Electronics,* Delmar Publishers, Albany, New York, p. 7, 47, 124, and 131, 1979.

Technical Guide No. 10—High Performance Drives—Speed and Torque Regulation, ST-352-100, Reference Information, Drive Operations, ABB Inc., New Berlin, WI, p. 12–21. Jan. 1996

Technical Guide No. 101—AC Drives vs. DC Drives—Evaluating the Alternatives, ST-352-101, Reference Information, Drive Operations, ABB Inc., New Berlin, WI, p. 5–13, Jan. 1996.

Technical Guide No. 108—Adjustable Speed Drive Accessories—Encoders and Tachometer Generators, ST-252-108, Reference Information, Drive Operations, ABB, Inc., New Berlin, WI, p. 2-10, March 1997.

Index